Writing Aids

THROUGH THE GRADES

ONE HUNDRED EIGHTY-SIX DEVELOPMENTAL WRITING ACTIVITIES

Ruth Kearney Carlson

California State College, Hayward

Teachers College Press

Teachers College, Columbia University

The poem "The Broken 'V' " on pages 110–111 is reprinted from volume 4 of *Windsor's Budding Poets* (Windsor, Ont.: Windsor Council, International Reading Association, Border Press, 1969) by permission of the author, Michael Keck, an eighth-grade pupil at the Oakwood School, Windsor, Ontario.

MANUFACTURED IN THE UNITED STATES OF AMERICA

*Dedicated to
the memory of
David H. Russell,
one whose humaneness
and scholarly ways
have exercised
a profound and lasting influence
on those who knew him*

Contents

Introduction

WRITING AS A TOTAL ACT OF EXPRESSION

Many books concerning writing aids present composition writing as an activity with a stimulus-response mechanism. They imply that a motivator turns on a faucet and a stream of beautiful, effective words flow out into predetermined communication channels. In other words, the embryo author responds like a monkey jumping through a hoop. Other authors, of the free-expression philosophy, imply that the child author creates little gems spontaneously, magically, and intuitively; no outside teacher or adult dare tamper with the writing process or product. Unfortunately, writing is not an easy activity; it involves the total being in a process of learning a more and more complex skill.

While educators have frequently implied that writing consists of a balancing of impressions with expression, they somehow eliminate certain essential in-between steps. The process of writing can be arranged in a hierarchical chain of learning experiences, which might be presented as follows:

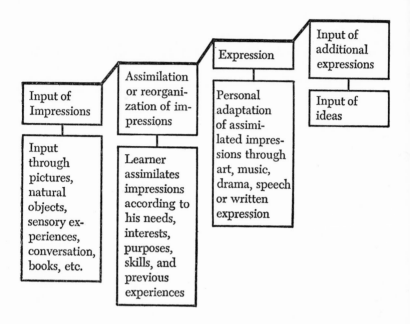

This hierarchical chain is not really so simple, as much writing involves many processes. Barricades are frequently thrown up between each link of the chain, and the young author, thwarted, fails to reach a higher level of progress in composition skills. Sometimes, for instance, he reaches the expressive stage, but, handicapped because of skill deficiencies, he may stay on a plateau until he acquires a competency in syntax and such English mechanics as spelling and penmanship.

Writing Aids Through the Grades will present some ways in which the undeveloped, immature child author can, through the use of some practical, creative ideas, be helped in improving his writing skills.

RUTH KEARNEY CARLSON

April 1970

1

THE EBB AND FLOW
OF WRITING

Several years ago, a language laboratory teacher was working with a group of Chicano boys and girls who had problems with English as a second language. This teacher, a college student, asked the children to write about gold-mining experiences as an enrichment idea for a unit in California history. She had these pupils enthusiastically construct imaginative miners' lamps, using fluted muffin papers attached to strips of paper; each little Chicano child dutifully wore his miner's lamp. The teacher provided the following instruction for writing:

> Imagine you are in Grass Valley or Nevada City, California, and are digging gold. You are going down, down into the dark earth. How will you feel? Write about it.

The classroom lights were then turned off to give the effect of darkness in a mine, and were later turned on so the children could see to create.

The pupils began to write. Most of them managed to compose a partial sentence, and a few labored dutifully until one sentence was constructed. The motivation was unique, the children were enthusiastic, but expression stopped. These pupils knew too little about California gold mining to think of any ideas; gold-mining episodes in 1849 were too far removed from relevant personal experience. Most pupils also lacked vocabulary fluency; they knew few words to come to their rescue. Spelling deficiencies hampered them; they couldn't even spell the few words they knew how to read. The assignment was unclear as

1

well, and the pupils were confused about the form and structure of the assigned composition. Children learn expression from numerous concrete, real experiences with their environment. They interact with their surroundings, and through such interacting they exercise more muscles of awareness. Writing about personal feelings is a rather intangible task, but most compositions that are to involve how a child feels should be about personal experiences and the cultural milieu in which the child lives.

In this chapter are suggested numerous multisensory activities, which should increase the observational power and environmental awareness of children. These activities include direct contact with such natural objects as leaves, animals, blossoms, and stones, as well as vicarious experiences—listening to recordings, viewing filmstrips, and listening to "concept" books, which help children understand such concepts as beauty, shapes, and growth. Indeed, children should have many listening experiences before they attempt to create an original tale. Experiences with traditional folk tales such as those of Scandinavia, Japan, and Africa help pupils to identify with persons living in other cultural environments, and related dramatic experiences based on these tales will make oral expression and writing relevant to the growing child. Proverbs, myths, legends, and fables also help pupils understand various literary genre, sometimes aiding them in developing a story-writing style based on a particular literary type. Most of the activities suggested in this chapter are designed to encourage the imaginative development of children's minds so they can create compositions more freely and uniquely.

MULTISENSORY ACTIVITIES: BUILDING
AN AURAL VOCABULARY

I. Sharing and Telling Activities

1 · PAPER BAG OBJECTS Kindergarten pupils love share-and-tell experiences, and conversational moments about something that is real and meaningful enlarge the vocabulary and increase the confidence of young speakers. If the children are sharing objects, they could sometimes carry them to school concealed in large paper bags and give clues to the hidden objects. The other children might try to guess the object from the owner's descriptive words and phrases.

2 · NATURE-STUDY OBJECTS When youngsters become tired and inattentive to informal sharing and telling experiences related to their personal lives, some sessions related to nature study can be profitable. The children should be encouraged to bring live animals or insects in safe containers, and each child should tell some of the things he notices about his hamster, goldfish, or rabbit. The other pupils should also use their senses to learn about the animal.

In the fall, when golden and bronze-red leaves fall to the ground, the pupils should each bring in some leaves and discuss them and the various trees from which they come. A "bulletin board" could be made with branches of trees, each child placing his leaf on a branch or twig. The teacher can help pupils to identify trees, but emphasis should be placed on observation skills.

3 · CHILDREN'S LITERATURE The classroom should have a diverse collection of beautiful children's books. The children should be encouraged to read these books in a left-to-right direction, even though they only read pictures. Picture-reading builds a readiness for the later reading of books and stories. A child and the teacher or two children can turn the pages of a book and discuss what the story might be. Sometimes pictures in an imaginative child's book encourage a child to tell his own creative story. Such a book is *A Cat Story Told in Pictures* by Elliot Gilbert. At other times, the teacher may read the real story.

4 · IMPROMPTU PUPPETS During work periods the teacher can help the pupils to make simple paper-bag or stick puppets, after which the teacher or an aide could help the children recreate such stories as "Peter Rabbit" or "Three Billy Goats Gruff." The impromptu playlets should then be shared with the total kindergarten circle.

Sometimes other forms of creative dramatics can be experienced. Children enjoy play-making in which creative rhythms and body movement are used spontaneously to recreate a story such as "Cinderella," or *Mike Mulligan and His Steam Shovel* by Virginia Lee Burton.

5 · WHISPER STORIES   Young children like a personal, one-to-one relationship between an adult and themselves. Sometimes whisper stories are possible if teacher aides or paraprofessionals are available to record the whispered words. A child volunteers to tell a "whisper story," tiptoes up to the older person, and whispers his words. The adult serves as a recorder, typing the story on a typewriter, then, if the child knows how to read, asking the child to read it. If the child has not learned to read yet, the recorder reads the story orally and asks the author if he wishes to make any changes. Many first-grade pupils struggle to write a story of one or two sentences, but some whisper stories 400 words in length have been recorded.

II. Experiences with Feeling

6 · FEELING BOXES   An attractively decorated "feeling box" adds to the excitement of learning through the sense of touch. Kindergarten and first-grade children can reach into a feeling box and touch such diverse objects as sandpaper, a string mop, fur, velvet, salt, and steel, and discuss one or more.

7 · A "FEELING" BULLETIN BOARD   Some teachers make tactile or "feeling" bulletin boards, but it is important to arrange the displays low enough so the children can *feel* objects. One class glued a large number of objects such as cotton, wool, steel wool, leaves, and silk to cardboard. The children felt the objects and created original similes, such as:

> The cotton feels like a rabbit's tail.
> The steel nail is as cold as ice.

8 · "TACTILE" PARAGRAPHS   One language laboratory teacher arranged thirty different objects along classroom window ledges, including such items as an artichoke and scraps of velvet material, and numbered each item. The children went to the window ledges in pairs, one blindfolded and led by his partner. The blindfolded child touched objects, tried to identify them, and then went back to his seat to write a descriptive paragraph using tactile sensations. Then the partner was blindfolded and did a similar task with new objects, which were substituted for the original ones on the window ledges.

9 · A FEELING WALK   Children love to go out on feeling walks. One class went on such a walk and brought back such objects as glass, twigs, clods of dirt, tinfoil, and leaves. These were arranged on a table with a sign that said, "The Things We Touch." A first-grade child wrote:

MY SENSE OF TOUCH

A tree trunk is rough
And mud is squashy.
Some wood is smooth.
Other wood is rough and tough.
I felt two small leaves
Shiny and smooth and cool.

10 · DEVELOPING IMAGERY AND VOCABULARIES   A language laboratory student, Rosemary Lane, conducted several sessions with kindergarten children in which she worked with them to develop their imaginative power through talking about personified objects and imagination. Miss Lane asked, "What is imagination?" Misty said, "It's when one thinks of something that isn't there," and Brett volunteered, "It's when you see something that really isn't— like I'm friends with a tiger and I live in a jungle and ride on him."

An imaginative story, *Did a Bear Just Walk There?* by Ann Rand and A. Birnbaum, was read, after which the discussion turned to living things such as flowers, trees, hummingbirds, bears, and toads. Miss Lane asked if animals or plants could have secrets. Allan said, "I think so because the trees whisper to the winds and then bend and blow."

In order to stimulate imaginative power further, certain objects—such as a feather, some fur, a rubber frog, and a doll—were placed in a "magic basket." Volunteers went to the basket and felt an object; then, without looking at it, each child dictated his personal story. The three dictated stories that follow indicate differences in maturity level, imaginative power, and verbal fluency.

I think I touched a squeaky frog. He probably lives under a bush.

RICKY

I felt a furry dog who turns into a camel whenever he wants to do it.

TOMMY

This is a baby bear who lived in a family of bears in the woods. They have their own airplanes and one day they had a picnic. They went in their airplanes to Santa Cruz. Then they walked along the beach, but they didn't go swimming because bears don't have bathing suits! Then they got back in their airplanes and flew home.

CINDY

11 · BRINGING NEWS THROUGH FINGERS   Mary O'Neill has written a sensitive book, *Fingers Are Always Bringing Me News.* Such verses about the fingers of children and others as those entitled "City Fingers," "Country Fingers," "Grown-up Fingers," and "Old Fingers" offer sensitive impressions of parts of the world seen through the sense of touch. After experiencing the book, pupils can make finger pictures by tracing around their own fingers and decorating the tracings with crayons or poster paints, or they can make finger paintings of objects they like. And after studying the format of a simple news story, the pupils can write brief news articles describing an event through tactile sensations. Some children might like to select a person such as the postman, the paper boy, or the dentist and write a descriptive paragraph focusing upon the person's tactile experiences. Other pupils may wish to add another poem to the O'Neill book in the style of the author.

III. Experiences with Shapes

12 · SHAPES AROUND US　Children can become conscious of some basic shapes—such as the triangle, rectangle, and circle—if resemblances are pointed out to them. Sometimes a flannel-board can be used; pupils can put square objects together on the board, using additional lines to make such figures as an odd animal, a dog, or cat. If vocabulary words are being taught, shapes can be matched with appropriate words. A good book on shapes is *The Wing on a Flea, A Book About Shapes,* written and illustrated by Ed Emberley. This book is effective; the author ingeniously looks at the shapes of unusual objects around us and lets us see, among other things, that the wing of a flea and the tail of a fish are triangles.

Coronet Films has released four filmstrips, under the general series title, *Stories About Shapes.* The individual filmstrips are titled as follows: "A New Shape for Freddy," "Triangles Everywhere," "The Lost Rectangle," and "A Circle in the Sky."

13 · A WALK NOTICING SHAPES　The boys and girls can go on a walk out-of-doors and note different shapes on the walk. Then they can return to the classroom and talk about the rectangles, circles, and triangles they observed. Rebus stories, using pictures in place of certain words, can be written.

14 · CLASSROOM SHAPES　The children can observe things in the classroom in order to discover objects shaped like circles, rectangles, and triangles, then create composite creatures, using many shapes together to form a new object. The figure should then be given an imaginative name, such as Cora Circle or Triangle Pete.

15 · SHAPE PARAGRAPHS　One language laboratory teacher, Miriam Shein, distributed many colored construction-paper shapes to her second-grade pupils, who then pasted shape pictures on Manila paper. Each child created a two- or three-sentence paragraph about his picture. On the following day the children were asked to turn their pictures upside down or sideways and create a different story paragraph.

16 · COUPLETS　Children can create simple couplets about shapes:

Hopscotch in a square
Boys and girls must play fair.

Let us circle round and round
And sing together a happy sound.

17 · A CLASS BOOK   A committee of pupils can create their own *Wing of a Flea* class book, using pictures of various natural objects and composing lines about the shapes seen in each.

18 · A COOPERATIVE BULLETIN BOARD   A cooperative bulletin board can be arranged using various objects, each particular shape organized into its own category. The children can make labels for the categories using neat manuscript writing.

IV. Experiences with Movement and Sound

19 · DANCING A STORY   Young children enjoy dancing a story, and can imaginatively identify with almost any story that is related in music or on spoken recordings. Ann Lief Barlin has created a series of stories that have accompanying recordings, including *The Magic Mountain, Little Duck, The Toy Tree,* and *The Brave Hunter.* Each album contains one seven-inch $33\frac{1}{3}$ rpm (LP) record and a thirty-two- or forty-eight-page storybook. One side of the record has music and narration; the other side has music only, to free children for improvisation and free interpretation. Betty Rowen in *Learning Through Movement* suggests numerous ways in which language and movement go together. She also demonstrates ways to do story dramatizations of such classics as "The Sleeping Beauty," using the Tchaikovsky music.

20 · SOUNDS AROUND US   Pupils can become conscious of noises and use onomatopoeic words naturally in their stories if words are created to imitate sounds around them. When sounds are talked about abstractly, the use of onomatopoeia is difficult. Numerous books about sounds are available, and one interesting one is Vana Earle's *The Busy Man and the Nighttime Noises.*

In this book the noise of crickets, the chirps of sparrows, the sounds of owls—"to wit, to woo"—and the noises of a cat are all heard at nighttime. Pupils could be encouraged to create words to imitate sounds heard in the daytime. A "sounds" book can be created, utilizing such titles as "Sounds We Hear," "Sounds Around Us," "Sounds in Daytime," "Sounds at the Zoo," or other appropriate titles.

21 · A RHYTHM-INSTRUMENT STORY Children can have fun creating a rhythm-instrument story together. This is appropriate for any grade level. Younger children may need more assistance in getting the story initiated, so an adult can relate some of the story sequences and children can add sound effects and lines for the story. Older pupils can work in couples and use rhythm instruments to add sounds at appropriate places in an original story.

22 · A TAPE-RECORDED SOUND STORY Children love to experiment with sound effects. Some sounds come out quite differently when magnified by mechanical means, such as a microphone. Certain sound effects have been developed by radio stations for use in radio plays. These are quite realistic: for instance, rice grains rolled on a tin pan sound like a storm and coconut shells beaten against the breast or legs sound like the galloping of hoofs.

A class can take a story that includes much imagery and possibilities for sound effects and record it on a tape recorder, adding appropriate sound effects, or the children can create their own story in a round-robin style. Somebody can initiate the story, then another child can signal that he is ready and continue on with the story, adding sound effects to accompany the narration. The noise level gets high when pupils are experimenting with sound, so some practicing may take place during free periods.

23 · THE LISTENING ELF Sometimes story time becomes too noisy, and pupils excitedly shout to one another without learning to take turns. Language laboratory student Rosemary Lane created a listening elf. A flannelboard figure of an elf with three sets of ears—large, medium, and small—was fashioned, and then

Miss Lane made up a story about a very special forest elf, presenting the ears in sequence. When large elfin ears were replaced with tiny little ears, the children softened their voices so they wouldn't hurt the elf's little ears. In this way the pupils showed some special listening sensitivity. Later some "listening elf" stories were created.

V. Experiences in Seeing: Color and Art

24 · FILMSTRIPS AND RECORDINGS   A large number of filmstrips and recordings can be used to supplement the experiential backgrounds of pupils and help them to develop their imaginative power and vocabularies. A helpful series designed for use with preschool, kindergarten, and primary children is *Stories About Colors,* issued by Coronet Films. These six stories include "The Purple Flower," "The Orange Pumpkin," "The Yellow Bird," "The Green Caterpillar," "The Blue Balloon," and "The Red Car." A silent version (C134) is fully captioned, and the sound version (S134) has three twelve-inch records. Besides teaching about colors, these filmstrips also offer some emotional content, such as feelings of loneliness, unhappiness, or friendship. Suggestions for using the books *Hailstones and Halibut Bones* by Mary O'Neill and *What Is Color?* by Alice and Martin Provensen accompany the series. Children can create original similes or metaphors orally after viewing these filmstrips, or they can create their own stories about color, spring, autumn, or other related topics.

25 · STORIES AND POETRY MOTIVATED BY CROCKETT JOHNSON STORIES   Two or three books by Crockett Johnson can stimulate pupils to create picture books and color stories. One of these is *Harold and the Purple Crayon* and another is *A Picture for Harold's Room.* In the first story, Harold goes out to take a walk with his purple crayon. When he needs something, such as a dragon, he merely draws a purple dragon under a tree. As the pages unfold, Harold draws more and more interesting things. The other book is quite similar, but uses instead imaginary pictures drawn for Harold's room.

Each child can select a crayon and create his own poem or story about a color, focusing upon one particular one, such as green, yellow, blue, or red. Each book can be named after the child creator, as *Jim and His Blue Crayon* or *Mary and Her Black Crayon*.

26 · LINES AND ORAL STORYTELLING   Another, similar book, which focuses more on lines and less on color, is *Lines, Spines, and Porcupines,* written and illustrated by Anne S. Samson. Children can take crayons and make many imaginary creatures and buildings using lines. They can then get into groups of three and tell oral stories about their line pictures.

27 · MASTERPIECES OF ART—OBSERVING AND EXPRESSING IDEAS Art appreciation lessons can correlate with language expression at all grade levels, although details of an art composition are presented differently to primary-grade pupils than they are to children in upper grades. One kindergarten teacher gives successful art appreciation lessons, using such diverse artists as Rembrandt and Paul Klee, by showing large reproductions of an artist's work and asking the pupils to talk about each one. What do they see? What colors does the artist use? Do they like the painting? If they don't like it, why? These young people use their own vocabulary words to express such things as space, color, line, and composition, recording their ideas on a tape recorder.

28 · STUDYING REPRODUCTIONS, WRITING STORIES   One first-grade teacher obtains reproductions of paintings from art galleries and museums, and a picture of the week is displayed. A helpful book for this and similar projects is *The First Book of Paintings: An Introduction to the Appreciation of Pictures* by Lamont Moore. This book selects certain pictures and discusses them in relation to such qualities as line, shape, space, light, color, pattern, balance, rhythm, contrasts, and unity. For instance, Botticelli's *The Adoration of the Magi* is discussed under line, and *The Madonna of the Chair* by Raphael is presented in relation to unity. The pupils could view some of these pictures and then write one- or two-sentence stories about each artist or each reproduction. Later, the stories might be placed in a book, *Artists We Know*.

Older children can look at art reproductions and discuss their own impressions. They can also study the biographies of certain famous artists and compose biographical sketches. Some third-grade teachers have successfully taught their pupils to write three-sentence biographical sketches of artists, but these stories are usually teacher-directed.

29 · CHILDREN'S PICTURE BOOKS   Some sense of the emotional intensity and feeling represented in art can be presented by showing pictures from children's books that are beautifully illustrated. Such pictures as those by Symeon Shimin in *Dance in the Desert* by Madeleine L'Engle create both awareness and appreciation of good children's book illustrators. Pupils can write biographies of different artists, using as guides the brief biographies included on many book jackets.

30 · PICTURE MOTIVATION   Learning to read pictures is an interpretative-perceptive skill. Many primary-grade teachers display a number of large pictures (travel folders are a good source of picture material), and an adult leader helps the children to interpret the pictures, extending imaginative ideas and sometimes helping the children to juxtapose scenes and make a more dramatic story climax. Also, a child can be encouraged to add other characters or animals to a picture. Questions can be asked, such as:

> What might happen to this mother hen and her chicks if a coyote came into the yard? What sounds might the coyote make? What might the chickens do?

VI. General Observation Activities

31 · "IT'S A GOOD THING" BOOK   A book that emphasizes many multisensory experiences is *The World Is Many Things* by Mircia Vasiliu. This book takes each of our senses, starting each time with the line, "It's a good thing to have ———" For instance, if we have eyes we can see sunrises and sunsets, and we can also see the robin's-egg blue dress of a little girl or the sparkling flashes of a city's neon lights. This book can be used for five different days. On each day the children should think of various things that can be experienced through the use of one of the senses, listing them on a story chart. Later, the five story charts can be arranged in sequence and placed in a class book. The class book could be bound by covers decorated either with finger or gadget paintings or a collage showing pictures of eyes, ears, fingers, noses, and mouths, accompanied by the words "It's a Good Thing," or some other title selected by the children.

32 · NUMBER STORIES AND POEMS Numbers are marvelous sources for both stories and such verses as couplets or quatrains. Such numbers as one, two, three, four, and five, for instance, have many possibilities in rhyme. A fun book for young children is *Fingers Come in Fives* by Oliver G. Selfridge, with drawings by Murray Tinkelman, in which the author cleverly shows the significance of numbers in our lives. The number four, for instance, calls attention to the four walls of a room, four seasons, four different tastes, and four directions of the compass. Even dogwood flowers have four petals. The children can select a number, look around them, and find things their number represents. Then they can create number stories or poems.

Another, similar number book is *Take a Number* by Mary O'Neill, which may stimulate children to write other interesting number poems.

EXERCISES IN IMAGINATION

33 · COMBINATION OF OBJECTS INTO A STORY Such classics as "The Little Red Hen," "The Pancake Man," and Wanda Gag's *Millions of Cats* and *The Funny Thing* can be read and shared with a listening circle.

The pupils can then take two or three objects, which can be miniature toys, and combine them in a new way for a story.

For instance, if a green snake, a miniature sailboat, and a Scottie dog were used, the leader could initiate the story with such phrases and clauses as:

Once a green snake crawled . . .

I saw a green snake with eyes of golden fire crawling . . .

The children could then be encouraged to go on with the story by naming the Scottie dog and adding other episodes.

Sometimes a teacher can hold up ordinary classroom objects and help the children to personify them in a story. For example, a ruler, a book, and a pencil can come to life and have many exciting experiences.

34 · ADVENTURES OF "*" (GRADES 7 AND 8)   Several highly imaginative films are available, such as *Dot and Dash, Fiddle De Dee,* and *Adventures of "*."* Color and shapes interact with each other to form unusual images, and, since soundtracks serve as background, some emotional content underlies each film. Pupils viewing such films learn to think imaginatively as abstract shapes and shifting colors interweave with each other to form new pictures in their minds.

Harriet Hatch, a language laboratory teacher, used *Adventures of "*"* with adolescents who resented writing. She showed the film to children in five different classes. For some groups she provided explanations, an introduction, and an emotional setting. In other classes the film was merely turned on, and the pupils had no introduction except the direction that they would be expected to react to it in writing. The hero of this highly symbolic film is an asterisk that assumes a more or less human appearance as it passes through infancy, childhood, and adolescence into adulthood and fatherhood. In these classes, some pupils wrote philosophical essays about the meaning of life; others created imaginative stories, one of which started with the words: "Hello, my name is Asterisk Googenheimer." One pupil titled his paper "Adventures of Humphrey Asterisk." Humphrey's father was Spiro Asterisk.

35 · POETRY AWARENESS AT THE KINDERGARTEN LEVEL   A kindergarten teacher, Patricia Hartman, developed poetic awareness with young children through a sequence of several activities involving poetry. She constructed a miniature merry-go-round, using animals created from corrugated cardboard. An individual poem was created for each animal on the merry-go-round, if no such poem was available from anthologies or other printed sources.

The poems were recited, the children giving some of them in choric verse. They also sang songs with rhythmical verses. Mrs. Hartman presented free verse and rhymed verse forms so the pupils would understand that all poetry does not necessarily have to rhyme.

After many experiences with poetry, a day for poetry creation was planned. A tape recorder was used, since these young pupils could not write independently. If a child wanted to share his own poem with other pupils in the kindergarten he said, "I have a poem." He was given a microphone, and he dictated his ideas. One of these was:

CAT MEOW

A little cat meowed
Mama cat—mama cat
Guess who I am?
Meow—meow.

Mike presented a couplet about himself:

My name is Mike
It rhymes with trike.

Another boy said:

Poems, poems
What is a poem?
Anybody know?
I know.
Fish-dish.

A fourth child said:

WHAT IS IT?

Does a dog go "meow"?
No!
Does a cat go "meow"?
Yes!
Does a fish go "meow"?
No!

Later the children listened to all of their recorded poems and proudly announced that they were poets.

36 · THE WISHING THEME (GRADES 1 AND 2)   Wishes make highly imaginative stimuli for creative stories and simple expository paragraphs written by young children. A lesson on wishes can sometimes be, as well, a sociometric device by means of which the teacher can understand her pupils better. Numerous books that illustrate wishing ideas are available, two of them being *Tico and the Golden Wings,* by Leo Lionni, and *The Wishworkers,* written and illustrated by Aliki. The Lionni story is about a little bird who has no wings and a wishing bird who can grant secrets. The story can be beautifully developed through the use of flannelboard figures. In the little story *The Wishworkers,* a foolish bird named Twiddle asks for such silly wishes as to become as large as an elephant, to have the legs of a fox, and to have the head of a lion. He becomes quite a mixed-up, miserable creature until another character in the story, Bellaglinka, intercedes with the Wishworkers and uses one of her own wishes for Twiddle.

The children might enjoy doing several things:

1. They can create beautiful wishworker birds in glorious colors, using 3-D materials.

2. They could add another episode to *The Wishworkers* in which Twiddle becomes another odd creature.

3. They could make fantastic animals, fashioned so they are part bird and part animal. The animals can be made of egg

cartons, pipe cleaners, and scrap materials, and they should be named.

4. The children could write personal, poetic letters to the Wishworkers in couplets. These letters can be posted on attractive leaves made from construction paper, with the words formed from imaginary "bird pecks" (dots formed into letters).

5. They might dramatize the story of *Tico and the Golden Wings* by using a few simple properties and printed signs.

37 · ALADDIN'S MAGIC LAMP WISHES   Another wishing theme was developed with first-grade children, using a silver gravy boat to represent the magic lamp that granted wishes with the help of a genie. The teacher told a simplified version of "Aladdin and His Magic Lamp" and read a poem, "I Keep Three Wishes Ready," by Annette Wynne, from the *Arbuthnot Anthology of Children's Literature*. The children tiptoed up to the teacher, rubbed the lamp three times, and went back to their desks to draw pictures of their three wishes. Later, the boys and girls gathered in small conversational groups, shared their pictures, and talked about their wishes.

EXPERIENCES WITH THE CULTURES AND LITERATURE OF OTHER LANDS

I. Nursery-Rhyme and Folk-Tale Activities

38 · A MAGICAL FLYING SHIP (GRADES 2 OR 3)   This imaginative story-writing lesson will probably be more successful when pupils have had enough geographical knowledge to understand differences in various parts of the world. Many picture-story books are available on cities and countries around the world. Bemelmans has introduced Paris and France through his books *Madeline* and *Madeline's Rescue,* and children have been introduced to Japan through such books as *Crow Boy* by Taro Yashima or *Meiko* by Leo Politi. Many filmstrips and new film loops teach geographical concepts about the boat people of Hong Kong or

Pygmies of the Congo. The beautifully illustrated folk tale, *The Fool of the World and the Flying Ship,* as retold by Arthur Ransome with pictures by Uri Shulevitz, offers motivational ideas for voyages through the air in a wonderful flying ship, which can sail the waters of the sea or soar through the clouds and skies. Pupils can create further episodes for this story by going on imaginary voyages to other places in the world.

39 · NURSERY RHYMES FROM JAPAN   Several collections of nursery rhymes should be available on the reading table, and the pupils can recite favorite ones. Then the teacher and children can share a Japanese Mother Goose book, *The Prancing Pony, Nursery Rhymes from Japan,* adapted from Japanese verse for children by Charlotte B. DeForest with *kusa-e* illustrations by Keoko Hida. One of the Christian educators of Japan, the Reverend Tasuka Harada, collected over a hundred Japanese folk poems and made literal translations. Miss DeForest was asked to translate these into English verse.

Some of the poems in this book are refreshing and different and of interest to younger pupils. Such verses as "Sleepy-Sparrows," "The Barefoot Bat," and "The Penniless Hawk" are delightful. And to give the children the idea of kusa-e artwork, the effect of which is partly a montage but is designed in such a way that figures seem to float or move, pictures from the book can be projected on a screen with the use of an opaque projector. Kusa-e figures are also extremely simple, and many of them have the effect of origami paper-folding. One of the most attractively illustrated verses in the book is "A Flower Lullaby," in which the mother, going to pick flowers, puts them in her gown and forgets to come home for some time. The pictures for this poem are mosaic-like, with hundreds of delicate little squares of yellow, purple, blue, green, and lavender paper fluttering into a flower pot like the green hills. Another, similar one, called the "Thorn Song," depicts a lady in her kimona being caught by a thorn.

Children can select such subject matter as birds, dragons, fireflies, the moon, beetles, cats, puppies, snowmen, melting snowflakes, flower lullabies, shimmering rivers, thorn trees, lonely seagulls, prancing ponies, long-nosed elves, little bats, or wild geese.

After a child has selected his subject, he can think about an idea for a poem describing his feelings. The quatrain form can be taught through the use of such a poem as "Wild Geese Flying," with its rhyming pattern of *aabb,* or "The Spinners," with its pattern of *abab.* Questions might be asked to motivate thoughts. For instance, a poem about fireflies could be encouraged through such questions as:

What are fireflies? When do we see their lights? Where might a firefly light? Would you like to have a firefly party with a special feast spread out on the lawn?

The teacher and children may compose some group quatrains on pets, the moon, or a rooster, but individuals should be encouraged to experiment with personal poems as soon as possible. And to illustrate the poems, the children could have a wide selection of paper, with various textures and shades of color, and might experiment with collage effects using both gay and subtle colors. The collage can be created like a puzzle. After a child feels his picture bits are placed in a style he likes, he can paste them in place.

Another section of the DeForest book discusses a Japanese form of poetry, the *haiku,* which is unrhymed verse of 5,7,5 syllables that express a breath of wonder about something in nature. Pupils who are uninterested in formal rhyming couplets or quatrains may wish to create haiku verses to correlate with their collage pictures. (Haiku will be taken up at greater length in Chapter 4.)

40 · Japanese folk tales and magic animals (grade 3) Many cities of Japan honoring traditions and artists are full of sculptures that depict animals fabled in legends or mythology. An interesting volume is *Magic Animals of Japan* by Davis Pratt and Elsa Kula. The authors, on a visit to Japan, became aware of the animal figures, sculptures, and figurines placed in various artistic settings. Since most of these animals were magical and mythical, the authors collected as many tales about them as they could. One of these tales, "The Great Spirit of the Toad," is a modified Good Samaritan tale in which a man named Jiraiya wanders throughout the countryside, helping those in need and giving aid to the weak.

This and the other tales are brief ones, and third-grade pupils may enjoy rewriting them in the form of simple shadowgraph plays. Figures can be cut out of construction paper and mounted on sticks or wires. A simple shadowgraph stage can be made from a corrugated box, with white wrapping paper for a background. A standard filmstrip projector can be used effectively as a light source; pupils can experiment with the location of the light, which can come from either above or behind the screen to form the shadows. In creating a play, the pupils can add other figures, and can use sound effects and music. A narrator sets the stage or announces the scenery or setting. In the story "The Great Spirit of the Toad," the following could be scenes:

Scene I   The Gang of Thieves
Scene II   At the Home of a Kindly Woman
Scene III   The Great Spirit of the Toad

Characters could be:

Narrator
Jiraiya
Kindly woman
Great Toad Spirit Man
Needy villagers

The children can dictate the narrator's part and dialogue into a tape recorder so they can spend their efforts manipulating the shadowgraph figures. Some ideas for the construction of figures for shadow plays appear in *Silhouettes, Shadows and Cutouts* by Norman Laliberté and Alex Mogelon. More help on shadow plays is available in *Exploring Puppetry* by Stuart and Patricia Robinson.

41 · WONDERFUL ANIMALS THAT NEVER WERE Children are fascinated by tales and descriptions of fabulous beasts and monsters. Adults think of the horror and cruelty associated with beasts, but children's acceptance of such nightmarish creatures as the ones in *Where the Wild Things Are* by Maurice Sendak shows that the imaginative wonder of childhood reaches beyond the realm of adults. A new book about monsters is *The Most Wonderful Animals That Never Were* by Joseph Wood Krutch, illustrated by Pauline Baynes. This volume explores the lore behind such creatures as unicorns, basilisks, and mermaids and is designed for persons of all ages. Older pupils will enjoy *Knights, Beasts and Wonders: Tales and Legends from Mediaeval Britain,* fifteen tales and legends first written down in the Middle Ages and later retold by Margaret J. Miller, with illustrations by Charles Keeping.

The children can create three-dimensional figures of fabulous beasts and monsters and give the beasts original names. They can then write stories or character sketches about the creatures.

42 · Tengu, goblins, and trolls   Part of the folklore of most of the world consists of folk creatures—goblins, leprechauns, Hawaiian menehunes, or trolls. These creatures, intermingled in folk tales and imaginative fantasies, usually represent the forces of evil. In *Magic Animals of Japan* by Davis Pratt and Elsa Kula one learns about a goblin creature, the *tengu,* who lives in the mountains and woods. One type of tengu is a birdlike beast with a beak, feathers, and claws. A second type of tengu has human characteristics, including a long nose. He dresses in feathers and wears a tiny cap. One story in this book, entitled "Don't Tease the Tengu," is about a woodcutter, Toshi, who tries to tease the tengu and gets such a terrifically long nose that it is tied around a tree.

In Norway, in the evenings, after chores were done, the Norwegians sat around hearth fires and listened to storytellers relate tales of princesses being captured by trolls and of Soria Moria Castle, filled with pure gold, tales created to explain the origin of natural phenomena. Most Scandinavian folk tales include odd creatures with magic powers, and in *A Folklore Map of Norway,* painted by Jørleif Uthaug and with a text by Pat Shaw Iversen, these strange creatures of Norwegian folklore are graphically portrayed. There are trolls, whose relatives were probably the frost giants in the days of Odin and Thor. Some trolls have fifteen or more heads, and, while they frequently carry away princesses, are soon outwitted by them. Man-bears are part-mortal creatures who at times shed human features and take on the qualities of bears. Old Erik is kind of a devil, as he has cloven hoofs and causes strife, but a clergyman can remove him through a pinhole. *Heks* are witches who cast spells and have remedies for ailments, and the Hulder is a beautiful woman with a cow's tail, which she tries to hide under her skirt. The *nisse* are guardians of farms and wear long gray whiskers and red caps, and at Christmastime a bowl of cereal with a pot of butter in it is put out for them. Troll hags are as fierce as trolls, and huge enough to hurl boulders at unwary travelers or people in wedding processions. Akelad is a male Cinderella, a cinder lad who sits by the fireside poking ashes. He is the hero of many Norwegian tales. Another book of interesting folklore is *A Time for Trolls: Fairy Tales from Norway* by Peter C. Asbjörnsen and Jörgen Moe.

After the children have listened to many folk tales from such countries as Japan and Norway, they may like to have a folklore festival. Large sketches of creatures can be painted on tagboard, or the pupils can work together to create a folklore mural. This could be a map of different world areas with cutout figures of trolls, tengu goblins, and Akelad figures. Or the children can have a folklore storytelling festival based on Akelad tales. The central figure can be Akelad, to whom different daring events can occur each day. A simulated hearth fire can be built, and the children can sit around the fireside and listen to imaginary tales created by their classmates.

43 · AFRO-AMERICAN FOLK TALES AS A GENRE In recent years blacks have become much more interested in Afro-American literature as part of the cultural heritage of their people, and the African folk tale is becoming a popular form of black literature for young children. Four books of African tales are *Folk Tales and Fairy Tales of Africa,* selected by Lila Green and illustrated by Jerry Pinkney; *Tale of a Crocodile: From a Congo Folktale,* written and illustrated by Ann Kirn; *African Village Folktales,* written and illustrated by Edna Mason Kaula; and *The Dancing Palm Tree and Other Nigerian Folktales* by Barbara Walker.

The volume by Lila Green includes tales from Sierra Leone, Ghana, Ethiopia, Uganda, Zanzibar, West Africa, and the Congo. A glossary gives a pronunciation of African words.

The Congo folk tale, *Tale of a Crocodile,* has some of the qualities of "The Little Red Hen." Rabbit tries to get Crow, Goat, and others to help him frighten away the crocodile from the plantain so his family can have leaves to eat, but finally Rabbit does the job himself with his little rabbits.

The book *African Village Folktales,* by Edna Mason Kaula, includes tales from the Hausa, Ashanti, Mishona, Nyakyusa, Gogo, Chagga, Sukuma, and other peoples. It also includes a map with numbers on it, referring to the place of origin of the folk tales. Each folk tale is preceded by some information about the culture and life of the people.

The Nigerian folk tales retold by Barbara Walker are mostly gathered from the Yorubas. Barbara Walker writes that African storytelling ceremonies frequently open with a riddle. Then the storyteller enters into the story itself by acting out events, using bodily movements, and singing the songs or chants of the characters. Listeners take part in the telling by beating drums, playing instruments, and adding sound effects to the tale. If the storyteller does a good job, the audience claps and cheers. After listening to several folk tales from these or similar books, pupils can sit around an imaginary campfire and develop oral round-robin tales by having each pupil add an episode to his neighbor's part of a story.

44 · AN AFRICAN FOLK TALE MAP   After the children have listened to enough of these stories, they can construct a large map of Africa, then draw pictures or cut out silhouettes representing the tales and paste them in the area of the African tribe from which each tale originated. Each child can then tell a tale about his picture.

45 · THE ELEMENTS IN A FOLK TALE   The children can study the elements of any folk tale, particularly those of African tales. Some of these elements are:

Setting: Certain words in the story may serve to locate it in a particular locale. For instance, animals such as tortoises are characteristic of people living in a particular climatic area.

Foreign words and names of characters: Words from the native language are often used in a folk tale, just as characters in a folk tale often have names derived from the native language. Glossaries give language cues. For instance, the glossary of the African folk tale book by Lila Green includes such native African words as *injera* (common pancake) and *Abunawas* (the name of a rascal hero).

Style: Some peoples repeat certain stylistic devices throughout their stories. Nigerian tales, for example, begin with "Far away and long ago in a small village . . ."

Cultural hero: Some African peoples use a certain cultural hero, such as Abunawas, the rascal hero, or Anansi, the spider, in many of their stories.

Explaining the origins of things: Some folk tales explain the origin of natural phenomena. For instance, in the Congo story "The Prince Who Wanted the Moon," one learns the thinking of a people who feel that the dark spots on the moon are marks made by the bumping of someone's shoulders.

Moral: Many tales have a moral. In the Nigerian story "Test of a Friendship," in which two friends argue about a hat, the point of the story is that good friends should examine both sides of a question without anger.

After listening to many African tales, the children should create an original tale in the style of an African folk tale, using the criteria of a folk tale, established by the class and outlined above, as an evaluative measure.

46 · PANTOMIMING FOLK TALES   A committee of pupils can work together to practice telling a tale in the style of the Yorubas of Nigeria. Some committee members can beat drums at appropriate moments, others can offer sound effects, and a chief storyteller can pantomime the tale by reenacting the major events.

47 · DRAMATIZING FOLK TALES   Most of the folk tales in *The Dancing Palm Tree and Other Nigerian Folktales* can easily be dramatized, and animals made out of corrugated boxes, with the head and tail of each animal sticking out at each end. The story "Tortoise and Barbarinsa's Daughters" can be the source of an original drama in which the tortoise is made out of corrugated boxes and simple murals with palm trees form background scenery. This story could also be depicted beautifully as a shadowgraph play.

II. Fables, Proverbs, Legends, and Myths

48 · FABLES (GRADES 4 THROUGH 6)   Most modern children are uninterested in the fable as a story for enjoyment, but fables are part of the cultural heritage of our civilization. Didactic lessons simply stated in fables are quoted frequently, but allusions have no significance unless the listener or reader has knowledge of the basic fable. One of the many versions of the famous collection of fables originating in Greek literature, *Aesop's Fables,* is the Illustrated Junior Library Books version with drawings by Fritz Kredel. Such classic fables as "The Dog in the Manger," "The Wolf in Sheep's Clothing," and "The Fox and the Grapes" appear in this collection. La Fontaine's *Fables* are usually translated from the French in poetry form, and a modern collection of Russian fables is *15 Fables of Krylov,* translated by Guy Daniels and illustrated by David Pascal.

A fable is a brief moral tale that gets over a wise saying or hint on behavior through the actions of an animal figure. For instance, a donkey goes out to a field and calmly chews the prickly thistle in the lane, thinking how happy he is with his food; the application is "one man's meat may be another man's poison." The famous race between the hare and the tortoise was won by the slow, methodical tortoise, with the admonition that "slow and steady wins the race."

In a typical animal story the reader usually gets a description of the animal and develops some feeling for it and its actions. For instance, in "The Tramp and the Skunk" from the DeJong book *Smoke Above the Lane,* one has empathy with the little skunk who kept the tramp company in the railroad car. In a fable a person feels little sympathy for the principal animal character, since he is presented as an abstraction, not really as a personality.

A teacher can select numerous morals or aphorisms from various fables and list them on the chalkboard or on a lesson sheet that contains samples of the fable style. Some of these are:

Some begrudge others what they do not enjoy themselves.
Appearances are often deceiving.
Honesty is the best policy.
Do not trust flatterers.
Don't bite the hand that feeds you.
There is no arguing a coward into courage.
Prepare today for the wants of tomorrow.
Do not count your chickens before they are hatched.
The smaller the mind, the greater the conceit.
Necessity is the mother of invention.

The children could then write a story, in the fable style and based on one of the above morals, in which an animal teaches a moral or a lesson. Some pupils may wish to rewrite some of the *Aesop's Fables* in the form of couplets or quatrains. Many other morals can be obtained from any basic collection of *Aesop's Fables.*

49 · PROVERBS   A proverb is a pithy saying that condenses the wisdom of experience. It is usually a simple application of a general truth, such as "a rolling stone gathers no moss." Proverbs of the Bible offer numerous examples of moral virtues and contrary vices; Proverbs 1:5 says, for instance, "A wise man will hear and will increase learning; and a man of understanding shall attain unto wise counsels." A collection of proverbs called *African Proverbs* has been compiled by Charlotte and Wolf Leslau, with decorations by Jeff Hill. These have been collected from the peoples of Ashanti, Baguirmi, Buganda, Basutoland,

Cameroon, the Congo, Ethiopia, Ghana, Guinea, Ivory Coast, Kenya, Liberia, Madagascar, Niger, and other African countries.

The teacher can have three-minute thought writing lessons daily. Each day a collection of proverbs can be listed on the chalkboard. The pupils can ponder over their meanings for a few minutes and then write simple paragraphs, explaining the significance of the proverb in notebooks they keep for the purpose. For instance, the pupils could consider such proverbs as these of Senegal:

Nobody tells everything he knows.
A heart cannot be bent like the arm or knee.
Speak only to those who understand you.
It is safer to travel alone than with an evil companion.

50 · LEGENDS (GRADES 5 THROUGH 6)   A legend is generally an unauthenticated story from an earlier time that is thought to have some historical basis. Often a legend focuses upon a cultural hero, who is sometimes part man and part god. Most cultures have basic legends that are part of their heritage. A Mexican legend, beautifully narrated by B. Traven, is *The Creation of the Sun and the Moon*, illustrated by Alberto Beltran. This is the story of Chicovaneg, an Indian hero who wants to rekindle the sun after it has been captured by evil spirits. The quetzal bird assists him, and they travel to the ends of the earth until Chicovaneg leaps far up into space and grasps the nearest star. He races from star to star, salvaging bits of silver light from each, which he ties to his shield. Then, as he reaches the apex of the skies, his shield becomes the new sun. Another part of the legend depicts the rabbit Tul and Chicovaneg's son, who create the moon to light the pathway for men at night. Two portions of this same legend describe what happened to the earth when there was no sun and again what happened to the earth when the sun was restored to it by Chicovaneg. The children can write an imaginative descriptive scene entitled "The Earth Without a Sun" or "The Return of the Sun to the Earth." Other students may wish to create a roller movie or script depicting the sequences of the story about the hero, Chicovaneg, and the sun.

51 · DEVELOPING WRITING STYLE THROUGH GREEK MYTHS AND LEGENDS (GRADES 6 THROUGH 8)   Most presentations of Greek myths and legends are stereotyped accounts of stories that seem to have little relevance to the modern child. Instead of reading one version of "Arachne," "The Pomegranate Seeds," or "Pyramus and Thisbe," the pupils should obtain the same stories handled by different authors. For instance, *The Arbuthnot Anthology of Children's Literature* contains two different versions of the King Midas myth, one called "Midas" and the other called "The Golden Touch." A good source is *Greek Myths and Legends as Retold by Eminent Mythologists,* compiled by James R. Squire and Barbara L. Squire. This volume includes Robert Graves's description of the palace of Olympus, a pictorial, dramatic one. Here one sees King Zeus on his polished black marble throne adorned with gold, a throne reached by seven steps colored the seven colors of the rainbow. Students reading this description can absorb details that don't appear in many stories of the gods. Olivia Coolidge has written the version of "Phaeton, Son of Apollo" in this book, but many variants of this tale have been told. Other myths told by Olivia Coolidge appear in *Greek Myths, with Selected Episodes from the Trojan War.*

A committee of pupils can divide a group report so that each student is responsible for one Greek myth. Such myths as "Phaeton, Son of Apollo," "Arachne," "Cupid and Psyche," "Niobe," "Daedalus," "Midas," "Pyramus and Thisbe," and "Baucis and Philemon" can be selected. Each pupil should study some geographical and basic historical facts about Greece and should consult at least three different versions of the same myth. Then the myth should be rewritten by (1) introducing more pictorial images clarifying the scenes; (2) using more picturesque language, such as strong nouns and vivid adjectives; (3) enhancing the characterization of a central figure by rounding out his character as the myth progresses; (4) rewriting moments of tension or climax in a more dramatic style; (5) eliminating minor characters who might confuse the reader.

Young authors should write a page or two of description and

dialogue. Then they can dictate what they have written on a tape recorder and play back the tape to listen for smoothness and naturalness of style, as well as for sincerity and clarity. Then the story can be recast and typed or written in cursive or manuscript writing. Authors should read their myths over many times, listening to the music of their words. This is one lesson in which revision plays a major part. Creative professional authors are dismayed to find modern students so careless about their own responsibility for writing quality. This myth-recreation lesson, designed to focus upon writing style, should encourage many revisions of an original tale.

52 · CREATION OF AN ORIGINAL MYTH (GRADES 4 THROUGH 8) Most persons have dispensed with a firm belief in mythology, since scientific discoveries can account for most events of the universe and also offer convincing explanations of such natural phenomena as the origin of the sun or moon. Myths may be fictitious, but they do explain the culture of peoples. Each child should try to imagine that he is visiting a primitive group of people. He should describe the geographical location and cultural traditions of the group and create some myths. For instance, a child might be a Yoruban and write a myth called "How Tortoise Got His Shell" or "How the Moon Got Its Craters."

2

COMPOSITION WRITING AS AN ARTISTIC EXPRESSION

INTRODUCTION

The writing of a composition can be compared with the creation of a painting. A painting can be spontaneous or carefully planned and executed. A primary-grade pupil, for instance, experimenting with water colors or tempera, can splatter paints on an easel and sometimes, unexpectedly, create a spontaneous, natural, fresh picture. An older child, on the other hand, takes a course in the theory and practice of art fundamentals and learns that form and line, shape and texture, color and spatial perception have certain functions in an artistic composition.

Written composition can also be spontaneous or carefully executed. If a child is able to sense tone, mood, and unity, he can create a bit of prose or poetry that is fresh and unhackneyed. And if a child has also had a good deal of experience in observation, several directed thinking experiences, some knowledge of the structure of both paragraph and composition, an enriched vocabulary, and some exercises in motivation, he can plan, purposefully, a paragraph essay of high quality. Older children can profit, too, from some experiences in proofreading and revision.

Numerous thinking skills applicable to writing situations are listed in *Teaching for Thinking: Theory and Application* by Louis E. Raths, Selma Wasserman, Arthur Jones, and Arnold M. Rothstein. Paintings that might be used in art criticism are included in *Art Fundamentals, Theory and Practice* by Otto G. Ocvirk, Robert O. Bone, Robert E. Stinson, and Philip R. Wigg and *The First Book of Painting: An Introduction to the Appreciation of Pictures* by Lamont Moore.

OBSERVATION AND THINKING EXPERIENCES

53 · OBSERVING   No author can express himself clearly unless he thinks logically or imaginatively. Certain thinking activities aid writing, and the first of these is *observing*.

Such a biography as Jean Lee Latham's *Anchor's Aweigh: The Story of David Glasgow Farragut,* and others of Latham's such as *Drake: The Man They Called a Pirate, Carry on Mr. Bowditch,* and *Trailblazer of the Seas* refer frequently to observation skills; navigators of historical sailing vessels, for example, had to be constantly alert to changes in weather and tides. Some observation experiences for children follow:

1. Looking at a ship's log. In connection with this, even young primary-grade children might like to try keeping a sample diary or journal.

2. Noticing the itinerary of a traveler.

3. Looking at photographs and slides of people and describing them orally or in writing.

4. Focusing attention on setting or scenery and describing geographical locales.

5. Studying the narrative and descriptive properties of a work of art such as *The Nut Gatherers* by Adolph William Bouguereau or *House by the Railroad* by Edward Hopper.

6. Planting an avocado seed, carrot top, lima bean, or sweet potato in water and observing and describing daily changes.

54 · COMPARING   Students can observe many items in their environment. Comparing one thing they see with another is a basic thinking skill valuable in composing paragraphs. A few comparing activities follow. The children could:

1. Compare rabbits in a story such as *Peter Rabbit* with rabbits in *Rabbit Hill* or *The Velveteen Rabbit.*

2. Compare a folk song with a tall tale or folk story.

3. Compare paintings by modern artists such as Paul Klee and Piet Mondrian.

4. Find similarities between flowers and a painting or between a painting and a written composition.

5. Note likenesses between such makes of automobiles as Toyota and Datsun, find resemblances between Chevrolet, Pontiac, Buick Skylark, and Oldsmobile Cutlass.

6. Compare two birds, a skylark and a blue jay.

55 · CONTRASTING Another thinking skill consists of contrasting, or finding differences between, objects and persons in the environment. Boys and girls can look for differences between many things, such as:

1. A painting by El Greco and one by Edvard Munch.

2. A still life by Henri Fantin-Latour and one by Paul Cézanne.

3. *Rouen Cathedral* by Claude Monet and Sandro Botticelli's *The Adoration of the Magi.*

4. A poem by Robert Frost and one by Carl Sandburg or E. E. Cummings.

5. A sulphur butterfly and a swallowtail.

56 · CLASSIFYING The children can use various classifying skills to organize objects into categories having some relationship with each other. They could classify such things as:

1. Names of fruit trees and evergreen trees.

2. Books about sailing, sports novels, mystery novels, and science fiction.

3. Occupations characteristic of jungle areas and of the Arctic or Antarctic.

57 · COLLECTING AND ORGANIZING DATA In constructing paragraphs children need to experiment with ways of gathering data related to a central topic. Pupils can classify some of the following:

1. Jobs of fathers and of mothers, gathered in a class census survey.

2. Favorite foods and foods disliked.

3. Episodes of a novel or story, organized to focus on either humorous events or on sadness or hardship.

4. Ways books are organized in the school library or in a city library, based on a survey and including a report on the Dewey Decimal System.

58 · Summarizing Essays and other types of nonfiction literature use the device of the summary frequently. Novels, too, are often summarized by readers. Children can learn one technique of summarizing by participating in "group talk." The pupils gather in groups of five with a chairman to discuss a particular topic of interest to all others in the group. Rules of behavior are established, and students are given a time limit for discussion. At the end of the stated time, a pupil summarizes the salient points of discussion.

STRUCTURAL FEATURES OF THE PARAGRAPH

59 · Developing paragraph sense in primary children Young boys and girls need many thinking experiences before they become cognizant of the structural features of a paragraph. Unfortunately, many of the basal readers being read in grades one, two, and three have poor structural features; paragraphs are short and supporting details are not descriptive enough.

Group paragraph-stories related to social studies or science will help give some sense of structure if ideas are focused upon concepts such as change, interdependence, or differences. Much work with oral discussion and summary charts is helpful. For instance, pupils can write paragraphs on such subjects as:

1. Tools of the Zulus
2. Machinery used in a supermarket
3. Vehicles of space exploration
4. Foods of Alaskan Eskimos
5. Foods of Amazon natives
6. Language of animals

The "pocket chart" is an aid in helping young children under-stand some of the logic of good paragraph structure. If the class is studying about the supermarket, the teacher and pupils can consider one main idea, such as "Supermarket workers use many kinds of machines." Pupils can read about supermarkets in easy reading books, or they can take a trip to a nearby supermarket. After they learn about some of the machinery used in super-markets, the teacher can focus discussion by writing a topic sen-tence on a strip and placing it in a pocket chart, as:

Supermarket workers use many kinds of machines.

Then such supporting ideas as the following are printed on tag-board strips:

1. The butcher cuts meat with a meat slicer.
2. A meat wrapper uses a wrapping machine, which seals paper on the meat.
3. The checker uses a cash register.

Volunteers among the children can place these strips in the pockets of the pocket chart underneath the topic sentence, after which the teacher and pupils can work cooperatively on a para-graph that incorporates these ideas. The teacher can then pre-pare some sentences that are unrelated to the main topic, such as: "The butcher sells beef, ham, and chicken," or "The checker is polite to customers." These sentences, on strips, are then sub-stituted in the chart under the topic sentence about workers and machines, and the children learn what happens to a paragraph when the logic is altered. During the earlier stages of paragraph writing it is helpful for children to learn that a good topic sen-tence has a controlling idea and other sentences should relate or support the main thought. After experiences such as these, many young pupils can write fairly logical paragraphs about topics being studied in such subjects as health, science, and social studies.

60 · Discovering main ideas—the topic sentence and controlling idea Many paragraphs written for young readers focus upon clearly written ideas, with the topic sentence usually either the first or second sentence. Children should learn, however, that sometimes topic sentences in dramatic, narrative sentence sequence come as the last sentence or as a surprise element. For instance, in Chapter 1, "The Animal's Point of View," in *The Language of Animals* by Millicent E. Selsam, one reads the following paragraph:

> A school of minnows comes close to shore, and as we approach their silvery bodies flash in motion. The whole school goes off in another direction. Flocks of starlings come in to roost on a winter evening and shift and turn and dive together with the greatest precision. The monkeys in a zoo, the dogs on a street, the chickens in a barnyard, the minnows, the starlings, and most other animals have ways of communicating with each other.*

In this instance the topic sentence comes as the last one in the paragraph. The controlling idea states that *most animals have ways of communicating with each other.*

The children could go through numerous magazines and newspapers and cut articles into paragraphs. Colored pencils could then be used to underline the topic sentence of each paragraph.

61 · Finding the controlling idea To help young authors locate the controlling idea in a paragraph, a nonfiction article in a basal reader or magazine can be selected by the teacher and divided up into separate paragraphs, and each child given the responsibility of reading one paragraph. Each reader should then select the topic sentence of his paragraph and place it on the chalkboard or write it with a flowbrush pen with colored ink on lined newsprint chart paper. Then the controlling idea of the paragraph—the word, phrase, or clause that definitely points out the central idea in the paragraph—can be underlined

---

* Millicent E. Selsam, *The Language of Animals* (New York: William Morrow & Company, Inc., 1962), p. 9.

with chalk on the board or with another color of ink on the paper. Some examples of topic sentences, with the controlling ideas underlined, follow:

Without doubt, Maria was my greatest friend.
The store on Via Alamitos was expensive.
Dionysio, the character in the Mexican novel, has proved to be a quivering coward.
The government space program involves careful training of human cosmonauts.

62 · PARAGRAPH RELAY   From a textbook, the teacher can select four paragraphs, of comparable length, each of which has a stated topic sentence and definite controlling idea. The paragraphs should be duplicated and numbered 1, 2, 3, 4, and four rows of pupils assigned to work in a paragraph relay—row one on paragraph one, row two on paragraph two, and so on. The first person in each row will write the topic sentence from his paragraph on the board or on a large piece of lined newsprint chart (24 x 36 inches). The second child will underline the controlling idea or most important fact in the sentence. The third pupil will place a supporting sentence under the controlling idea, and the fourth pupil will place a second sentence after this one. This process will continue until all sentences of the paragraph have been organized in order. The teacher or an aide will judge the clarity of the thinking of the pupils who have participated in the relay. Time should not be a major factor, as too rapid writing may ruin penmanship.

A sample paragraph:

The "Day's Eye" or Daisy

The "Day's Eye" flower is commonly called a daisy. The daisy opens up when the day is begun. It closes up at night when the sun goes down. It grows rapidly and crowds out new grass and hay crops. It is called "The Farmer's Curse" because it is such a pest.

Child one:

The "Day's Eye" flower is commonly called a daisy.

Child two:

Daisy

Child three:

The daisy opens up when the day is begun.

Child four:

It closes up at night when the sun goes down.

Child five:

It grows rapidly and crowds out new grass and hay crops.

Child six:

It is called "The Farmer's Curse" because it is such a pest.

63 · SCRAMBLED PARAGRAPH SENTENCES   Paragraphs can be cut from old workbooks, magazines, and newspapers, then cut up into sentences and placed in envelopes, which should be clearly labeled and coded so the paragraphs won't get scrambled up. Each pupil should draw a different paragraph envelope, after which he should arrange the enclosed sentences in good paragraph order. In some instances, several sentences might be arranged in a different order without destroying the coherence of the writing.

64 · VOCABULARY-BUILDING   Vocabulary-building in relation to paragraph construction is a continuous process. Pupils should consult dictionaries frequently, and vocabulary charts organized according to topics or categories should be available. Colors, weather terms, and art terminology such as "form," "line," "shape," "value," "texture," and "space" help. Certain synonym charts such as "words to be substituted for *said*," are invaluable. Several synonym books should be in the study center reference section. Some of these, such as Roget's *Thesaurus,* are available in cheap paperback editions but are difficult to use. Primary pupils can be helped with *In Other Words: A Beginning Thesaurus* by W. Cabell Greet, William A. Jenkins, and Andrew Schiller, a book on synonyms, antonyms, and sets. Elizabeth Kirtland has compiled *Write It Right: A Handbook of Homonyms.* Some teachers have had their pupils make picture-dictionary homonym books. In such a book, "son," for instance, could be a picture of a boy, while "sun" shows the sun with its blazing rays. Junior high pupils will find many uses for *The Comprehensive Word Guide* by Norman Lewis (Doubleday), and many other word-guide books are available in paperback form.

65 · USING PAINTINGS AS THEMES IN PARAGRAPHS   Paintings not only provide excellent subject matter for paragraph writing, but, because of their own structure, enable students to see paragraph structure more clearly. For instance, the writer can select a picture and focus on that part of the painting which interests him most. The statement concerning this focal point can then become the opening sentence of a paragraph. Either art books, such as *Composition in Pictures* by Ray Bethers or *Looking at Pictures* by Kenneth Clark, or reproductions of masterpieces of art, which can be found in the form of large posters, may be used. Students should note that the subjects of pictures can be painted or viewed from more than one point of view. In Otto G. Ocvirk *et al., Art Fundamentals Theory and Practice,* for instance, there appears an unusual picture by Rufino Tamayo entitled "Animals." The animals of the title are depicted as different species of savage beasts or brutes with snarling teeth.

A student's description might be:

> Wild beasts gnash their teeth in a picture by Rufino Tamayo, exhibiting brute cruelty. Cruelty is also seen in staring eyes, remnants of bones from former feasts, and by the stiff tails of the animals held in the air like piercing swords or spears.

66 · PROVIDING SPECIFIC DETAIL IN A PARAGRAPH   Young authors cannot write good paragraphs unless they know some interesting facts about their chosen subject. Scientists and historians are frequently able to compose interesting articles, as they observe data and organize it into written form, through the use of specific accurate details. For instance, Millicent E. Selsam's *The Language of Animals* includes a paragraph about mule deer that is clearly written, using specific details and vocabulary words relating to the subject:

> Mule deer, with their big ears, are well known in the Western part of North America. Careful studies show that these deer too have sound signals. An explosive snort warns other deer; bleating sounds exchanged between mother and fawns help keep them together. Under attack, a young fawn lets out a shrill piercing scream that brings the mother doe to its defense. . . .[*]

Children can be naturalists recording data from the field. Each author should observe one animal—a bird, a cat, a dog, or a duck—and take field notes. Later these notes can be organized according to significant data. For instance, if a child selects blue jays as the subject of his paragraph, he can take notes relating to certain topics:

1. Color of the jay
2. Food the jay eats
3. Flying habits
4. Cruelty and other birds
5. Greediness of the jay

Later, if the writer decided to focus on the cruelty of the bird, he might select the title "A Cruel Neighbor—the Jay."

THE STRUCTURE OF THE COMPOSITION: OUTLINING AND ORDERING OF IDEAS

67 · Developing outlining skills Outlining is often a tedious task, since it is not only repetitive in nature but time consuming, but it is a skill essential to good writing. The intricacies

[*] Ibid., p. 68.

of outlining can be developed in junior high school. Most pupils in elementary classes should be familiar with the following organization patterns:

I.
   A.
      1.
         a.
           (1)
              (a)
  II.

or

I.
   A.
      1.
      2.
   B.
  II.

Younger pupils can probably find controlling ideas in most well-written paragraphs. Older students in grades seven and eight can learn further skills, such as the noting of major and minor supporting sentences, and specific forms of paragraph organization, such as time order, space order, general to specific order, specific to general order, and the order of climax. Sixth-grade pupils can write two- or three-paragraph essays and junior high pupils can compose themes of four or five hundred words. Major parts of essays need to be outlined in order to provide coherence and unity to the total composition.

Ideas can be organized into either a sentence or a topic outline. The three parts of a sentence outline are the title, the thesis statement, and the body. The first word of each sentence is capitalized. The thesis statement is the controlling idea or central thesis of a paper, and helps to eliminate irrelevant material. If a thesis statement is sharply focused, the composition is much clearer; if the thesis statement is abstract or general, a paper is harder to develop.

Suppose a boy observes a sleeping barn owl. He might prepare the following thesis statement and outline:

Barn Owls

Thesis statement: The eyes of barn owls affect their nocturnal behavior.

I. Eyes of barn owls are sensitive to light.
   A. Owls see in daylight.
   B. Light hurts eyes of owls so owls sleep until dusk.
II. Owls sleep in daytime.
   A. Owls use ears and nostrils to find food in dark.
   B. Owls hunt food at night.

Pupils can write a topical outline with a thesis statement by carefully observing such environmental objects as sparrows, snakes, street gutters, and buildings. They can organize ideas according to various sensory images, such as those of touch, taste, smell, sound, and vision. For instance, an outline on the topic of street gutters could be organized according to visual or olfactory images.

68 · Trial outlining on the chalkboard In introducing outlining skills, some contests can be held at the chalkboard. Five pupils can select the same topic and view it from different aspects. For instance, suppose some fifth-grade pupils wished to write about folk tales and folklore. One pupil could outline facts on folklore, a second child could outline facts on folklore heroes of America, a third student could write on folklore games, a fourth pupil could outline facts on folk songs, and a fifth one could collect details from a folklore map of the United States. After books have been studied and notes taken, main ideas could be written out and glued to colored strips of construction paper, the five pupils then moving the ideas around until they seem logical. When a logical outline is developed, it should be copied on the chalkboard. The other pupils could discuss the clarity of thought and suggest the removal of extraneous ideas.

69 · "HIDDEN VILLAIN" GAME—EXTRANEOUS DETAILS Intermediate-grade children will enjoy the "hidden villain" game. Paragraphs should be used that are well written in many ways, but in which some "hidden villains" or extraneous data are included. A time limit is given. The pupils are to find the guilty parties, write them on strips of paper and put the paper strips in his own individual box or envelope marked "Hidden Villains." The pupil who finds the most extraneous-detail items in a certain period of time wins the game. He must prove to the other players that the information he has selected is not necessary.

70 · RA VOYAGES Expository paragraphs explain or tell how to do something climactically. The coherence of a paragraph is helped if sentences are organized in one of the five following orders: time order, space order, general to specific order, specific to general order, or order of climax.

Pupils might derive inspiration in constructing expository paragraphs from examining the story of the Norwegian explorer Thor Heyerdahl, who has won fame from sea explorations on primitive rafts, the most noted, until recently, being his *Kon-Tiki* voyage in 1947. In May 1969, after setting off from Safi, Morocco, Heyerdahl had his papyrus boat *Ra* towed out to sea, to prove that North Africans could have sailed to the Americas in reed boats over 3,000 years ago. Pupils can imagine that they are Thor Heyerdahl arranging for the cruise of the *Ra* and write a paragraph organizing plans for the voyage chronologically, or write several paragraphs in which the events are organized geographically in space, beginning in Safi, Morocco, and landing on the coast of some part of the United States.

71 · ORDERING OF IDEAS—THE CLIMACTIC METHOD The eyes of people all over the world focus on the exploits of astronauts as they orbit around the world, land on the moon, or splash down into ocean waters. Pupils can create two- or three-paragraph essays, explaining the exploits of space heroes, and organize their paragraphs according to the *climactic* method. Sentences in paragraphs organized in this way are arranged beginning with the least important details and leading up to the most important ones. For instance, a person might write about his day's events as follows: (1) His car engine shoots flames, stalls, and dies; (2) the car is towed to the garage; (3) he starts out from the repair department with a motor tune-up and a happy smile; (4) he runs out of gas on the freeway.

72 · Filmstrips as aids to space, time, and order-of-climax paragraphs   Filmstrips are usually organized in a straight narrative form or according to some factual order or concept. Unfortunately, too many unrelated facts are presented. Recently, a new concept, film loops, which focus upon one principal idea, was devised, but a class can achieve the same effect by working with ordinary filmstrips.

Three committees can be selected—one each for space order, chronological or time order, and order of climax. After the filmstrips are shown for the first time, they should be shown again, with the students in each committee listing episodes or facts related to his particular area. Each committee should take notes on ways sequences in the filmstrip could be regrouped and the script accordingly rewritten. Pupils using a factual filmstrip might need to be imaginative and suggest other possible sequences that will contribute to a more dramatic climax. For instance, if scenes of beautiful forests, lakes, and highways are shown, an appropriate climax might be scenes of a forest fire, a flood, pollution of lakes, and litter on the highways.

MOTIVATIONAL ACTIVITIES

73 · Organizing paragraphs by analogy   Analogy consists of comparing two things that are not alike but have similar characteristics. One learns about the unfamiliar through a comparison with something that is familiar or known. In *Life on the Mississippi*, Mark Twain compared a river-boat pilot's memory of the river to the problem of memorizing every detail of a city street in New York; a seventh-grade boy used the analogy of life and death as open and closed doors after he read the poem "Out Out" by Robert Frost. An apt analogy makes a paragraph more picturesque and clear. In a paragraph entitled "The Demon

Driver," an analogy might be made between the devil and an insane driver who takes dangerous chances with his own life and that of others.

74 · RECOMBINATION OF IDEAS IN NEW SETTINGS   After students have looked at a number of art masterpieces, their imaginations can be fostered by using observation and descriptive skills to combine ideas from two different pictures into a new setting. One teacher used *Fish Painting* by Paul Klee and a poster of men in a gondola-shaped vessel. The children, sixth-grade students, were asked to look at the pictures carefully and imaginatively, then to pick out a figure or character from one painting and place it into the other. Then the children were asked to create some narrative paragraphs using the new setting.

75 · COLLAGE PARAGRAPHS—Pupils can create collages by using magazine pictures, printed labels or newspaper heads, colored construction paper, and paste and paint. It is usually easier to create collages around ideas, such as "Faces in the Night" (faces of all kinds staring out of the darkness) or "Loneliness" (a mass of pictures of lonely people in deserted places). Pupils can make collage pictures that will set a mood or tone for the dramatic paragraph they will subsequently write.

76 · FACES (GRADES 3 THROUGH 8)   Much is revealed through faces. We see more than a person's features; we see the inner feeling or mood that affects the expression. Eth and David Clifford have written a photographic story, *Your Face Is a Picture*. This book contains pictures of children from different countries throughout the world; some faces are smiling, others are covered with tears, and still others show anger. Some faces reveal hunger and other faces make a plea for friendship and an escape from loneliness.

A committee of pupils can collect a large number of pictures of people from magazines, newspapers, travel posters, or other sources. These pictures can be grouped together in certain categories and placed in folders or large Manila envelopes. One category could be called "Next-Door Neighbors." Another one might be "Neighbors Far Away," and still another might be "Anger," its opposite "Friendship." After the pupils have organized the pictures into appropriate classifications, a photographic essay can be created. Pictures can be organized as montages or grouped on separate pages of a book. If a book is made, the group of authors should study the format of a book carefully and organize theirs with a title page, copyright page, foreword, table of contents, index, and probably a glossary.

77 · SATIRE AND PARODY (GIFTED SEVENTH- AND EIGHTH-GRADERS) Satire is a technical form of literary expression that uses sarcasm, irony, or wit to expose abuses or follies. A satirist usually mocks something in the current political scene, and to be effective he must pick well-known persons to satirize, as well as write his descriptive passages in a literary style, using classical references. A very famous vehicle of satire is Swift's *Gulliver's Travels*. To cite more modern examples, newspaper columnists such as Russell Baker, Arthur Hoppe, and Art Buchwald create satirical pieces about people—mayors, presidents of universities, governors, or movie stars—and current political problems—unemployment, antiballistic missiles, and militants.

Teachers can save satirical columns from newspapers and magazines to use as examples, and pupils can create satire related to the local political scene by using literary allusions with which they are familiar. The teacher can also provide examples of these.

78 · CARTOON SILLIES FROM NEWSPAPERS Teachers can collect a large number of political cartoons, comics, and other cartoons, such as those from the sports page. These can be distributed and used to motivate ideas for paragraphs, stories, and poems.

79 · WANT ADS AND PERSONAL COLUMNS The daily newspaper is a resource that can be heavily used for ideas. Pupils can study want ad columns to learn the style. They can select an odd object or antique, describe it, and offer it for sale. The personal column of the newspaper can be recreated, with literary figures begging others to come home: Romeo can leave messages for Juliet. And, in an advice-to-the-lovelorn column, Venus can give counsel to the lonely girl in love with Jupiter or Apollo.

80 · IMAGINATIVE INVENTIONS AND IMAGINARY LANDS Many pupils love to create imaginative machines of the Rube Goldberg type, with all kinds of gadgets and conveniences. One class invented some ingenious desks with several devices to aid in play and study, and some pupils have fabricated homework-saving machines.

A few classrooms have established imaginary governments in strange parts of the world, such as the Arctic. Pupils can invent a new language, a different form of government, strange types of residences, a special flag, and other symbols, and they can explain these inventions through news articles in newspapers, letters from people in the invented land, diaries, and other such devices.

SUMMARY

As we have seen, the ability to compose paragraphs throughout the grades can be developed through thinking activities, creative motivational devices, assistance in structural paragraph formation, and activities using many items in the environment, as well as through vicarious experiences with books, slides, movies, and the radio. Various devices for evaluating paragraphs have been suggested in *Sparkling Words: Two Hundred Creative and Practical Writing Ideas* and *Language Sparklers for the Intermediate Grades,* both by Ruth Kearney Carlson.

It is highly important that written expression be evaluated in a manner to increase competence, but the teacher should not undermine the confidence and self-concept of the young author who is just beginning to learn new skills of expression.

3

SPELLING PROBLEMS AND
THE FLOW OF EXPRESSION

Too often children, provided with ample motivation to encourage them to write, cannot do so because of spelling deficiencies and other mechanical problems such as handwriting. Writing is a total process; when young children have spelling difficulties, the flow of language will either trickle slowly or dry up completely. The following writing aids are directed, with the exception of the last few, toward primary-grade pupils.

ACTIVITIES TO START THE CREATIVE FLOW

81 · TAPE-RECORDED STORIES When children have immature spelling and writing skills, the tape recorder can come to the rescue. Groups of five or six children may sit around a tape recorder and dictate their stories into the microphone. Later, they may listen to their own words and evaluate their tales.

Many things can be used to start the flow of language, such as art, music, or colored slides. Language laboratory student Rosemary Lane's group of first-grade pupils did a unit on color and language. A prism was brought to class and the children learned that a ray of light refracted in the prism produced a spectrum of red, orange, yellow, green, blue, indigo, and violet. Terms about colors were discussed. Then the children painted pictures, each child concentrating upon one color, after which each picture was pasted at the top of a piece of art paper and a pocket was pasted on the back of the art paper. Each child

47

dictated his color story into a tape recorder, but eliminated an ending to his story. A second child listened to the first child's color story on a tape, then wrote an ending for the story and placed it in the pocket on the back of the picture that accompanied child number one's story.

Many first-grade pupils become discouraged when asked to write lengthy stories, but they can easily create two or three sentences that can supply an ending to a story.

82 · "WILD THINGS" AND SPELLING PROBLEMS   Another group of children taught by Rosemary Lane made paper-box animals or monsters, using shoe boxes and such scrap materials as feathers, velvet, colored cord, egg cartons, yarn, and moss. The teacher worked with the children to develop imaginative qualities for their creatures. An animal with three legs and two heads, a robot, and other highly imaginative creatures were made and colorfully painted in brilliant colors.

On the following day, the teacher asked the pupils to write about their wild things. The following was helpful:

WILD THINGS

I am a _____. My name is _____. I live in _____.

The teacher wanted the pupils to develop an originality in writing that would match the fantastic shape of their cardboard-box "wild things." She asked them to use odd names, to create strange words. But, since these children were hampered with spelling problems, they could only use words like "pig," "deer," or "giraffe." The lesson was stopped and the children worked on names by using sounds an animal might make as part of the name. They duplicated the name if it had one syllable—for example, one doglike wild thing was a "Ruff Ruff," and a piglike animal was an "Oink Oink"—and added syllables, such as "Quacky Wacky" and "Ducky Lucky," if a longer name was desired.

After the teacher and pupils worked on names, little stories came slowly as thought was disrupted and focus was placed more on original names than on a narrative sequence of events. (This work on the creation of interesting names should probably have been done in a preceding lesson, not at the time of creation, since the exercise on original name creations interfered with a narrative story sequence. These young children learned to write original names, but could not create a story episode.)

83 · A "WILD THINGS" ART GALLERY   Miss Lane showed some reproductions of paintings—one of these was *Fish Magic* by Paul Klee and another one was *A Girl with a Watering Can* by Auguste Renoir—and discussed the title of these and the other paintings with the class. The children learned that paintings are often identified by having an artist give them a title and his personal signature. The boys and girls were encouraged to go to art museums with their parents to note titles of art masterpieces. Each child then looked at his "wild thing" and gave it a title, including its name. The title was neatly affixed to the animal so the name became a part of it.

84 · EXTENDING IMAGINATIVE CONTENT ON "WILD THINGS"   On a subsequent day, Miss Lane read *Where the Wild Things Are* by Maurice Sendak. Then she called attention to the individual cardboard animals created by pupils in the class and asked such questions as:

> Where might your wild thing live? Where could your wild thing go? What are some things that might happen to your creature?

Pupils wrote brief three-sentence stories telling about events that could happen to their "wild things."

85 · IMAGINATIVE COMPLETION BLANKS   First-grade children often have a limited spelling-usage vocabulary. If their flow of thought is interrupted by idea gaps and spelling problems, children feel frustrated. Sometimes a series of questions makes the writing process merely a set of questions and answers, with a resulting loss of sequence or narrative flow in the child's product. On the other hand an imaginative set of completion blanks is sometimes desirable in initial writing lessons, to prevent problems encountered from making writing tedious.

MY DOG

I have a dog and his name is Cindy. He has soft brown fur which _____ when I touch it. One day Cindy and I went _____ _____. He leaped into the water of the green lake and pulled out a _____.

This type of lesson controls imaginations quite a bit, but sometimes an initial successful experience in an exercise like this is better than unusual creativity at this stage of maturity. The teacher should be careful, however, to stop using imaginative completion blanks as soon as pupils can work independently.

SPELLING AIDS

86 · SPELL IT AS IT SOUNDS A child is trying to record his thoughts as rapidly as possible when he comes up against a necessary word that he wants to write but cannot spell. For instance, he has decided to write a story called "A Crocodile Tale." He has a picture of a crocodile, and he has read factual books and folk tales about crocodiles. He starts writing:

One day on the Congo River I met a _____

He asks the adult for help. The teacher or aide should not stop the writing process by insisting that the spelling be perfect, but should say: "Spell it as it sounds." The young author might spell the word any way—"crockodile," "crokodyl." The word is spelled *as it sounds* to the ear of the child. The aide might help the child sound out the word by pronouncing it more clearly, but little time is spent on perfect spelling of words at the momentous instant of creation. Spelling corrections come at the proofreading stage or elaborative aspect of the creative process.

87 · MAGIC WRITING (GRADE 1) Sometimes "magic writing" keeps ideas flowing. A child writes his sentence story independently and makes mountain-peak lines for words he cannot spell. For instance, consider the story about a "Never-Never-Land

Flower," which is written to correlate with an imaginary flower created by the child artist.

Never-Never-Land Flower

This is my /\\/\\/\\/\\/\\/\\
It is a Never-Never-Land /\\/\\/\\/\\/\\/\\.
It has hearts and /\\/\\/\\/\\/\\/\\ in
the center. It /\\/\\/\\/\\/\\/\\ and
/\\/\\/\\.

Later, the child reads his story to a teacher or aide and words are substituted for the magic-writing lines.

This is my flower. It is a Never-Never-Land chrysanthemum.
It has hearts and arrows in the center. It tinkles and sings tunes.

In most cases pupils can remember the words that they want to place where the magic-writing marks are. They tell the teacher or aide the word and the helper writes the correct spelling above the mountain-peak lines. Later, if this is an important vocabulary word, the child can practice spelling it independently. Spelling practice, however, should not come at the time of creation.

88 · PICTURE DICTIONARY AIDS   Numerous picture dictionaries should be available in work centers. During reading circle time or during periods of individualized reading, children should be instructed in ways to use the picture dictionary. It is important to have some other dictionaries in the classroom as well, since a child gets quite frustrated if he tries to spell a word and can't find it in his reference source. Some picture dictionaries are: Albert Harris and Mae Knight Clark, *My Self-Help Dictionary;* Albert Harris and Mae Knight Clark, *My Word-Clue Dictionary;* Lillian Moore, *The Golden Picture Dictionary,* illustrated by Beth and Joe Krush; and Wendell W. Wright, *The Rainbow Dictionary,* illustrated by Joseph Low. It is important to spend several sessions on picture dictionaries, to enable the child to become quite familiar with both their novelty and utility. Otherwise, he will spend so much time thumbing through the pages of the reference book that he will forget and not have the time to complete his written composition.

89 · PERSONAL PICTURE DICTIONARIES   Some primary children have made attractive personal picture dictionaries organized from A to Z. Pictures of things whose names begin with a certain letter of the alphabet are grouped together on one or more pages, each picture identified by a label neatly printed in manuscript writing. The children can use these words in creating original paragraphs and stories.

90 · VOCABULARY KINESTHETIC BOXES (GRADE 2)   Sometimes the kinesthetic spelling approach is effective at the second-grade level and can be adapted to paragraph- and story-writing experiences. (A kinesthetic spelling approach is some method by means of which the child gets a feeling for the spelling of a word in his muscles rather than visually or orally. He often traces words with his fingers and files them in an "A to Z" box.) In this approach, the child learns to spell a word he needs as he finds some use for it.

Suppose a second-grade child decides to write some realistic sentences about an urban supermarket. A skeletal framework or sentence supplied by the teacher using the child's ideas, such as the following, gets the young author started:

> The Lucky Supermarket is near our (1) _____. It is on (2) _____ Street. I go (3) _____ at the supermarket and buy milk and (4) _____ for Mom.

The four words or phrases that the child wants to use in his composition are (1) *house,* (2) *Via Mercedo,* (3) *to shop, shopping,* or *buying things,* (4) *Nucoa* or *margarine.* Each child has an "A to Z" box. These can be purchased commercially, but they can also be made from sock or shoe boxes, and using lined strips of paper approximately 4 x 12 inches.

When the child is writing his sentences and comes to a word he needs, such as "house" or "apartment," he turns to an aide, teacher, or older pupil. The aide asks the child to repeat the word, then prints it in manuscript writing on a strip of paper.

Then the child traces the word three times with his fingers and repeats the word. The word is printed again on the chalkboard and the child takes his word strip and compares it with the word on the board. When he thinks he knows the word, he writes it in his story and files it behind the correct alphabetical word in his word box. He does the same for the other words he does not know how to spell. (Note that it is tedious to do this with too many words on one day. Ordinarily enough words or sentence outlines should be supplied so the child doesn't have to stop too frequently.) On the following day, the word strips are reviewed. The child uses each word again in context, and it is listed in a "word help" book kept by the teacher. At intervals the child is given more experiences with words, such as the ones described below.

91 · CATEGORY GAMES   Category games can be developed, in which words from the "A to Z" boxes are first put into categories and then used in stories, poems, or sentences. Categories, which are frequently used in relation to a social studies project, such as the study of the supermarket, can be chosen by the children with the help of the teacher. For instance:

Laundry	Fruits	Vegetables	Meats	Canned Goods	Frozen Foods

A child might have the words "string beans" and "corned beef." "String beans" could be placed in either the vegetables, canned goods, or frozen foods columns, and "corned beef" in either the meat or the canned goods column. Later, pupils can create two- or three-sentence paragraphs using words in one category. A sample paragraph might be:

PRODUCE DEPARTMENT

We visited the produce department. We saw orange <u>carrots,</u> yellow <u>squash,</u> and green <u>lettuce</u> and <u>cabbage.</u> We saw green <u>sprouts,</u> which smelled like <u>cabbage.</u>

The words that are underlined were formerly placed under the category "vegetables."

92 · WORDS BY CATEGORIES AND CLASSIFICATIONS As primary-grade pupils study different subject areas, words can be organized into categories and classifications and color coded. For instance, if pupils are studying Zulus of Africa as part of a third-grade unit of social studies directed toward concepts, certain words are needed repetitively. These should be placed on a chart, in word categories organized by the children in any way they wish. Different-colored sheets could be used for different subject areas—canary yellow for social studies, green for health, blue for science. Or color codes could be organized according to different classifications.

93 · GLOSSARIES AND STORIES BASED ON A THEME Pupils should become accustomed to the use of the word glossaries at the backs of basal readers, simple geography and history books, and other books used in content subjects. Pronunciation aids and the alphabetical arrangement of words should be taught as part of the reading lesson.

One California third-grade teacher, working with first-grade children who had spelling and reading deficiencies, taught the importance of glossary use the following way: The pupils were Mexican-American children who were learning English as a second language. One of the basal readers had a mouse story, and when the teacher saw that the hitherto apathetic boys in the group enjoyed the story content, she found several other mouse stories in other books. The pupils began to develop a vocabulary listening list, and then each child in the group wrote his own mouse story in a personal style. The teacher made a vocabulary listening list or glossary, in which children could recognize visually words they heard, for each story, and the child and teacher wrote some simple comprehension questions as well. The pupils worked on the style of books, putting together a title page, copyright page, table of contents, and the glossaries, and then each story was arranged in a *Mouse Reader* with an accompanying illustration by the author. The book was placed on the reading table for children in other reading groups to read and was later presented to the school library.

94 · STORY ART FOLDERS Teachers working on an individualized basis with children have found story art folders a help. Commercial story folders are available, and some schools purchase English workbooks that have pictures, vocabulary, and spelling aids for young authors, but unfortunately workbooks are designed for mass production and sale and lack personalized motivations directed to the needs, interests, and skills of a particular group of pupils. Story folders can be used by groups of four or five pupils in a group writing lesson directed by the teacher or they can be used independently as a free-time activity, in which each child writes a story based on the pictures or stimuli in a folder. Stories are placed in the folder after they are written or they are numbered to correspond with the number written on the folder and handed in to the teacher when they are completed.

Story art folders can be as artistic and elaborate as the teacher desires to make them; however, such criteria as variety and versatility, needed vocabulary words, imagination starters, and relevance to children at a particular grade level should be applied to the construction of such aids before any other consideration. A simple method of making a folder is to take a 12 x 18-inch piece of colored construction paper and fold it in the middle. In the upper left hand corner of the folder an illustration can be pasted, either made by the teacher, or, if the teacher is not artistic, cut out of a magazine. Suggested titles or questions can be placed under the picture. For instance, suppose a picture of a giraffe chewing a spring bonnet bedecked with flowers were chosen. Titles for this could be:

An Odd Diet
Beauty Is Within
Hats for a Giraffe
A Strange Flower Diet

Questions or stimulators might be:

1. Write a paragraph about the lady who wore this bonnet.
2. Write a descriptive paragraph about the giraffe.

3. Write a story of this giraffe in the first person or as if the giraffe were going to tell the story.

4. Write a story of the lady in the first person or as if the lady were talking about her zoo experiences.

5. Prepare a script for a simple puppet play in which conversational bits by the lady and giraffe are given as direct conversation with quotation marks around the conversation. For example:

"Ouch!" said Mrs. Cornpopper as the giraffe snatched her hat.
"These cornflowers and daisies should taste good," said Maizie, the giraffe at the Brookfield Zoo.

Spelling and vocabulary words that might be needed:

1. giraffe
2. zoo
3. bonnet
4. flowers

Three-dimensional articles can also be used in story folders to motivate thinking. For instance, a large number of different buttons could be glued on a piece of paper, along with such questions as:

Where have these buttons been?
If these buttons could talk, what might they say?

Each story folder can be numbered and placed in an attractively decorated story file box. The box can be covered with gift paper, gadget-painted paper, or wallpaper samples.

95 · STORY VOCABULARY STRIPS   Some teachers make a collection of words that are needed by pupils in their classrooms, some using cut-out strips of paper, with the strips rolled up like scrolls, others the back of wide adding machine tape. These words are organized around the room in special areas. Games can be played with vocabulary spelling strips to help the children learn to locate words rapidly.

96 · BASIC SPELLING WORD LISTS   Many children are familiar with the basic spelling word lists that, based on research studies, are compiled according to the number of times a word is used at various levels of difficulty. These words are studied in spelling workbooks, which are graded according to level of difficulty. After the pupils have studied the basic word lists for spelling, the words can be arranged into categories that are more useful for writing purposes. For instance, seasons can be used. All words appropriate to, say, the Christmas season can be transferred from a basal speller to a list under the heading "Christmas." "Families" might be another category. In each instance, the basal spelling workbook is the source of the words.

COOPERATIVE STORY ACTIVITIES

97 · Cooperative chart experience stories   The cooperative chart experience story is a standard procedure for most primary-grade classes. This is a group story in which children dictate sentences and the teacher becomes the scribe. (Quite frequently, the cooperative chart story becomes more teacher-directed than child-created. This is so when the teacher puts words in the mouths of the children and does not permit them to express themselves naturally.)

A cooperative experience story derives from a common experience known to several first-graders. Some children see a snake on the way to school; several boys and girls visit the zoo; one group of children goes to a circus; other pupils go to a car race. The teacher usually records thoughts rapidly in manuscript printing on either large newsprint paper (24 x 36 inches) or on the chalkboard. First of all, the story is recorded exactly as it is presented by children volunteering phrases or sentences:

Our Trip to the San Francisco Zoo

We went to the zoo.
We went to the zoo on our school bus.
The driver got lost.
We saw lions.
We saw elephants.

> We saw an anteater.
> We loved the flamingos.
> The monkeys were funny.
> The monkey spit on us.
> We came home.

The pupils should be encouraged to read the dictated lines to see if there are ways in which they might sing a better tune. Ordinarily, young children's ears are attuned to the fluency of folk and fairy tales, and they resent short, isolated, dull sentences.

The writing of experience stories is a good way to teach children the techniques of expanding and contracting sentences, helping them to form compound and complex sentences in a natural way. Thus, some of the sentences in the experience story might be:

> We went to the San Francisco Zoo on our school bus.
> We saw funny animals such as monkeys and anteaters.

Primary-grade pupils can also be encouraged to use proper nouns and colorful adjectives. For example, the bus driver was Mr. Bosco. So a child might say, "Mr. Bosco who drove us got lost." Some sentences using colorful adjectives might be:

> The anteater has a spiky snout and sticky tongue. Its sticky tongue sticks like glue.

After pupils are satisfied with an experience story, several procedures are possible.

1. The teacher can make two copies in neat manuscript printing. The second copy can be cut up into phrases and words. On another day, groups of children can match words and phrases with the master story.

2. The cooperative story can be typed on a ditto master so each child can have his own copy as a reading-writing aid.

3. Important words can be put on the chalkboard or on dupli-

cated masters. The children can find other contexts in which to use the words, as well as work on oral sentences using them in different sentence structures.

98 · COOPERATIVE CREATIVE STORIES OR POEMS   Experience stories are used quite extensively in primary-grade classrooms, but few teachers use cooperative creative stories as extensively as they could. In working on such a story, it is perhaps easier to keep the thread of the story in mind if some central characters are chosen and used in different episodes. An excellent idea is using characters from a classic story of which the children are fond; for example, younger boys and girls love Beatrix Potter stories, even though her books are too small to be seen at any great distance, and *The Tale of Mrs. Tittlemouse* has imaginative possibilities. The story can be read to the children and certain characters can be listed on a "Mrs. Tittlemouse Chart."

> Characters: Mrs. Tittlemouse, a wood mouse
> A Beetle
> Mother Ladybird
> Fat Spider
> Babbity-Bumble Bee
> Mr. Jackson
> Mrs. Butterfly
> Funny Conversation: "Tiddly Widdly"
> Buzz! Wizz! Wizz!

Each day one episode for a Mrs. Tittlemouse story can be dictated by some pupils working with the teacher. The pupils will have read the list of characters, and will either be able to say the names or consult the chart, which includes many words with which they are familiar. They can also insert bits of dialogue from the "funny conversation" part of the chart. Each episode can be illustrated and, after the teacher writes it down in manuscript writing, can be combined with the others to make a room storybook.

99 · COOPERATIVE STORIES WITH CULTURE HEROES   Black, Spanish-American, Oriental, or other children coming from a minority group can develop cooperative creative stories around their own people and experiences. Chinese stories would use characters with Chinese surnames, and Mexican or Puerto Rican stories would use Spanish names. Urban black children could create stories about the experiences of blacks in an urban area. Large picture montages with which the children can identify can be used for motivation. A word chart can be made up, including not only words frequently used but words, names, and places used specifically in the neighborhood, such as the following:

WORD LIST OF OUR NEIGHBORHOOD

Mrs. Pendoza's store	adiós
Pablo	buenos días
Mercedes	centavos
Rio Mercado Avenida	

The children can work cooperatively to create a certain culture hero. For instance, Pablo could be a naughty child who gets into difficulty in the community but is aided by adults, among them a friendly priest. He can do such things as rescue an alley cat or, as he comes out of the store, he can be challenged by his friend Juan to a race, in which he drops the eggs he was sent to the store to buy.

ACTIVITIES FOR ADDED INCENTIVE

100 · THE LANGUAGE-EXPERIENCE APPROACH   One of the most beneficial aids to writing fluency is a language-experience approach, which is a practical writing situation involving several skills—speaking, reading, writing, spelling, and memorizing. This procedure, which is more effective if the teacher has two or three aides to assist her, works as follows:

1. The student, using manuscript printing, writes a personal story that is relevant to him. It can be realistic or imaginative. When he does not know the spelling of a word he writes the initial part of the word and draws a line.

WADDLES THE DUCK

Waddles the duck walked down to the p_____ at L_____
M_____. His little baby d_____ walked after him. They
went "quack quack quack." Waddles was the m_____ duck.

2. A teacher's aide or an older student goes to the author and
asks him to read his story. The author is complimented and the
story copied with correct spelling and punctuation.

3. The original story is lightly crossed out.

4. The child is asked to read and spell orally the corrected
version of his tale.

5. Then the author is told that he is to have a quiet thinking
time to himself. He rereads the story and practices spelling his
words quietly in any way he desires.

6. When the child thinks he knows the correct spelling and
content of his story, he turns his paper over on the back and
writes it from memory. Usually he succeeds. If he does not, he
studies his story again until he can write it independently without looking at the model.

7. The author then finishes by illustrating his story with a
picture.

Much supportive work goes on in connection with the procedure described above. The teacher gives sound clues, phonetic
or phonemic lessons, and other aids, usually during another part
of the period. These supporting activities are usually not done
during the actual writing process, since drills and exercises tend
to interfere with the free flow of thought. The child learns all
kinds of ways to concentrate upon words. Encouragement and
positive reinforcement are given him to enable him to feel confident in his writing ability. For instance, if a child does outstanding work according to his developmental level, his story
can be printed on a large sheet of heavy paper and decorated
with attractive illustrations, such as pictures painted with poster
paint.

A helpful source for teachers of young pupils is *Language
Motivating Experiences for Young Children* by Rose Engel,

which gives many suggestions for multisensory experiences related to oral and written expression, as well as to dramatic play.

101 · STORY OF THE DAY   Tales are to be communicated, and pupils will expend greater effort on theirs if they know that others are going to read them. Several motivational devices can be used to encourage more attention to the mechanics of English. For example, for an extra-time activity, a picture can be displayed, each child writing his own story about the picture. The teacher collects the stories, and the best one becomes "Story of the Day." Efforts should be made to rotate the honor.

102 · A "BEST STORY" BULLETIN BOARD   Language laboratory student Rosemary Lane painted a beautiful peacock picture and placed it at the top of a bulletin board over the title "Something to Strut About." The best three or four stories of the class were displayed, and new stories were put up each day.

103 · A CLASS LITERARY MAGAZINE   This can appear four times a year. An editorial staff can be selected, and the best articles and stories, which will later appear in the magazine, can be chosen by the pupils themselves.

104 · A CLASS STORYBOOK   A class storybook can be created and decorated with montages showing bits of imaginative thinking such as flowing bubbles, bits of goldenrod fluff, and silk costumes. Storybooks can be exchanged with another classroom in the school or in other schools.

105 · CHILDREN'S HOSPITAL WORK   Pupils can write letters to children who are in a children's hospital or to those who are homebound. Delightfully attractive story or poetry books, too, can be sent to the ill or crippled children. Delicate tissue-paper fairyland scenes can add imaginative luster to the writing.

SPELLING AND VOCABULARY AIDS FOR INTERMEDIATE-GRADE PUPILS

Many of the spelling aids suggested earlier in this chapter should also be used with intermediate-grade children. If a fourth-grade child is highly original and is trying to create a story about a green dragon or a trip beneath the sea, he becomes thwarted if a teacher focuses upon absolutely correct spelling at the time of creation. Most intermediate pupils have some spelling sense based on previous years of schooling and can write a word that has some semblance of its correct spelling. The author has read over 5,000 children's stories written by intermediate-grade pupils as part of a study, and no more than two or three stories were indecipherable because of spelling.

The initial draft of a paragraph or story should probably be written without too much emphasis upon the mechanics of perfect spelling. Later, after the first stage of creation, such paragraphs or stories can be proofread and corrected by the child and teacher.

Older children who have negative self-concepts and have had repeated failures in writing stories and paragraphs should probably have more lessons in oral composition; these should precede writing. For instance, pictures can be placed on corrugated cardboard or construction-paper "story-starter" cards. These cards can be distributed to the pupils and a time limit of five or ten minutes be set for each of them to construct a story in his mind. After the time is up, each child can hold up his picture and tell a story. Round-robin storytelling devices also aid verbal fluency. A story is initiated by the teacher with such a starter as: "The fog is a mysterious monster. One night . . ." Many sixth- or seventh-grade boys who resent assigned composition exercises enjoy relating ghost stories, adventure stories, or tall tales. These can be dictated into the microphone of a tape recorder.

Intermediate-grade pupils can also use story boxes, vocabulary charts, personal word dictionaries, dictionary skills, and category exercises to advantage, as well as the language experience techniques indicated earlier in this chapter. This is particularly beneficial if these children are deficient in reading and writing skills. Three exercises directed toward older pupils follow.

106 · TYPEWRITTEN STORIES Some intermediate-grade teachers follow many aspects of the language-experience stories suggested for primary grades. Children who have considerable deficiencies in reading and writing can dictate a story to an aide.

The aide types the story, then the author practices reading his own tale. Later the child can be encouraged to type his own story.

107 · GROUP DICTATING OF A TAPED STORY   In urban areas in recent years, several books have been written through the device of having people dictate their experiences and feelings directly onto a tape. This approach makes for much more fluency of style, and sometimes a distinct emotional tone is set. For example, after a child has visited an art gallery and purchased art post cards, he could dictate his ideas about his visit. Or, if a child has observed a fight in his ghetto neighborhood, he could dictate his impressions of the fight. Such stories are frequently sociological in nature, as is the book that John Holland has edited from tapes, *The Way It Is: Fifteen Boys Describe Life in Their Neglected Urban Neighborhood.*

108 · AN INDIRECT APPROACH TO SKILLS   An interesting approach to the mechanics of English was followed by Carie Stegall, a Texas teacher, who published the results of her experience in *The Adventures of Brown Sugar: Adventures in Creative Writing.* Her pupils claimed that they hated English, so she imaginatively encouraged them to improve their English by writing a book at the fourth-grade level. The children chose her Pekingese dog as the subject for the book, and, as the book developed, they created their own text by practicing skills related to their writing needs as authors. These needs included outlining, finding synonyms for "said," and learning rules for punctuation.

Many children in intermediate-grade classes may enjoy doing a long-term project that uses a real person or animal in several episodes. The repetition of the same characters and settings assists both word fluency and spelling difficulties.

4

ORIENTAL POETRY AND OTHER SYLLABIC VERSE FORMS (FOR THE INTERMEDIATE GRADES)

Syllabic verse is a form of verse in which, as the name implies, stress is placed upon a certain number of lines, each of which contains a specific number of syllables, rather than upon stanzas made up of metrical foot patterns as in more traditional verse forms. Syllabic verse is also less lyrical and less rhymed than the more traditional forms; some people feel, in fact, that syllabic poetry might even be called "prose poetry."

One principal advantage of a poetry-writing experience in syllabic verse for young authors is this limited emphasis upon formal rhyme and stanzaic patterns. Inexperienced writers working on rhyme spend more time on nonsensical rhyme exercises than they do upon aspects of thought and mood. Syllabic poetry as written in English usually focuses upon something symbolic, a central mood, and a clear image or idea.

While *haiku* poetry probably illustrates one of the most well-known types of syllabic verse, there are many other types that this chapter will consider, including the *tanka, renga, senryu, cinquain,* and *lanterne* forms, as well as others.

ORIENTAL POETRY

In recent years Westerners have become interested in Oriental patterns of poetry, especially the form known as *haiku*. This is a form of verse written in 17 syllables, which are divided into three lines of 5, 7, 5.

It is important for students to understand some of the basic qualities of haiku before writing a verse, otherwise writing just becomes a gadget or a stunt of counting syllables. To begin with, good haiku poetry is both related to nature and seasonal in character, most poetic examples reflecting man's closeness to nature in a way that, without explicitly stating the season, the season is understood; a Japanese reader will recognize the time of year from certain key words. A volume explaining seasonal symbols clearly is *A Net of Fireflies: Japanese Haiku and Haiku Paintings,* with verse translations and an essay by Harold Stewart. For instance, springtime includes February, March, and April and is revealed through such images as the Japanese nightingale, butterflies, frogs, cherry blossoms, plum blossoms, wisteria, and peonies. Summer is May, June, and July, and such words as "cuckoos," "fireflies," "goldfish," "morning-glories," and "evening breezes" connote this season. Autumn includes the months August, September, and October, and appropriate images might be the Milky Way, wild geese, quails, chrysanthemums, maple leaves, and ivy. Winter includes November, December, and January, and symbols of the season include frost, ice, hail, winter moons, withered fields, camellias, and mandarin ducks.

A second quality of haiku is the expression of the "ahness" or "suchness" of things. Nothing is too insignificant to be worth expressing in this poetic form: a frog breaks the silence of a spring evening; a tranquil willow tree weeps by a stream; the pelting hail pounds a merchant's back; a cricket grieves near a scarecrow's sleeves, and a swallow darts forth from the nostril of a Buddha fashioned in bronze. Each experience he observes is significant to the creator, a principle that extends to the interrelationship between man and nature: man looks at Fujiyama so long that the mountain becomes a part of man, and man becomes a part of the mountain.

A third quality expressed in haiku is the immediacy of the moment. The verse is written with the eye of the poet upon a sparrow, or on the swirling sea; the author is an experiencer. The poet Basho writes of willow leaves falling while he and his lord listen to a bell, and Hokushi looks at the ashes of a burned cottage as cherry trees scatter their blossoms over the dull grayness; Kakei sees a dull bucket being pulled from a gloomy well, but a pink camellia bloom lightens the darkness; Issa depicts a mooing cow slowly coming into view. Both poet and reader feel a relationship to the happening of the moment or instant of time.

A fourth haiku quality is its image-making one. If the reader sees no image, the verse is either poor in construction or the experiencer has an impoverished background. Each verse should offer a delicate painting in miniature. The poet Chiyo, for instance, goes to a spring to draw a bucket of water, but when he sees morning-glories clinging around its sides, he journeys on to another one; Kikaku depicts the murmuring sea with one vermilion torii gate looming up through the early mists, and Chora writes of plaintive plovers disappearing as the moon sinks away and daylight arrives. If an author reads haiku orally, a listener can close his eyes and relive a moment of beauty.

A fifth quality of haiku, not present in all poems and usually not evident in creations by amateurs, is the expression of an unfinished statement. The author creates a bit of verse that the reader interprets his own way, each person extending the verse in his imagination according to his personal observations and cultural background.

A sixth quality of much haiku verse is its focus upon an individual incident, object, or creature. Ordinarily, the poet does not depict a group of willow trees; he looks at one willow tree so it is almost personified in his consciousness, as he will also look at one frog or one heron. Soseki rebukes a cricket who reminds him of autumn, and Taigi depicts the bee and butterfly playing tag in different peonies.

A seventh quality of haiku is its contemplative spirit. Many Japanese poets have studied Zen Buddhism, and some artists immerse themselves in this philosophy for decades before they create verses of note. Some readers of haiku can sense this quality of "becoming," the ceaseless struggle to reach a sense of "being." Westerners may not accept some of the philosophic tenets of Zen Buddhism, but they do feel refreshed by the quiet feeling of dignity and sense of repose a poet expresses as he shares a simple experience; these qualities are very evident in Noritake's scene of blossoms falling and butterflies fluttering to a branch to take their place, Buson's view of drops of dew delicately perched on brambles at sunrise, and Boncho's depiction of a black-ribbon river darkening a deep snow scene.

Some haiku verse expresses the transience of life—the feeling that life is but a fleeting moment. Sometimes, as the Oriental poet depicts a fluttering blossom, a twittering bird, or a croaking frog, one senses that this glimpse of loveliness is evanescent and fleeting, that it lies suspended for one moment of beauty and then passes away. Basho, for instance, writes that the hour of the morning-glory must end, and Onitsura notes the bursting of spring buds into blossoms and compares the falling petals to the days of his life, which soon pass away.

A ninth quality of haiku, self-evident in every form of good verse, is economy of statement, or understatement, closely related to the quality of the unfinished statement, already discussed. Haiku is similar to *haiga* or *sumi-e* paintings, in which there are spaces that must be mentally filled in by the beholder. Basho writes of a night heron shrieking at the lightning, but one does not see the total pattern of action—it must be completed by the imagination of the reader.

Some activities related to Oriental poetry—both haiku and other—follow. Most Oriental poetic forms have a similar philosophy and form to that of haiku, but vary their structural patterns.

I. Haiku

109 · HAIKU VERSE IN ENGLISH   Pupils of all ages may wish to experiment in writing several different types of haiku verse. This is a writing experience that can be done either at a surface or depth level. Inexperienced amateurs would work on syllabic patterns only, helped sometimes by using a pattern form with dashes for syllables, as follows:

Line	Syllables
1 – – – – –	5
2 – – – – – – –	7
3 – – – – –	5

But before attempting to create haiku verse, students should have many listening and reading experiences relating to the poetic form. Numerous books are available, among them:

1. Behn, Harry, trans. *Cricket Songs: Japanese Haiku.* With pictures selected from Sesshu and other Japanese masters. New York: Harcourt, Brace & World, Inc., 1964.

2. Beilenson, Peter, trans. *A Haiku Garland: A Collection of Seventeen-Syllable Classic Poems by Basho, Buson, Issa, Shiki, Sokan, Kikaku, and Others.* With decorations by Jeff Hill. Mount Vernon, N.Y.: Peter Pauper Press, 1968.

3. Beilenson, Peter, and Behn, Harry, trans. *Haiku Harvest.* Japanese Haiku Series, vol. 4. Decorations by Jeff Hill. Mount Vernon, N.Y.: Peter Pauper Press, 1962.

4. Henderson, Harold G. *Haiku in English.* Rutland, Vt.: Charles E. Tuttle Company, 1966.

5. *Japanese Haiku.* Translated from the Masters of the Seventeen Syllable Poetic Form (Basho, Buson, Issa, Sheki, Sokan, Kikaku, Ransitsu, Joso, Yaha, Boncho, and others). Mount Vernon, N.Y.: Peter Pauper Press, 1955.

6. Lewis, Richard, ed. *The Moment of Wonder: A Collection of Chinese and Japanese Poetry.* Illustrated with paintings by Chinese and Japanese masters. New York: Dial Press, Inc., 1964.

7. Yasuda, Kenneth. *The Japanese Haiku: Its Essential Nature, History, and Possibilities in English, with Selected Examples.* Rutland, Vt.: Charles E. Tuttle Company, 1966.

Samples of haiku verse can be given to pupils to show them the structural form; however, it might be remembered that haiku verse-writing is an experience, not just an act of counting syllables. One teacher preceded verse writing by giving the class an opportunity to investigate many different objects relating to nature, including mounted specimens of insects and grass, a beautiful live dragonfly, pictures of cherry blossoms, and slides showing beautiful, natural scenes.

A sample haiku follows:

> Wrinkled waves below (5)
> A silver-sheeted bowl rim (7)
> For scarlet ibis (5)

110 · MAKING SEASONAL DICTIONARIES Most countries do have various seasons, although the seasonal months may differ from those of Japan. For instance, all of California does not have all of the seasonal variations that Japan has—or that even other states in the United States have—but some parts of the state have distinct seasons. In fall a Californian might think of falling elm leaves and bronze chrysanthemums, and in spring chartreuse blades of grass, almond blossoms, and, perhaps, blustery winds; summer could mean roses, watermelons, and cantaloupes.

To heighten children's awareness of the seasons and the words or concepts that fit each one specially, a valuable class or individual project can be the making of seasonal dictionaries. Either each child can make a personal seasonal dictionary and decorate it with water-color paintings, or four class committees can be formed, with each committee responsible for one large, attractively illustrated seasonal dictionary representing one of the seasons.

111 · SYMBOLISM IN FLOWERS AND PLANTS Younger pupils are uninterested in symbolism, but preadolescents are quite fascinated with the symbolic connotation of flowers. Many books on *ikebana,* or Japanese flower arranging, are available in libraries, art stores, and in schools. A beautiful but expensive volume is *The Art of Arranging Flowers: A Complete Guide to Japanese Ikebana* by Shozo Sato, which has several pages in the bibliography devoted to flowers and their traditional symbolic implications. A committee of pupils could prepare a special report on

"The Symbolism of Flowers," the report enhanced by using an opaque projector to project illustrations of flowers.

112 · Two-line, rhymed Oriental verses Much haiku verse is not translatable in a typical syllabic pattern of 5, 7, 5 syllables. In fact, a slavish addiction to this form gets tiresome. Such a volume as *A Net of Fireflies* has some beautiful translations that are presented as rhymed couplets. After the pupils have experienced enough unrhymed verse in the 5, 7, 5 syllabic pattern, they may wish to create some verses in the Oriental style patterned after the Stewart translations. These lines are not hindered by such restrictions of pattern as meter, but move along freely to express an idea:

> Bright acacia shimmers on brown rocky bank
> With yellow fluffy balls retreating before the sun that sank.

113 · Haiku as an unfinished statement Pupils at most age levels have little difficulty with the syllabic pattern of haiku, and most boys and girls easily comprehend the seasonal and nature qualities of the verse form. Grasping the "unfinished statement" idea, however, is more difficult. This "unfinished statement" is a verse that is incomplete enough to stimulate completion by its reader. Such a verse is:

> And as the blossoms fall
> Clouds of white gather
> At the bottom, and then . . .
>
> Ken

One teacher, Francis Valente, did some interesting work with some intellectually-gifted fourth- and fifth-grade pupils. He aroused interest in haiku by setting up a colorful bulletin board decorated in orange, yellow, lavender, and green, and with samples of Japanese calligraphy in squares. About a week before the actual writing lesson was presented, the teacher wrote the words "Haiku is coming!" on the chalkboard. When he initiated the lesson, he discovered that ten pupils had brought in definitions for haiku and all the pupils in the class had discovered its meaning. Several verses were written on the chalkboard and the pupils discussed their brevity, simplicity, openness, and seasonal qualities.

On the following day eight haiku poems were interpreted, and two children brought in original verses they had written. The next day was spent experimenting with light, sound, and things in nature, and in a subsequent lesson Japanese art pictures were displayed.

A three-line haiku verse about scattering blooms was read and the pupils were asked to interpret its meaning. One child wrote the following:

> The blossoms of spring are all around me. As I sit and gaze about I see only living things. As a warm wind scatters the blooms about, I smell their fragrance. Then I say to myself, could these blooms be me? As the wind blows, then could it be the wind blowing me through life?
>
> SANDY

Another child reacted to a haiku poem about snow and mountains with a definition: "*Haiku* is a short poem with pictures that make you think about what is said."

Sixteen haiku translated into English were duplicated for these pupils, and they selected verses they liked and interpreted them through the use of phrases or summary sentences. In related activities, several pupils voluntarily created haiku booklets while other children experimented with such other forms of verse as *cinquains* and *tankas*. Some haikus follow:

> In the meadows of Spring
> Lies the blues of Winter behind
> Itself, until . . .
>
> KEN

> The caterpillar
> Is sleeping in his cocoon
> And then? . . .

In the heavy world's
Shadow, I watch the sputnik
Coasting in sunlight.

CHERYL

114 · COMMITTEE CREATION OF HAIKU VERSES After the children have listened to many poems and become familiar with the verse form, committees of three pupils each can create cooperative haiku verses. First a beautiful landscape scene such as a waterfall tumbling over rocks can be shown to help motivate pupils to write haiku verses related to nature, after which the children, as practice before breaking up into committees, can create a class haiku. Student teacher Cheryl Graef mounted ten beautiful landscapes, among them pictures of horses, roses, tumbling waters, ships, waters, and rainbows. The pupils formed into committees of three and the chairman of each committee selected a picture. The committee looked at the scene together and wrote original haiku verses, sharing the results with the others in the class. The poems were neatly printed with flow-brush pens and mounted on scrolls decorated with water colors. The scrolls were then hung up with colored cord or yarn.

115 · A HAIKU EXPERIENCE THROUGH FILM A vicarious experience with the beauty of such objects in nature as trickling waterfalls, a frog, and dramatic cloud effects is to be found in a film issued by Coronet, *Haiku: An Introduction to Poetry.* The musical accompaniment to the film is provided by Kiu Haghaghi, a composer and musician from Iran who plays the *santour,* an ancient Persian stringed instrument similar to the dulcimer, with a total of eighty strings and a range of three and a half octaves. Much haiku verse is woven into the sound track of the movie, making the haiku experience an effective one.

The Weston Woods Company has also issued a film, *A Day Is Two Feet Long,* which, too, is designed to give viewers an appreciation for natural beauty.

Children should probably have had much experience with haiku in English before viewing either one of these films. And, after viewing one of them, little talking should follow, as conversation might break the mood and alter the viewers' impressions. Sometimes it might be necessary to experience a film, talk about it briefly, and then rerun it. After viewing one of these films, pupils can be given a chance to write a descriptive prose piece or some haiku verse on one of the impressions he received from it.

116 · LINKED OR CHAIN HAIKU VERSES Traditional haiku verse, as we have seen, is characterized by its economy of form and unfinished quality. Some students may enjoy writing linked or chain haiku poems. The poet can select a subject from nature, such as trees, cats, dogs, horses, or frogs, or an abstract subject, such as loneliness, courage, or love. For instance, he might select a subject such as "My Siamese Cat." Then he might write six haiku verses in which he presents aspects of the world as seen through the eyes of the cat. These might be linked together through such a title as "Views of a Cat."

Better chain haiku is interlinked in such a way that the lines in each verse are related to each other in the context of the poem. An example follows:

FOR WHAT?

Slimy crawly snail
Creeping slowly to the rose
Distorting petals;

In a lacy trail
Of a creature's cruel taste
Of velvet wonder.

II. Tanka and Senryu

117 · TANKA *Tanka* verse is composed of a haiku verse (known as *hokku* when it is part of a tanka poem) plus two more lines, seven syllables each and known as the *ageku*. The entire poem totals 31 syllables.

Tanka pattern

Line		Syllables	
1	– – – – –	5	⎫
2	– – – – – – –	7	⎬ hokku
3	– – – – –	5	⎭
4	– – – – – – –	7	⎫
5	– – – – – – –	7	⎬ ageku
		31 syllables	

Tanka verse is similar to the haiku form, but the addition of the two lines of seven syllables each cap the verse and make it sound more complete, producing a different effect from haiku.

THE QUEEN

Pearl dew is kissing (5)
The dainty queen butterfly (7)
She is a monarch (5)
In golden robes of bronze orange (7)
Reigning in royal glory. (7)

118 · TANKA PARTNER GAME In China, couples or family members used to work together to create tanka verses at parties and poetry contests. Usually, an "Emperor" declared a certain theme or subject and couples cooperated, one person writing the first three lines, or opening hokku, and a partner capping the tanka with two concluding lines of seven syllables each. Young authors enjoy composing poems or couplets this way.

119 · LINKED TANKA At one time Oriental poets wrote poems using linked verses. The popularity of chain verses has diminished in recent years because the haiku pattern is more diminutive and exquisite, as well as more modern in style. Children, however, may enjoy writing chain tanka, which consists of writing two related tanka verses and unifying them with a title.

Two samples of linked tanka verses written by children are:

ABRAHAM LINCOLN

Abraham Lincoln
Modest though he was and kind
Quiet too at times.
He loved to read books on law
Good hard worker with the plow.

Hard reader he was
Gray, shabby books on shelf
Tried law work he did
Abe did an excellent job
President of the country.

STANLEY

CURIOUS MAN

Scantily-clad man
Walking proudly down the street
Your gold ring shining . . .
Looking at a crowd in wonder
Pushing on with great concern.

There . . . a thin lady
Her hands stretched out for money . . .
The man turned away,
Then stopped, and gave her a coin . . .
Money for a blind beggar.

JOAN

120 · SENRYU OR FANPIECES   The *senryu* is a combination of the best qualities of haiku and an epigrammatic idea. An epigram is a witty, brief statement that focuses upon a human weakness or turns a traditional idea into another thought by a cleverly stated phrase. Thomas E. Sanders in his book *The Discovery of Poetry* includes several illustrations of fanpieces. A typical fanpiece has 14 to 16 syllables. It contains a paradox, communicates by means of an implied metaphor, and sometimes uses such poetic elements as alliteration, consonance, and assonance. Fanpieces are similar to haiku in their simplicity, but they are didactic, or teach a moral, and sometimes include a paradox.

An example of a senryu or fanpiece follows:

SIGNIFYING NOTHING

Between the talks and written word
All that I uttered; so absurd!

CARLSON

III. Activities Based on Japanese Verse and Other Japanese Arts

121 · HAIKU AND OTHER JAPANESE ARTS   Cindy Martin, a student teacher, presented several lessons on haiku that correlated art, music, and poetry. She asked the children to review things they already knew about Japan, after which she played the record, "Sayonara," and she and the children discussed differences between Japanese and Western music. Two girls put on Japanese kimonos and presented a dance to the tune of "Sayonara." The teacher and pupils discussed the simplicity of Japanese dance movements and gestures.

At another session some pictures of Oriental screens, painted with simple brush strokes, were displayed. A flowering cherry branch was used as a model, and after a demonstration of simple brush strokes in the Japanese style was given, the children were encouraged to paint in that style, using light gray construction paper and black, pink, and white tempera paints.

In another lesson the pupils were informed that simplicity was not only a quality of art, it was also a principal aspect of good writing. After several haiku verses by professional Japanese poets were read in English translation, a class haiku was composed and written on the chalkboard. Then springtime was given as a theme and the pupils wrote verses. A bulletin board, entitled "Springtime Haiku," was arranged and poems and pictures were framed with black paper and exhibited on a white background that had been washed with pale pink, yellow, orange, and lavender water colors.

On following days pupils composed original haiku verses and continued to read poems created by Japanese poets. More haiku displays were set up, this time using simulated rice paper as a mount for the poems. The "rice paper" was made the following way:

Gray construction paper, which was to form the background for the rice paper, was cut in the shape of a square or rectangle and fresh flower petals arranged in a design on it. Some paper tissues were pulled from a box, separated, and a thin sheet placed over the entire surface of the construction paper and flowers. A solution of white glue and water was made, and a brush saturated with the solution was brushed lightly over the tissues. This process was continued until the tissues were completely saturated. A little lumpiness, caused by the flower petals placed underneath and similar to the whiter grains in real rice paper, appeared. The simulated rice paper was dried, after which the children took the original poems they had written and pasted them on the rice paper.

A few of the original verses follow:

> Who are you seven,
> Growing up to be eleven,
> But soon will be old.
>   BOBBY

SPRINGTIME

> In the Spring dogwood
> Blooms across a crown and nail marks
> God's own special tree.
>   LISA MARIE

122 · PAINTED JAPANESE FANS   Japanese art forms should be blended with poetry, and the Japanese fan is a beautiful art piece. A little volume, *Painted Fans of Japan: Fifteen Noh-Drama Masterpieces,* edited by Reiko Chiba, offers an excellent introduction to this form of art, since it reproduces some of the painted fans used in traditional Noh dramas. The painting usually conformed to the shape of the fan. The folding fan or *ogi* was probably invented in Japan in the eighth century. In Japan, fans have been used for many purposes—to fan charcoal burners, to use as an offensive or defensive weapon, to be carried to weddings, or to accompany the chants and lyrics of a dance drama as a sort of dance motion. Chiba states that travelers frequently carried map fans as they journeyed along the highway.

Children may enjoy painting scenes on paper folded in the shape of fans, accompanying the scenes with some haiku or tanka verses related to them.

123 · GOLDFISH SIGNATURES AND "TELEGRAMS" As pupils continue to work with abbreviated statements or phrases, they begin to appreciate the delicacy and power of few words. Modern advertising billboards get their messages cleverly across by using a few telegraphic words with white spaces between, similar to the manner of a Japanese *sumi-e* artist, who places his brush on the paper and leaves expanses of white space between the dark blobs of ink. The Charles E. Tuttle Company of Rutland, Vermont, has issued an unusual book of poems entitled *Gold and Fish Signatures,* by Paul Reps. An interesting Japanese art, as described in the book, consists of fish rubbings. A fish is brushed on one side with sumi or black ink and pressed against rice paper so it will leave its signature on the paper. A fish wiggles for several minutes after it is pulled from the water; sometimes a fish splotched with sumi ink is allowed to wiggle across the paper, giving squirming, active motion to the painting. (Poetic signatures of fish are known as *gyotaku* and are also described in *Gyotaku: The Art and Technique of the Japanese Fish Print* by Yoshio Hiyama.)

The Reps book gets its messages across through simple telegraphic phrases or words illustrated with simple pictures made up of black strokes or smudges employing both "goldfish signatures" and brush painting. For instance, a trunk of a bamboo might be shown, or a piece of root, along with such words as "Bloom will come." This short phrase, more than would a lengthy descriptive paragraph, vividly depicts the renewal of life in spring through growth and the fresh new beginnings of plants. The author also explores the interrelationship of man and nature.

Pupils may enjoy writing telegraphic messages and illustrating them with brief forceful brush strokes, using paint or ink. The project, of course, will be enhanced if the pupil uses his best handwriting. The telegraphic messages themselves should be quite abbreviated, no more than phrases of two or three related words.

Boys and girls might also like to try crayon rubbings; they may not have fish available for rubbings, but they can experiment with the technique by placing a sheet of thin paper over an object such as a leaf, a root, or a weed and rubbing over the paper with a crayon to create a pattern. Another helpful book on the subject is *Rubbings and Textures, a Graphic Technique* by John Bodor.

124 · PIXIES   A type of poetic and artistic expression similar to that in *Gold and Fish Signatures* by Paul Reps might be developed in the style of a cartoonist. For instance, Jack Wohl had a column entitled "Pixies," which appeared in the May 4, 1969, issue of the *Chicago Tribune* magazine. One picture accompanied by a few brief words can depict more than a lengthy story or poem.

One picture depicts an open match package, with a statement to the effect that one only gets noticed by striking.

Another picture shows two E's. The E to the left has the traditional three horizontal parts, while the E to the right has four. The first E says to the second E, "Nobody likes a hoarder."

Pupils with a gift of humor can draw simple cartoons or cut out pictures from newspapers and magazines to create their own "Pixies."

125 · SUMI-E PAINTING AND HAIKU VERSE   The study of sumi-e painting helps the artist to extract the beauty hidden in nature and shows how to communicate that beauty with simple brush strokes. Students may wish to experiment with sumi-e painting and haiku verse correlated as a unit. A helpful book for this project would be Jack McDowell's and Takahiko Mikami's *The*

Art of Japanese Brush Painting. The painting may be created first and the verse related to it or the verse may be created first and the painting then can illustrate it.

126 · BIOGRAPHY IN POETRY AND PHOTOGRAPHS A beautiful biography of the Japanese poet Issa is entitled *Of This World: a Poet's Life in Poetry,* by Richard Lewis. The poet's life is illustrated, not only with striking photographs, but with illustrative poetic verses. Pupils may enjoy selecting a biography, writing part of his life story and illustrating it with haiku or tanka verses.

127 · A CLASS HAIKU BOOK Susan Jacques, a student teacher, worked with haiku verse in a class composed mostly of Mexican-American students who had had little experience with poetry but who had previously had much observational experience with nature-study specimens. Several samples of haiku verses were duplicated, giving the children the opportunity to experience the poetic form visually and orally, after which they created their own haiku verses. Susan obtained a book of wallpaper samples and the children selected wallpaper, to complement each poem, on which to mount their work. For instance, one child wrote

STARS

Twinkle like fairies
Running here and there
to guide the sun
PATTI

and mounted it on a piece of wallpaper covered with stars and dripping dots. A dramatic piece of black wallpaper with a silver and green pattern on it was chosen for the verse

CAT

It makes not a sound
as it runs through the dark night
Seeking adventure
PATTI

A piece of brown wood-grained paper backed the poem

The old oak is wise,
On a clear hot summer day
But lonely as night

TERRY

These mounted verses were displayed on a bulletin board decorated with miniature cherry blossoms fashioned of pink and
purple tissue paper and the word "Haiku" written in imitation
of Japanese calligraphy. Later, the verses were mounted in a
class book, the covers of which were decorated with cherry
blossoms and a butterfly, and mounted on Japanese rice paper.

128 · FLOWER ARRANGEMENTS AND WRITTEN EXPRESSION   One
Japanese boy in a sixth-grade California classroom brought a
bouquet of flowers from home and made it into an exquisite
arrangement. Some pupils wrote poems about the flowers, using
Oriental verse forms; other students wrote paragraphs in which
they described the beauty of the flowers from different viewpoints. Numerous books are available on Japanese flower arrangements. One of these is *A Treasury of Japanese Flower Arrangements* by Tatsuo Ishimoto.

OTHER SYLLABIC VERSE FORMS

129 · THE CINQUAIN   The poetic verse form called the *cinquain* was originated by Adelaide Crapsey, a fragile minister's
daughter who suffered from tuberculosis and spent much of her
life writing poetry while she was a patient at Saranac. Her delicate, atmospheric poems suggest the Japanese style.

The pattern of the cinquain is five iambic lines organized as
follows: one foot in the first line, two feet in the second, three
in the third, four in the fourth, and one in the fifth. This poem
can be organized through the use of syllables.

Pattern of the Cinquain

Line		Syllables
1	– –	2
2	– – – –	4
3	– – – – – –	6
4	– – – – – – – –	8
5	– –	2

The organizational pattern of the cinquain gives the form a rising and falling, emotional feeling that is quite poignant. Several representative cinquains can be found in *The Discovery of Poetry* by Thomas E. Sanders. An example of a cinquain is:

THE CITY

People
Callous and cold
Hurrying scurrying
Squeaking bleating blaring noises
Bedlam.

CARLSON

130 · THE DOUBLE CINQUAIN The double cinquain loses its delicacy, beauty, and poignancy, but it is an interesting poem for experimental purposes. Creators of the double cinquain merely double the number of syllables or iambic beats to a line, so the pattern becomes:

Line		Syllables
1	– – – –	4
2	– – – – – – – –	8
3	– – – – – – – – – – – –	12
4	– – – – – – – – – – – – – – – –	16
5	– – – –	4

Here is a seventh-grade girl's first attempt at a double cinquain:

TRADING RAT

A trading rat (4)
With a long and ugly gray tail (8)
A large sniffling nose on a very saddened face (12)
The squirming small body twisting through a great and huge
  brown doorway (16)
Replacing gifts. (4)

131 · CHAIN OR LINKED CINQUAIN VERSES These verses also
lose some of the delicacy of the Crapsey cinquain verse, but
some children enjoy linking several individual cinquains together
under one topic.

The following poem, about a cannibal flower, gets considerable
feeling in its three linked verses:

DEVIL FLOWER

Blossom
Devil Flower
Baiting small helpless flies
Venus flytrap is a demon
Flytrap.

Flower
Grotesque blossom
Living in nature's realm
Living by the law of nature
Kills flies

Venus
Traps small victims
Long arms close upon fly.
Life and death in man's nursery
Cruel trap.

RICKEY

132 · THE LANTERNE The *lanterne* is a delicate syllabic form
organized visually into the shape of a Japanese lantern. The
structure of the verse gives it a rising and falling feeling.

Line		Syllables
1	–	1
2	– –	2
3	– – –	3
4	– – – –	4
5	–	1

My
kitten
fluffy as
vanilla white
cones
PAT

133 · CHAIN OR LINKED LANTERNES   Interesting effects can be obtained by linking several lanternes together. After a chain lanterne is written, each verse could be posted on a miniature Japanese lantern and hung in a chain on colored cord, or pasted on colored tissue paper and suspended from a paper-flower tree. A chain lanterne by a seventh-grade boy follows:

My
Dog is
A pretty
Cocker spaniel
Dog.

He
Is black
And white on
His two front paws
But,

Spot
My dog
Was run down
By a fast black
Car.
JIM

An unusual chain lanterne poem, created by a fourth-grade pupil and depicting the cycle of life through an egg and bird, appears in *Language Sparklers for the Intermediate Grades* by Ruth Kearney Carlson, pages 91–93.

134 · THE CAMEO   Most persons visualize the cameo as a gem of different colored layers, with a design carved in relief on one and the other layers serving as background. The *cameo* poetic form, created by Alice Maude Spokes, consists of seven lines of 2, 5, 8, 3, 8, 7, 2 syllables respectively, each line ending with a strong word.

RUNNING

Hurt deer (2)
Rustling in the grass (5)
So young to leave and oh so scared (8)
Running hard (3)
By sages and trees so swiftly (8)
Until it reaches safety (7)
Then gone! (2)

BILLY

135 · DOUBLE AND CHAIN CAMEOS   Some pupils enjoy creating either double cameos, by doubling the number of syllables in each line, or chain cameos, by linking two or three cameos together by means of a single subject or relating the action of verses together.

After a cameo has been written, it can be illustrated by a silhouette-type of figure, to relate the cameo poetic form to the idea of the gem. Interesting ideas for cut- and torn-paper silhouettes appear in *Silhouettes, Shadows and Cutouts* by Norman Laliberté and Alex Mogelon.

136 · THE PENSEE   The *pensee* verse form, created by Alice Maude Spokes, is made up of five lines of 2, 4, 7, 8, and 6 syllables each, and each line ending with a strong word. An amusing vignette written in this style follows:

LITTLE GIRL

Small girl (2)
With big brown eyes (4)
Her brown hair so long and straight (7)
Face dirtied from eating ice cream (8)
Chocolate coated child! (6)

Some writers may wish to create double or chain pensees by doubling the syllables in each line or linking two or three pensees together.

137 · THE SEPT   The *sept* form, originated by Etta Josephean Murfey, has a pattern somewhat like the lanterne, as it builds up syllables and then drops them. It is a seven-line poem with a syllabic pattern of 1, 2, 3, 4, 3, 2, 1.

Rare (1)
Gleaming (2)
Emerald (3)
Dew-kissed pine branch (4)
Shimmering (3)
Spicy (2)
Fresh (1)

138 · THE SEPTET   The *septet,* originated by Mary Owen Lewis, is a seven-line poem with a syllabic pattern of 3, 5, 7, 9, 7, 5, 3.

Haughty bird (3)
Parading proudly (5)
Flashing brilliant blue body (7)
Across lemon blossoms and roses (9)
Frightening sweet humming birds (7)
Away from flowers (5)
A cruel jay (3)

139 · THE VIGNETTE   Flozari Rockwood has created the *vignette* form, with its pattern of seven lines of 2, 4, 4, 6, 7, 7, 3

syllables respectively and strong ending words. A vignette is a
short piece of verse that describes things delicately and subtly.
And because the term also describes a running ornament of
leaves and tendrils used in architecture or to decorate a book,
vignette verses are probably most suited to nature themes.

SWAN LAKE

Pearl swan (2)
Beautifully (4)
Gliding in pond (4)
Graceful ballerina (6)
Reenacting musical (7)
Tale of Tchaikovsky music **(7)**
Poignantly. (3)

140 · THE QUINTET   The *quintet* verse form, developed by
Mary Owen Lewis, is arranged in five lines of 3, 5, 7, 9, 3 syllables respectively, each line ending with a strong word. It originated as a delicate, fragile pattern that described scenes vividly
and pictorially.

Redwood tall (3)
Overpowering (5)
Pygmy man and steel machine **(7)**
Racing along suicidal freeways **(9)**
Still power. (3)

5

TRADITIONAL AND EXPERIMENTAL VERSE FORMS

In Chapter 4, considerable emphasis was placed upon syllabic prosody, which measures the number of syllables per line with little regard to the stress of those syllables. In this chapter, however, we will be concerned with more traditional forms involving such principles as the poetic foot consisting of one stressed syllable and one or more unstressed syllables, the different rhyming patterns, and such stanzaic patterns as the *couplet, tercet,* and *quatrain.* Other traditional forms—the *triolet,* the *sonnet, free verse,* and the *ballad*—will also be discussed, along with a number of more experimental poetry types, including *concrete poetry, chirography,* the *diamonte, poems with visual analogies,* and *reduced language poems.* And all of the forms discussed will be accompanied by numerous creative activities children might enjoy.

As this book is not designed as a poetry handbook, however, many poetic forms will be eliminated. A teacher interested in knowing about poetic meter and poetic form may wish to consult such volumes as *Poetic Meter and Poetic Form* by Paul Fussell, Jr., *Poetry Handbook: A Dictionary of Terms* by Babette Deutsch, *The Forms of Poetry* by Louis Untermeyer, and *The Art and Craft of Poetry: An Introduction* by Lawrence Zillman.

MORE TRADITIONAL VERSE FORMS

141 · THE COUPLET   The couplet, the simplest form of formal poetry, consists of two lines of poetry that are bound together by rhyme (rhyme scheme, *aa*). The metrical line might be any length. Robert Browning used couplets to create dramatic monologues of great beauty—"My Last Duchess," for instance—and Robert Frost used the couplet effectively in his poem "The Tuft of Flowers." Eve Merriam has a poem called "Couplet Countdown" in her book, *It Doesn't Always Have to Rhyme*, and Professor Swigly Brown teaches the couplet form in *Take Sky: More Rhymes of the Never Was and Always Is* by David McCord. Some activities involving couplets include the following:

1. Have the pupils write a couplet about a favorite holiday.

2. Have the children create two couplets and connect them into a *quatrain*, or four-line verse. This rhyme could be used in a card for Valentine's Day, Mother's Day, Fourth of July, a birthday, or some other occasion, and the card decorated with a delicate water-color painting. Such couplets should be neatly printed in manuscript writing.

3. Have the children combine couplets into a dramatic monologue similar in style to the poetry of Browning. The monologue should be created for some well-known character.

4. The pupils might like to write a "couplet countdown," in which the couplets get shorter and shorter in length.

5. Have the children try a "couplet countup," in which couplets get longer and longer.

142 · THE QUATRAIN   The *quatrain* is a four-line poetic form that can consist of any metrical pattern and be written utilizing several rhyme schemes: *aabb, abcb, abab,* or *abba*. Students who become interested in specific poetic metrical names may wish to experiment with iambic or trochaic meter. Iambic is the simplest one, and is the basic meter for blank verse. Iambic meter can be represented by "hello" (˘ ´). Trochaic meter, or the trochee, can be represented by ´ ˘, in such words as "brother," "mother," "searing," "rocker."

Here are some quatrains written by children:

WINDOW SILL GARDEN

A window box of roses
Makes everyone stand still
To see a garden growing
Upon a window sill.

ANITA

CALICO CAT

She struts along, her head held high
Showing her beauty and likes to preen
She knows her word is law
She finds quite soon that she's the queen.

JOYCE

During preliminary work with quatrains, children should work with ideas, images, and picture thoughts more than they should with meter. In fact, drill on specific meters such as iambic, trochaic, anapestic, or dactylic should probably be avoided unless there are pupils who are curious about the formal names.

Some activities with quatrains include the following:

1. Have each of the children write a quatrain about an animal he has closely observed; after the children have written one quatrain, they might add another that shows a different aspect of the same animal.

2. One of the best-known poems by Robert Frost, and a good one to use with children, is "The Pasture," which is composed of two quatrains written in such a way that the rhyme is quite subtle. A student might study the poem carefully and create a poem of his own about some animal in a different setting. It could be about a city cat foraging for food in an alley; it might be about a boy fishing.

3. Have the children observe a grasshopper, bee, aphid, or some other insect carefully and create a quatrain.

4. Have them write two quatrains, one describing a city scene and the other one a country scene.

5. The children could write quatrains about outer space.

Claudia Lewis has included many space poems in her book
Poems of Earth and Space.

6. Some children might write quatrains about mechanical man
in a computerized world.

143 · THE TERCET OR TRIPLET   The *tercet,* or *triplet,* consists
of three usually fairly short lines, rhymed or unrhymed, and can
be written utilizing many rhyme schemes, such as *aaa, aba, baa,
aab,* or *abc.* The *haiku* might be one example of a tercet. Tenny-
son uses the tercet pattern in "The Eagle," which appears in
Sound and Sense: An Introduction to Poetry by Laurence Perrine.
Harriet Monroe has used tercets in her highly structured poem
"In March," which appears in *The Hollow Reed* by Mary J. J.
Wrinn. Some sample tercets by children appear in *Sparkling
Words: Two Hundred Practical and Creative Writing Ideas* by
Ruth Kearney Carlson. Some activities involving tercets follow:

1. Have each child write a poem about the wind, rain, snow,
or some other weather phenomenon, using two tercets.

2. Have the children write tercets about one season, then add
three more, one for each one of the remaining seasons.

3. The pupils might like to write some linked tercets about
a person whom each child has carefully observed in a bus or on
the street.

4. Have the children write tercets about wild or zoo animals.

5. Have them write a tercet about a flower, in which the
author must demonstrate the use of at least two senses.

144 · THE TRIOLET   The triolet is a dainty, exotic form of
verse consisting of a single eight-line stanza that uses only two
rhymes. It is built on a refrain of two lines, which begin and end
the triolet. The pattern is *ABaAabAB.* Adelaide Crapsey wrote
a triolet, "Song," and Austin Dobson wrote two triolets, "The
Kiss" and "Urceus Exit." In "Write Me a Verse," appearing in
Take Sky: More Rhymes of the Never Was and Always Is, by
David McCord, Professor Swigly Brown teaches the triolet, illustrating his teaching with several verses.

A beginning poet can write a triolet by first working a skele-
ton structure and thinking of the rhythmical pattern:

Line

1	_____	A ⎫ Refrain
2	_____	B ⎭
3	_____	a (rhymes with A in refrain)
4	_____	A (identical line as A of refrain)
5	_____	a
6	_____	b (rhymes with B in refrain)
7	_____	A ⎫ Refrain
8	_____	B ⎭

A seventh-grade girl created this triolet in memory of the persons honored on Memorial Day:

MEMORIAL DAY LAMENT

Today and tomorrow	A
Dark days of our grief	B
Our suffering and sorrow,	a
Today and tomorrow,	A
Send pangs of much sorrow	a
To memories so brief.	b
Today and tomorrow	A
Dark days of our grief.	B

145 · THE SONNET A typical Petrarchan or Italian *sonnet* is a lyric poem of fourteen lines revealing a single thought or feeling or mood. It is divided into two sections, each of which expresses an idea, one related to or deduced from the other. Mary J. Wrinn has compared the two parts of a sonnet to the upper and lower lip of a sweet pea: each has a separate function but both work together to give the flower its bloom. The sonnet's principal idea is developed in the first eight lines, or octave; the secondary idea, or corollary, can be found in the final six lines, or sestet. The octave sets a problem, asks a question, draws a picture. The sestet applies more ideas, makes comments, or offers a solution. A good sonnet links the two parts together into one idea. One poet has compared the movement of a sonnet to a rocket: it is launched into the sky, gathers momentum, reaches its zenith, and then falls softly in a sprinkling of stars.

This sonnet form was developed in the fourteenth century in Italy. The rhyme scheme of the octave is *abbaabba,* the two *a's* in the middle of the octave giving unity to the stanza. The rhyme scheme of the sestet is *cdecde* or *cdcdcd.* One of the most beautiful Italian sonnets in the English language is "On First Looking into Chapman's Homer" by John Keats, even though it contains a slight geographical inconsistency. Another much-quoted work is *Sonnets from the Portuguese* by Elizabeth Barrett Browning.

The Shakespearean sonnet is somewhat less rigid than the Italian, since it includes seven rhymes. It consists of iambic pentameter, with a rhyme scheme of *abab, cdcd, efef,* and *gg.* The closing couplet caps the sonnet and summarizes the central idea of the poem.

Novices who are creating a sonnet for the first time may wish to work on a Shakespearean sonnet, beginning with the couplet first. This might mold the sonnet into a tighter form.

Students will probably not be able to create a perfect sonnet until they have had much experience with prosody, which might not come until the fourth year of high school. Many students, however, can get initial experience in writing sonnets by working on the basic sonnet pattern and not laboring with the intricacies of scansion. *Sparkling Words: Two Hundred Creative and Practical Writing Ideas* by Ruth Kearney Carlson includes three modified sonnets written by some seventh-grade pupils. Two other poems written by pupils in this same class follow:

ATOM'S FLASH

No day, no night will pass me still
Trickling, glowing streams run fast
Through the years I had my thrill
They're getting low because summer's passed.
The darkened night upon my sill
A succulent flower peeps through my sash
The window is open, I'm getting a chill
The waterways hit with a loud swift splash
In the far-away distance I hear the shrill

Sharp sounds resounding with a loud crash
That's ever around that distant hill
It whipped around and started to lash
Sandy desert and mountains or a city grill
Far over there, an atomic flash.

STANLEY

A DAY OF AWE

The grayish sky is gloomy as can be
It stays there always looking down at me
Darkness all around me slowly creeps
It sits in pale stillness as it sleeps
The sun is trying very hard to show;
I long to see its pale, pale glow.
It wants to shine its rays which are so bright
Oh look! It's almost coming into night.
The darkness all around me fades away
I didn't think I'd see this lovely day
The breeze that blows is very cooling now
Above my head it moves a drooping bough
The flowers which have beautified the day
Are closing in a very lovely way.

CHRISTINE

Pupils can write sonnets on almost any subject—love, war, peace, civil rights, discoveries, outer space, courage, learning, inventions, or anything they feel deeply about. Usually a sonnet should not be attempted prior to the seventh grade, and no child should struggle with scansion and prosody to the extent that his poetic appreciation is dulled.

146 · FREE VERSE   Although free verse follows no regular metrical pattern and recurrence of stress, it is not necessarily formless or unrestrained. The creator of free verse must be sensitive to rhyme, phrasing, and cadence and must work carefully to differentiate his poetry from prose styles of expression. The Matthew Arnold type of free verse uses a norm line of five feet with a dominant iambic foot and shorter lines organized around the pentameters. Such a poem is "Philomela." The Walt Whitman type of free verse is characterized by freedom from rhyme and regular metrical and rhymic pattern, as illustrated by his poem "When I Heard the Learn'd Astronomer." Whitman also uses the device of lengthening lines as parts of the poem progress, thereby offering strong climaxes, as seen in such poems as "Out of the Cradle Endlessly Rocking" and "When Lilacs Last in the Dooryard Bloomed." A third type, modern free verse, is not as regular as Arnold's free verse and is not as free as Whitman's. Modern poets rhyme or omit rhyme according to the tone of the poem and use a variety of rhythmical lines and phrasing. "The Twenty-third Psalm" can be arranged in a format resembling modern free verse.

Much recent modern verse uses ambiguity, ellipsis, and the device of "telescoping" words and ideas. Ambiguity used artistically is designed to offer two different images to the mind or ears of the experiencer, sometimes a pun. Ellipsis eliminates words needed to complete the syntax, but the gaps left by the omitted words can be bridged by the thought of the reader. "Telescoping" of words and ideas involves shortening and hyphenating words in order to render an idea more powerful. For instance, in "The Windhover" by Gerald Manley Hopkins, the poet uses the device on line two, "Daylight's dauphin, dapple-dawn-drawn Falcon." This speeds up the rhythm of the line and shortens what would normally be "dappled-dawn" to "dapple-dawn" by eliminating the final *d*.

Oriental and Hebrew verse make frequent use of rhythmical word patterns based on the cadence and modulations of the voice, the irregular spacing of accent due to the phrasal grouping of the words. E. E. Cummings illustrates this technique in his poem "Chanson Innocent," which speaks of a springtime world wonderful in its freshness and the marvel of mud puddles. His style frees the reader from formal verse scansion, but the poem still has form.

A child author is not skilled enough in prosody to work on poetic conventions such as intentional ambiguity and ellipsis, but children who are freed from the strictures of formalized rhythmical and stanza patterns and traditional metrical lines can create poems with cadence and an unforced stress of line.

Young children can create free verse best during moments of spontaneous experience, for it is at those times that a child sees images vividly and hears tunes naturally. For instance, the reader is sure that Stanley has observed a mother cat when he writes:

LIGHT MOVEMENT

Soft radiant glow
Dark cat sneaking by
Movements in the grass,
He hears.
As pale moon beams
He sees
A gopher in moonlight
He moves closer
Quieter
Looks, then jumps
Got him!
With a satisfied look
He carries it away
To eat.

This boy has not worked purposely for meter or rhythm. He has simply observed a cat carefully and reconstructed his experience with a natural, unforced rhythm.

In order to write free verse, some of the following suggestions might be helpful:

1. Provide numerous experiences in the out-of-doors; urban children can visit parks, stand on street corners, or visit museums near their homes.

2. Have the pupils work on diaries or journals, in which they should practice using a telescoped or telegraphic style of writing, employing short, simple phrases instead of more elaborate sentences. In sharing diaries, have the children work to eliminate pallid words such as "very," "nice," and "pretty," and try to include instead words that evoke clear-cut images or imaginative pictures.

3. Have the class listen to many poems by modern poets, such as E. E. Cummings, who work in a modified free-verse style.

The children should also have some experience reading numerous forms of Oriental verse, but only those that are beautiful in translation, not those that are merely a stereotyped syllabic pattern when translated into English.

4. Have the class collect numerous photographs and pictures that clearly and vividly depict landscapes and people and observe filmstrips and movies with the sound track turned off.

5. Encourage the children to listen to sounds around them. Encourage them, also, to imitate sounds; in this way the young authors can gain alertness, a sensitivity to various tunes, such as the tinkle of a Good Humor man's bell or the tolling sound of a church bell.

THE BALLAD FORM: FOLK SONGS AND THE BALLAD

The ballad is typically a narrative poem embodying a story or incident, originally sung or chanted to music. Ballads were traditionally concerned with the basic elements of life—death, love, intrigue, heroism, superstition, and tragedy—perhaps exemplified best by such ballads as "Sir Patrick Spens," "The Two Corbies," "Lord Randall," and the Robin Hood ballads.

They were also more concerned with action than developing characterizations of the central figures. In some ballads, the narration shifts to dialogue at the moment of heightened action. Dialogue is terse and to the point, and language is usually formalized. Traditionally, ballad creators use certain stereotyped terms, such as "milk-white steeds," "berry-brown horses," or "dapple-gray mounts." Steeds are shod in silver and gold, knights are usually gallant, and ladies are gay even at times of tragedy. Beds are often "soft and narrow," lips are "ruby red," and men are "true lovers."

English ballads are written in stanzas rather than in an uninterrupted series of lines. The *Viking Book of Ballads of the English-Speaking World* (edited by Albert B. Friedman), for instance, utilizes two principal stanza types. One is a stanza consisting of two lines of four beats each; the other stanza has four lines with the second and fourth lines rhyming and a pattern of four beats, three beats; four beats, three beats. And since ballads are folk poetry, they include such stylistic irregularities as wrenched accent and imperfect rhyme. Folk ballads do not force formal metrical patterns, but the ballad stanza is often the iambic quatrain, with its rhyme scheme of *abcb* and a number of variations, including a refrain of one or two repetitive lines, making overflow stanzas of five or six lines. In fact, repetition is a characteristic of many ballads, since the singers were reciting the tales from memory, and refrains were used to aid the memory and reiterate basic story parts. Hyperbole, as well as understatement, is also used frequently.

Some modern poets have taken the basic shape of the folk ballad and written literary ballads based on it; examples are "The Pied Piper of Hamelin Town" by Robert Browning, "The Ballad of the Harp Weaver" by Edna St. Vincent Millay, and "The Highwayman" by Alfred Noyes.

Many folk ballads have been collected by different scholars, but the most noted collection is a five-volume one by Francis James Child entitled *English and Scottish Popular Ballads,* in which introductions to 305 ballads are given. Using this collection as a base, Peggy Seeger and Ewan MacCall have issued *The Long Harvest,* a series of ten long-playing records, on which are presented forty traditional ballads and variations on them, including, in some cases, as many as eight different versions of a single ballad. The extensive notes that are provided with the album include Mr. Child's identifying numbers for many of the ballads, full texts, and a critical bibliography.

Note: Teachers using ballads with unsophisticated children may wish to eliminate verses they consider objectionable.

I. Ballad Study Activities

147 · A LETTER TO THE LIBRARY OF CONGRESS   A committee of pupils could write a letter to the Library of Congress, asking about references to folklore, the ballad, and sources for ballad collections.

148 · BALLAD REPORTS Pupils can use encyclopedias and books about folklore to prepare reports on the folk or the literary ballad. Such reports will be more interesting if they are accompanied by recorded selections or live music.

II. Activities Based on *The Ballad of America*

Numerous ballads relating to American history appear in *The Ballad of America: A History of the United States in Song and Story* by John Anthony Scott. The ballads in this collection lend themselves readily to classroom writing activities.

149 · DRAMATIZED BALLADS Some ballads lend themselves to pantomiming or dramatization. Pupils can take such a ballad as "Soldier, Soldier, Won't You Marry Me?" and rewrite it in the form of a playlet, giving stage directions. The Scott volume provides the music for the ballad, but it can also be chanted. Another interesting American ballad to dramatize is "Jenny Jenkins," a courting song of colonial days. In this ballad a lover is interested in the colors his sweetheart, Jenny, might wear, since a color indicated the attitude of the sweetheart. Red, for instance, stood for sin, blue for faithfulness, and white for purity. The lover asks her what color she is wearing once in every stanza. In dramatizing this, a girl could wear a certain color and a boy could sing the question to her.

150 · DOCUDRAMAS A *docudrama* consists of basic historical documents, music, song, and narration combined to depict accurately the historical or literary traditions of a country. In creating a docudrama, pupils can select any period of American history. Basic categories could include (1) The American Revolution, (2) The Early National Period, (3) Sea and Immigration, (4) The Westward Movement, (5) Slavery Days, and (6) The Civil War. Other docudramas could cover such topics as farmers and workers, immigrants, the Negro people, and the period between and since the two world wars. In recent years several books have been published that contain copies of authentic documents, including *To Be a Slave*, by Julius Lester, and *In Their Own*

Words, a History of the American Negro (Vol. 2 [1865–1916], Vol. 3 [1916–1966]), edited by Milton Meltzer.

Students will find *The Ballad of America* most helpful in writing docudramas, since many of the ballads will add much vigor to a depiction of American history. For instance, a contemporary account from the *Freeman's Journal* of January 21, 1777, describes a battle incident on Christmas Day and the marching song, "The Battle of Trenton," depicts the story. Another ballad, describing an incident in the fall of 1778, when the Americans were using floating mines or kegs containing gun powder ready to explode, is "The Battle of the Kegs," which was recorded by Martha Bennett King for the Children's Book Council.

151 · ORIGINAL RADIO PLAYS   Students may also use *The Ballad of America* to create an original radio play by utilizing some of the recordings listed in the last part of the volume. For instance, narration could be written to accompany various recordings listed under "Jacksonian America." Almost all general sections of the volume are represented by available recordings that relate to different historical periods. Pupils should probably concentrate upon one historical era, since recordings are expensive and few libraries have a large collection. In writing the script for a radio play pupils may want to provide for an announcer, station identification, and other things used on radio programs. Committees of students might write to their local radio station to get copies of scripts to use as models.

152 · WORK SONGS OF AMERICA   America has built its strength on the workers who have labored to earn a living while conquering the mountains, woods, and streams, and whose deeds have been immortalized in song. Students may enjoy organizing a program depicting the lives and activities of some of these workers through songs and pictures, using a tape recorder and filmstrip or opaque projectors. For instance, such songs as "Haul on the Bowline," "Off to Sea Once More," "The Greenland Whale Fishing," and "The Banks of Newfoundland" could be used in a program on seafaring life and fisheries. Parts of these songs could be recorded on a tape and played as appropriate pictures are projected on a screen.

153 · CREATING ADDITIONAL BALLAD VERSES   Students may enjoy adding new verses to ballads depicting the modern social scene. For instance, Woody Guthrie in "Plane Wreck at Los Gatos" described a wreck involving Mexican deportees. The words and music not only appear in *The Ballad of America* but have been recorded in *Songs of Woody Guthrie*. Pupils could add other verses telling more about the miserable life of the *braceros*.

III. Ballad Activities Based on the Local Scene

154 · BALLADS OF LOCAL COLOR—NOVA SCOTIA   Ballads are part of the folklore and cultural traditions of people. Collections have been made of ballads that are representative of a particular environment or geographical region of the world. One such collection is Helen Creighton's *Songs and Ballads from Nova Scotia,* and one ballad in the collection is "The Mary L. MacKay," a lengthy tale of a sea voyage from Portland, Maine, to Yarmouth Sound. A committee of three pupils could select this ballad and divide up responsibilities for interpreting the content to the rest of the class. One pupil could obtain a sketch of the ship; another student could select such seafaring terms as "haddocks," "Banks," "mainsail," "foresail," and "jib," and depict them pictorially; a third pupil could create a map of the ship's route.

155 · BALLADS OF LOCAL COLOR—THE LOWER LABRADOR COAST   Another local-color collection of ballads is MacEdward Leach's *Folk Ballads and Songs of the Lower Labrador Coast*. One ballad in this collection is the "Flying Cloud," which is known in both Labrador and Newfoundland. A group of adolescent boys might enjoy rewriting this couplet-style ballad in the form of a mystery tale about the famous clipper ship.

156 · BALLADS OF LOCAL HISTORY   In some communities, old-timers often remember ballads and ancient folklore. Students could interview local citizens and collect news items concerning grandfathers or older relatives. If the person being interviewed is capable of singing or playing an instrument, any lyrics or ballads he might know could be recorded through the use of a portable tape recorder.

Sometimes older citizens remember historical events, and after receiving the information about an event from an older person, a younger one might retell it. In some sections of Nova Scotia, Canada, for instance, superstitious stories are told about such things as a rocking stone or about an old man named Jerome, who was left to die on the edge of the sea with both of his legs cruelly amputated. Such tales can easily be rewritten in the form of a ballad.

IV. Ballad Activities for Younger Children and Gifted Preadolescents

157 · ROBIN HOOD BALLADS   An interesting volume for younger students is *A Bundle of Ballads,* compiled by Ruth Manning-Sanders and illustrated by William Stebbs. This volume includes nine ballads about Robin Hood, ranging from his birth and "Robin Hood and Alan-a-Dale" to "The Death of Robin Hood," most of which are in quatrain form with four lines to a stanza; "The Death of Robin Hood," however, has variant lines and a repeated refrain line. Sixth-grade pupils could read some of the classic stories about Robin Hood and create an original ballad based on some significant event in his life. If any pupils have difficulty creating rhythmical tunes, they could begin with two or three basic lines from one of these ballads and extend them into a longer ballad.

158 · FOLK BALLADS FOR YOUNGER CHILDREN   A helpful volume is *Folk Ballads for Young Actors* by John Jacob Niles and Helen Louise Smith, illustrated by Lee Ames. This includes stories, teaching suggestions, and songs for "The Frog in the Spring," "The Story of Noah," "Who Killed Cock Robin?" and "Posheen, Posheen, Posho." The latter story is probably the most interesting one, as well as quite brief. It tells the tale of Mr. Joe Mouse, Mayor of Posheen, who stubs his toe and ties it up with a blue silk ribbon. Susie Mouse, a little creature from Posho, is visiting Posheen and laughs at the Mayor. She apologizes when she understands his importance and receives the blue ribbon as a prize. A recording of this story is included. The pupils could dramatize the song as it is being sung or they could spontaneously reenact parts of the story as a choral verse group chants the words of the verses. Some boys and girls might enjoy adding new episodes. For instance, the man mouse could collect many other colored ribbons for his stubbed toe.

159 · BALLAD MAPS (GIFTED PREADOLESCENTS)   Committees of gifted preadolescents could consult various books of ballads and construct ballad maps, one committee working on a map based on details from the Viking book on American ballads and another on ballads originating in various other parts of the world. A third committee might obtain recordings of current ballads and create a map locating sites of events in ballads. Expository paragraphs could be written to accompany the maps.

V. Original Ballads

160 · COMPOSING ORIGINAL BALLADS BASED ON THE CURRENT SCENE   Pupils do not have to be skilled in musical notation to create original ballads. They can decide upon a particular rhythmic series of lines and create a ballad by beating out the rhythm on a drum or with sticks. As for subject matter, magazines and newspapers are replete with descriptions of incidents that could serve as sources for ballads: a fireman loses his life saving a worthless drunk or an innocent child; a youth rescues two swimmers from the pounding surf; soldiers perform heroic feats to help young children in a war-torn country. Any event having dramatic, relevant, contemporary interest can be recast into a ballad whose lines are organized in a quatrain or in a quatrain and a refrain.

161 · CREATING BROADSIDE BALLADS   Another type of ballad is known as the *broadside ballad*, since it was printed on a large sheet of paper known as a "broadside." One of the first ballad types to appear in printed form—previous ballads had been transmitted orally—the broadside ballad often contained allusions to current news topics, such as the hidden romance of a king or queen. The words of broadsides were often sentimental and the tunes diverse; in fact, sometimes the words were simply presented with the notation that the ballad would be sung to the tune of a popular folk song, hymn, or some other lyrical melody.

Pupils might like to select a popular tune with lyrical possibilities, listen to it several times, and create a broadside ballad to accompany the tune. The words can be printed in manuscript style on a large sheet of paper, along with decorations illustrating the principal event or episode in the ballad.

Bruno Nettl in *Folk and Traditional Music of the Western Continents* (Prentice-Hall) has described the broadside as well as other traditional folk music, including Negro folk music in the New World. The last two pages of this volume give a brief sectional bibliography and discography—and it should be noted, incidentally, that the series *Folk Music of the United States*, listed here and issued by the Library of Congress, is outstanding.

162 · BALLADS ORIGINATING WITH A REFRAIN   Sometimes imaginative pupils can create original ballads with very little motivation. One technique is to make a list of numerous refrains. Then a student can take one or more refrains and expand them into original ballads. Some refrains are:

> With a link and a down and a down . . .
> Down a-down, a-down, a-down . . .
> Hey! down a-down, a-down!

"Clootie," in the Ruth Manning-Sanders volume *A Bundle of Ballads,* has two lines that appear as lines 2 and 4 in each verse and serve as a refrain. These are "Jennifer, Gentle and Rosemary" and "As the Dove Flies over the Mulberry Tree." This particular ballad could be recited as a dialogue, with a chorus taking the refrain and a sole speaker reciting the rest of the lines.

VI. Hero Ballads

163 · BALLADS OF AMERICAN FOLKLORE HEROES   Some ballads about American folk heroes can be read, such as the legend of

John Henry or Pecos Bill. The appendix to the volume *The Ballad of Tradition* by Gordon Hall Gerould includes "Jesse James,"
"The Old Chisholm Trail," "The Lone Star Trail," "John Henry,"
and others. Pupils might like to select a popular folklore hero
and compose a ballad similar to one of these, using the same
rhythm and stanza style.

164 · BALLADS ABOUT HEROES AND BAD MEN   An excellent collection of ballads appears in *The Viking Book of Folk Ballads
of the English-Speaking World.* (Some of the ballads recorded
here are bawdy and should probably not be recited by younger
pupils.) Most boys like ballads of outlaws, pirates, badmen, and
heroes, and this Viking book contains many ballads about folk
heroes like John Henry and outlaws like Jesse James. In fact,
many of the Jesse James legends are included, legends about his
horsemanship, gifts to the poor, and the dramatic robberies he
was involved in. John Henry presents a better heroic image—
he was a gigantic Negro man who lifted a nine-pound hammer
and seldom stopped to rest.

Several ballads in the Viking volume, songs of cowboys, miners,
camp cooks, and buffalo skinners, deal with frontier episodes.
For instance, the ballad "Joe Bowers" tells about a miner who
fled to California in the 1850s to dig for gold. "Sweet Betsy from
Pike" is another gold-mining ballad.

Pupils might like to create a modified cowboy operetta, using
original ballads. Murals can be painted and used for stage settings, and the boys can dress up in cowboy clothes and the girls
in sunbonnets and aprons. In writing the ballad for the operetta,
the children can imitate the rhythm of the early ballads but
should create their own verses.

165 · BALLADS BASED ON HERO TALES   A group from four to
eight intellectually-gifted pupils in grades six to eight may wish
to write a ballad based on a traditional epic hero such as Sieg-
fried, Sigurd, Roland, or Beowulf. Some suggested sources for
epic heroes are *Hero Tales from the British Isles* by Barbara
Leonie Picard; *William Mayne's Book of Heroes: Stories and*

Poems, edited by William Mayne; and *Medieval Tales,* translated and adapted by Jennifer Westwood with illustrations by Pauline Baynes. Such a story as "Sir Orphee" or "Aucassin and Nicolette" from *Medieval Tales* can be used successfully.

One person can read the heroic epic tale to the other pupils or select an episode from a particular volume, such as one on King Arthur. The episode can be recorded on tape and listened to in a listening center that has enough sets of headphones for the group. The pupils should listen for a narrative progression of events, which can be listed by a recorder on a large sheet of paper or on the chalkboard. The students should then listen to several different ballads and select a rhythmical pattern appropriate to the story, after which the story should be rewritten in terse ballad style and taped. The student should listen carefully to the tape to detect weaknesses, such as wrenched rhythms. After the ballad has been revised, it can be recorded on tape and played back to the group, who should write the verses down from the dictated version.

VII. Ballad Dances and Games

166 · Dancing to a ballad   Teachers may enjoy reading *The Popular Ballad* by Francis B. Gummere and studying the characteristics of typical ballads as well as much on ballad history. A few pupils may enjoy creating an original dance as a ballad is recited or sung, the way the inhabitants of the Faeroe Islands did, as depicted in the Gummere volume. Some children may want to do the "Faeroe step," which is two steps left and one right, while singing to a ballad.

167 · Choreographing a ballad   Older adolescents who have seen modern-dance performances, or those who have viewed modern dances or ballets on television, may want to choreograph a dance, reenacting a dramatic tale that has been recorded in ballad form. The ballad "Frankie and Johnny" is frequently enacted in dramatic form, and the appendix to *The Ballad of Tradition* has a similar one, "Frankie and Albert." If creative movement or dancing is not possible, a ballad such as this one could be dramatized through pantomime.

168 · PLAY-PARTY SONGS AND POEMS   Folklorists and scholars such as B. A. Botkin, Louise Pound, and W. W. Newell have recorded numerous examples of the *game song,* which is similar to the ballad and folk song and is part of the tradition of frontier America, as is the play-party. The play-party was a rural gathering in which guests performed pantomimes and games to a tune and extemporized additional verses to existing poems or songs. This custom was not a substitute for dancing, as some religious groups that prohibited the dance allowed attendance at a play-party. Some game songs popular at play-parties were "Skip to My Lou," "Old Dan Tucker," and "Shoot the Buffalo."

B. A. Botkin's *The American Play-Party Song,* which was first published in 1937, contains a popular series of verses that were developed to the tune of "Shoo Fly" and that rhyme with the lines

> I feel, I feel, I feel
> I feel like a morning star.

The tune to "Shoo Fly" appears on page 306 of the Botkin volume. Pupils can create play-party poems and songs by writing other stanzas to this or other typical American game songs. Some children may enjoy having a play-party program, in which old customs can be described and acted out. Many poems were dramatized by persons at a play-party, in a way similar to ballads, a technique that really involved doing parodies of songs commonly sung by people throughout American history.

William Wells Newell, in his *Games and Songs of American Children,* discusses mythology and various versions of "London Bridge Is Falling Down." He also offers specific suggestions on a version of a song game related by an Irish domestic. Children might enjoy composing, and acting out, additional verses to this song.

CONCRETE POETRY AND RELATED EXPERIMENTAL
POETRY FORMS

I. Concrete Poetry

An unusual approach to modern poetry is presented in the volume *Concrete Poetry: A World View,* edited by Mary Ellen Solt. Some of the interpretations of modern poetry as presented in this scholarly volume are far too sophisticated and difficult for young pupils to grasp. However, some of the ideas present fresh viewpoints on art and communication.

Concrete poetry is strongly visual poetry that breaks away from some of the traditional poetic forms based on grammatical, syntactical patterns; in fact, it is more perceived than read, and the poet is more of a graphic designer than a "musician." This type of verse is closely related to concrete art, with its strong relationships of line, surface, and color as seen in the plastic arts, graphics, architecture, and industrial design. Concrete poetry can be put into different categories, such as visual or optic poems, phonetic or sound poems, and ones showing visual movements. Some of the following poetic experiments might be considered to be connected with concrete poetry.

169 · ART CHIROGRAPHY   The term "art chirography" appears in the scholarly footnotes appended to Chapter Three, "A Caucus Race and a Long Tale," of *The Annotated Alice: Alice's Adventures in Wonderland and Through the Looking Glass* by Lewis Carroll, with an introduction and notes by Martin Gardner. This is the scene in which Alice asks the mouse to explain why he hates C (ats) and D (ogs). The mouse, replying that it is a long and sad tale, proceeds to tell it, in the form of a poem written in the shape of a mouse's tail, with large print at the beginning of the tail and smaller print at the end.

Charles Peirce called this poetic form the "visual analogue of poetic onomatopoeia" or "art chirography"—the words patterned in a way to give a visual illustration of the poetic idea—and Clement Wood called it a "shaped whimsy," or a poem in which the typographical format indicates the theme. Such a poem is Aimee Jackson Short's "The Umbrella Man," which is about the English leader, Chamberlain, and which appears in "The Complete Handbook for Poets" in *Wood's Unabridged Rhyming Dictionary*. In modern times this poetic art form is used in advertisements, on book jackets, and for movie and television titles.

Children can experiment with chirography or visual analogues, relating the form to the theme or idea of the poem. For instance, they could do some of the following:

1. Write a poem about an auto race, arranged in the shape of a car on a race track.

2. Write a war poem to conform to the shape of a rifle.

3. Arrange a flower poem in the shape of a flower.

4. Write a weather poem in the shape of umbrellas or boots, or a violent weather poem depicted as a cyclone, in the shape of a funnel.

170 · MORE POEMS WITH A VISUAL ANALOGY   Some child may feel that a particular typographic form complements or reinforces the emotional content of a poem and reaches the reader in a way auditory images cannot. In such a form the idea behind the words is reinforced by the words themselves being arranged in a particular shape. For instance, a poem about tears or sorrow might be arranged in the shape of a teardrop. In one poetry anthology, *Windsor's Budding Poets* (Vol. 4), appears a poem, "The Broken 'V,'" by Michael Keck, a thirteen-year-old boy in the eighth grade at the Oakwood School. The shape of this poem quite effectively enhances the poetic idea.

THE BROKEN "V"

On
The horizon
I could see a
Long black line, V-shaped
I reached down and found my gun
Making sure it was ready for the kill.

They
Came closer
Until overhead
I placed my gun at
My shoulder, sighted
And squeezed the trigger.
And then I found   a
dead
goose
on
the
ground.

Children could think of a topic, such as sorrow, willow trees, swans, or dogs, and then draw an outline of the subject's shape. Then, after the poem is written, the words can be arranged within the drawn outline. *Types of Shapes,* a book by John Hollander, is a whole volume of poems arranged in various shapes, including a swan, a key, an umbrella, and an Eskimo pie.

The teacher should allow a free choice of subject matter, but list a wide number of possible subjects so the child who has no ideas won't be hampered. Explain and demonstrate various patterns of lines and develop subjects with which both boys and girls can identify. Possible other subjects include:

Poodle Dogs	Sun and Stars	Dancing
Great Danes	Ballerina	Motorcycle Tunes
Snow Swirls	Soul Music	Street Tunes
My Cat	Bugs	Jazz Rhythms
Racing to the Moon	Garbage Cans	Grasshoppers
Moon Orbits	Neon Lights	A Pile of Dirt

171 · REDUCED LANGUAGE POEMS Some concrete poets do much experimentation with words, reducing some words to letters and others to syllables. Some poets use whole words and arrange them in various pictorial combinations. One concrete poet, Eugene Gomringer of Switzerland, used the term "constellations" to express a poem as clusters of words related in response to a creative idea. He was interested in thoughts expressed in single words and used arrangement of words in space to help structure the poetic meaning. In other words, his poems were spatially structured ones, and he organized words so they could be read in several different directions.

Pupils can arrange letters, syllables, or words on a page in such a way that the idea will be expressed visually without resorting to the setting down of complete thoughts in metrical form. For instance, on the cover of the Solt volume *Concrete Poetry: A World View*, letters are arranged in strands to convey the idea of yellow forsythia flowers. In this case, letters take the place of words, including such descriptive adjectives as "graceful," "droopy," and "spritely."

172 · SOUND POETRY Paul de Vree of Belgium has been experimenting with sound poetry, using mechanical expedients such as tape recorders and sound tracks. De Vree's techniques are quite complex, but they could be adapted for intermediate students, using tape recorders to elicit a free-association type of response. Some ideas that have actually been tried with fifth- and sixth-grade pupils involve the use of a movie sound track. In one instance, a beautiful movie, *The Making of a River,* which was originally designed for secondary school pupils and adults, was shown to fifth-graders, who were enchanted with the beauty of the natural scenes. The pupils then closed their eyes and listened to such words on the sound track as "tiny fish troubled the sand," "ripplets of violet water," "falling in plumes of white." The pupils recorded phrases as they listened, then regrouped them into poems and paragraphs.

A similar experience, this time for sixth-graders, was based on the recording *Frank Sinatra Conducts Tone Poems of Color,* on which appear musical selections written to accompany poems, based on different colors, by Norman Sickel. Before hearing the record, the sixth-graders listened to the poem "What Is Gray?" from *Hailstones and Halibut Bones* by Mary O'Neill. Then they were told that they were going to listen to music in a gray mood and were asked to list phrases that might be gray such as "gray clouds," "gray fog wisps," "a furry gray mouse." After that the pupils listened to the recording and wrote their phrases. When the next part of the recording was played, the pupils were not told the color, or given any clues. This time, they wrote phrases according to emotions or feelings they had as they listened to the music. Some of the phrases were: "crackling fire," "roaring flames," "happiness," "speed," and "red sunsets," which meant that the color that most of the pupils heard in the music was—correctly—red. The recording was played again to give more tone or mood. Then the pupils created poems, using the phrases cr impressions they had jotted down while listening to the music. And after they wrote their own poems, the pupils listened while the teacher read them Norman Sickel's poems from the record jacket.

Some students may wish to follow the same procedure by listening to a recording entitled *Hi-Fi Hits,* which includes such selections of classical music as "Sabre Dance" by Khachaturian, "The Flight of the Bumble Bee" by Rimsky-Korsakov, Ravel's *Bolero,* or Enesco's Rumanian Rhapsody No. 1. A pupil may listen to the selection first, to get the impression of the total piece of music. Then he could listen to it again and dictate his phrases and impressions on a tape. Later the tape could be replayed and the selection heard again, allowing the student to indicate whether or not he wishes to make any changes. Later, the phrases could be recast either into free verse or into a poem of more standardized structure.

II. Other Experimental Poetic Forms

173 · POETRY-IN-THE-ROUND   Several years ago, the distinguished modern poet George Abbe popularized the idea of poetry-in-the-round by involving many audiences in the poetic experience of aural-audience interpretations. Abbe feels that a poet creates the central idea or focus of significance for a poem, but that the true making of the poem is not completed until an audience has expressed its feelings about and interpretations of the poem. In other words, an organic relationship exists between a poet and his audience; the reader becomes the "co-maker" of a poem. In poetry-in-the-round, an author initiates the poetic idea by reading his poem; the audience shares his thoughts and feelings by reacting to the poem in a personal, cooperative manner. Abbe expresses some of his thoughts in *The Incandescent Beast,* and some of these same ideas appear in his *You and Contemporary Poetry: An Aid to Appreciation.*

The poetry used for a poetry-in-the-round experience should have a certain amount of ambiguity or obliqueness; in other words, it should be open-ended, allowing for an extension of ideas by the experiencers, or audience. The following poetry-in-the-round procedures were followed with one group of sixth-grade students based on the poem "The Incandescent Beast," from Abbe's book of the same name:

1. The poem was read quietly and the pupils were asked to listen to the rhythm of the words and visualize images.

2. No discussion was held; students could consult a dictionary for unknown words, but no dictionary drill was given.

3. The teacher placed lines of the poem on the chalkboard, reciting them as they were written down.

4. The children were given paper and asked either to write down their feeling about the poem or to add other ideas.

5. As the pupils composed their ideas, the teacher recited dramatic phrases at intervals, a process that served to saturate them aurally with poetic words.

6. The words were then erased from the chalkboard and emphasis placed upon participation by the listeners.

7. Papers were handed in; the different aural-audience commentaries were read, with no attempt to focus upon the authors. Ideas and picturesque phraseology were complimented. Some of the poet's words were repeated by the child authors, but in most instances, such words were rephrased or placed in a different context.

Below is an aural-audience commentary by Ricky on the poem "The Incandescent Beast" by George Abbe:

DEEP CRIMSON FEAR

A dog lay silent, incandescent with fear. They say it had died, but it lived in the mind of the young boy. In rain, his teeth shone so bright. There he lay under a tree in a mist of leaves. This dog, the hope of all good, died on their feast day, but it was blessed before he went.

A boy with candy ball on a stick had a shiny red tongue. His money was gone. He stopped the longest to regard the movement of a black paw, pure licorice, through his eyes.

The sun of morning came slowly over the mountain range to remind him of what he tasted and saw. It must have been from heaven so far, or made of God. I do not know. The boy once more saw his own little dog which he loved so dearly. It had a brilliant bluish-green fur, but the fur was gone. Its white topaz eye seemed blinding, but through this brightness a dull mist surrounded the boy.

And the people that time of passing knew the dog had changed. An old bearded one of yesteryear saw blood on the poor beast. Gently, the old one brushed the fur from its face and imagined gems of richness. The boy came near and worshipped and he fell to his knees. He held his ruby candy closer to the gold through which the sky flashed. Death came, and the boy had no fear, no crimson fear.

174 · THE DIAMONTE (DEE-AH-MAHNTAY) This poetic form is in the shape of a diamond, but it is not necessarily related in substance to the symbolism of a diamond. The form was invented by Iris M. Tiedt and is described more completely in "A New Poetry Form: The Diamonte," which appears in the May 1969 issue of *Elementary English.*

The diamonte is arranged in a seven-line verse pattern, and has the following requirements:

Line

1 1-word subject (noun)
2 2 words (adjectives)
3 3 words (participles: *-ing, -ed*)
4 4 words (nouns related to the subject)

5   3 words (participles)
6   2 words (adjectives)
7   1 word (noun opposite in meaning to that subject which
      initiated the poem)

The beauty of the diamonte lies in the antithesis within it, the balance of opposing forces through the selection of nouns such as dark and light, gaiety and sorrow, winter and summer, speed and inaction. Note that the last noun on line 4 above is a "turning" word, which applies more to the antithetical noun at the end of the verse than it does to the subject noun at the beginning.

The following poem arranged in the shape of a diamond illustrates the form:

Volcano

fiery   vivid

leaping plunging   spraying

coals   sparks   flames   ashes

blackening sizzling ruining

starry   silver

highway

CARLSON

This diamond-shaped poem could be placed on a collage consisting of pictures of a volcano at different stages of eruption at various times of day balanced by a picture of a silver-ribboned highway decorated with crimson lehua or hibiscus flowers.

A pupil can create a diamonte about almost any subject close to his immediate experiential background—a flood, hurricane, disaster, tumbling waterfall, city streets at dawn and dusk, family happiness and sadness—and then place it in its most effective setting, a collage of pictures supporting the theme.

175 · SIMPLIFIED OR "POP ART" POEMS   One quality of modern communications is the "concentration and simplification" of language. Advertising art, newspapers, magazines, and other media look toward quick, visual word messages. "Pop art" is a realistic art style using techniques and popular subjects adapted from commercial art and such mass communication media as comic strips and posters. A poem derived from the idea of pop art would use few words and many symbols or pictures. A simple "pop art" poem could be:

GASOLINE HERE

Service Station 1 — 3 x Blue Chip	
Service Station 2 — 4 x Blue Chip	
Service Station 3 — 5 x Blue Chip	
Service Station 4 — 6 x Blue Chip	
Service Station 5 — 7 x Blue Chip	
Service Station 6 — 8 x Blue Chip	

COMPETITION

An understanding of this message involves having had a social experience with the use of trading stamps and the knowledge that gasoline stations are competing with one another by offering bonuses of trading stamps. For instance, Service Station 1 offers three times the usual number of stamps for a sale, while Service Station 6 offers eight times the number.

Students might study magazine, newspaper, billboard, and television advertisements, as well as comic strips. Using symbols from advertisements, students can create "pop art" poems in which the message is conveyed mainly through the symbol, and few words or letters are used.

176 · STRUCTURE-CONTENT POEMS   Both verbal and nonverbal means of communication are used in structure-content poems. A Brazilian poet, August de Campos, applied some of the principles of pop art to Biblical history. He created a Tower of Babel —but constructed of eyes, not ears. The poem was a montage of pictures of all kinds of different eyes arranged in the form of the Tower of Babel, along with a few abstract symbols and the words "Olho per Olho" (eye for eye).

Pupils can have fun using magazine pictures to express concretely an abstract idea. For instance, "gossip" could be depicted in a montage of many lips arranged as though their messages were being received by many ears of assorted shapes and sizes. "Courage" might be represented by a montage of several pictures representing feats of courage.

177 · TYPOGRAPHICAL OR NEWSPAPER POEMS   A teacher can work with pupils to create interesting visual, communicative ideas and reinforce abstract ones through the use of different typography, as well as pictures. For instance, poems based on such words as "war," "riots," "government," "education," "families," and so forth can be created from newspaper type and magazine pictures. A poem entitled "Families" might include miniature pictures of family members of different races performing different functions—eating together, conversing together, working together, playing together. Letters cut from newspaper heads could be used to form words describing the various activities, and placed near the appropriate pictures.

Another idea: the phrase "modern civilization" could be centered, in large type. Children might cut out such words and phrases as "war in Vietnam," "poverty," "hunger," "ignorance," "violence," "murder," "dope," etc., and group them around the large words in the center.

178 · PHOTOGRAPHIC POEMS   In recent years much emphasis has been placed on photographic poems, or poetry that expresses much more through photography than it does through auditory lines. Cameras are so reasonable in price that many young pupils have their own cameras, and they might enjoy using photography as a source for poetry. In many cases, the inspiration for a photographic poem can come about through thinking about a clever title or interesting phrase; some titles can be taken from the news media, while others the child author can originate. It probably would be helpful if pupils creating photographic poems had much experience with metaphors and similes, since metaphors can often be interpreted through the lens of a camera.

A photographic poet should select a basic theme or idea first, such as "the preciousness of little things," then take photographs of such small things as a violet, a hummingbird, or a drop of dew on a cobweb. After the photographs are taken, free verse inspired by the pictures can be created and the pictures then used to illustrate the poems.

Some children might even become interested in poetry through their knowledge of photography, by searching through poetry books to select poems that could inspire photographs. Whether they decide to make actual photographs of scenes suggested by poems or not, the fact that they can visualize such scenes so vividly usually means that they will enjoy the poems.

Two books with photography as the central core are *It's Autumn!* and *It's Spring!*, both by Sister Noemi Weygant. Both books are concerned with the relationship between nature and man, and involve a multisensory awareness of things around us. The poet is looking for resemblances; for instance, in "I'm Waiting" she sees in a dried-up tomato on a vine a possible use as a marble bag for a small boy. Another good photographic essay is *Black Is Beautiful* by Ann McGovern, with photos by Hope Wurmfield. In this essay photography and words work together in fostering the impression that beautiful things can be black.

6

WRITING IS A WAY OF FEELING (THERAPEUTIC WRITING)

Teachers can learn any number of techniques for teaching children to write, but the *feeling* content of writing is difficult to impart. Children and adolescents, however, can write with feeling about things that are important to them personally, and opportunity should be given them for some unstructured, free-expression activities. Free expression is valuable for all pupils—in fact, young authors frequently crave a free choice of writing activities completely unstructured by any outside authoritarian figure such as parent or teacher. Many children write spontaneously in journals, diaries, and voluminous notebooks, and one enthusiastic nine-year-old author was seen writing an original story on paper napkins in a restaurant, having no other available writing paper.

Most of the activities in this chapter, however, are of particular benefit to a slum-culture children, who are under such great tensions and feel such great need to release them. Writing under such circumstances becomes therapeutic in nature, and the teacher's attitude when conducting such activities should be one of understanding, sensitivity, encouragement, and trust. When an author writes truthfully and "tells it like it is," the teacher should accept the writer's contribution, even though the product may be shocking to a middle-class teacher unused to children in a slum culture.

179 · PAINTBRUSH STORIES   Years ago, Natalie Cole described some techniques of working with slum-culture children in *Arts in the Classroom*. She freed pupils to express themselves in many media—painting, sculpture, and writing—and, since she identified so closely with her pupils and classes, young boys and girls felt free to confide in her. As a result, these children wrote about life as they saw it; stories were written about ugly alleys and fathers who were mean or drunk. Large sheets of wrapping paper were spread around the room, and the youngsters painted the words of their stories with large vigorous strokes of their brushes. Each child wrote a story of his own.

Children can write stories about families, homes, stores, and people in their milieu, using large sheets of paper and the modern, easy-to-use flow-brush and Pentel pens that are commercially available now. Authors love a chance to see their words in vigorously rendered script.

180 · CHILDREN'S VOICES FROM THE GHETTO   The sociological climate is conducive to numerous expressions of life in ghetto cultures. Stephen M. Joseph has edited a volume entitled *The Me Nobody Knows: Children's Voices from the Ghetto*, a collection of poetry, essays, and autobiographical or fantasy stories written by slum-culture children, some of them shocking in their candor. Some titles in these chapters could serve as stimuli for original writing by the class:

How I See Myself	Anger
How I Feel	Fear
Things I Wish	Me, Myself, and I
The Story of My Life	Who Am I?
What I Love	When I Feel at Peace
Things I Hate	My Dreams
Alone	The Fight on Our Street
My Best Friend	My Neighborhood
Death	The Story of My Block
Grief	

181 · THE WAY THINGS ARE   John Holland has edited a revealing volume called *The Way It Is: Fifteen Boys Describe Life in Their Neglected Urban Neighborhood,* presenting the picture of a neighborhood as observed closely by boys living in it. Teachers can read excerpts from this volume, and encourage pupils to write descriptive paragraphs, poems, or stories about their neighborhoods and the people living in them.

182 · TAPE-RECORDED PERSONAL EXPERIENCE STORIES   Sandra Weiner in her beautiful book, *It's Wings That Make Birds Fly: The Story of a Boy*, tells a story as seen by a boy who could be in either Harlem or Watts, and whose innermost feelings are revealed. The story was obtained from the boy's own tape-recorded words, which were then edited by the author, who, an outstanding photographer, used photographs of the actual scenes to supplement the script. Teachers can make use of "listening corners" in a room and allow pupils to record their innermost thoughts. These thoughts should be considered so personal that they can either be erased immediately or edited and spliced together on a tape, which can then be kept in a permanent file.

183 · BEAUTIFUL BLACK THINGS   Black has always been symbolic of ugly things, such as darkness and fear, witches, bats, and cruel savages. Modern black children are being encouraged to think of beautiful things that are black to help instill in them a feeling of pride concerning the color of their skin. Ann McGovern's little book *Black Is Beautiful* reveals in words and photographs many black things around us that are beautiful: birds singing in the morning, long chains of trains in a station, shiny licorice, and black, silhouetted hillsides. Teachers and pupils can design a "Black Is Beautiful" bulletin board, on which pictures, photographs, and paintings of beautiful black objects around the children can be displayed. The children can also create individual and class books focusing on the black theme.

184 · AN IMAGINATION EXTENDER   A teacher can make a large black picture frame or a large black flannelboard. Pupils can look at the black frame or board and speak and write about the imaginative thoughts that come to them.

185 · FREE RESPONSE WRITING   One junior high school in a black neighborhood has started an unstructured creative writing studio, in which pupils taking the course as an elective write about anything they wish. The school has an annual literary magazine, but this is not the major motivation for the workshop.

One rule is *silence:* no student is allowed to talk or disturb others during the composing process. The students, who listen to recordings and tapes, view movies and filmstrips, and study painting reproductions in magazines and art books, can write or not write about each stimulus. If no writing is motivated, this is understood, but each student must turn something in at the end of a specified time. During certain parts of the period, "communication time," a time when the students share thoughts and writing with their peers, is called. Most of these students write poetry and love to recite their own poems, and each author keeps his own personal book.

186 · Pollution and destruction as a theme   One junior high school class did a photographic essay on the theme, "Pollution." Some pictures were taken of lovely natural scenes—the seaside, parks, trees, waterways, and beauty spots. Other photographs were taken of the places where man has polluted the countryside, by discarding beer cans and bottles, allowing filthy scrap heaps, abandoning broken-down cars on the roadways, filling the air with fumes from chemical plants, and scarring the landscape with ugly quarries. The pupils and teacher wrote narration and poetry to accompany the colored slides, and sang a popular song, "Pollution," as well as "America the Beautiful." This project had a significant impact on the lives of many pupils in the school.

SOMEONE WHO CARES

This book has offered numerous suggestions for teachers and other adults interested in helping youngsters find enjoyment and satisfaction in writing. And, in fact, the children's enjoyment and satisfaction very often communicate themselves to the adults who come in contact with them in a most remarkable way.

The poet George Mendoza, for example, was excited to discover that sensitive, powerful, poetic statements can come from children living in our urban areas. In his book, *In the World from My Window*, Mr. Mendoza portrays the world of the ghetto as glimpsed through the eyes of children. This collection of poems and drawings dramatically depict the life of children feeling the importance of being "just me" in a city where walks to school reveal abandoned houses and cars, condemned stores, buildings badly in need of repair, and dirt everywhere.

Virginia Olsen Baron became interested in poetry written by young people from some of America's minority groups. She wrote to schools in different parts of the United States and was overwhelmed by the hundreds of poems she received. From these she compiled a book, *Here I am! An Anthology of Poems Written by Young People in Some of America's Minority Groups*, in which, in such poems as "As I Sit" and "Hate," children write about their feelings, worries, temptations, and loneliness.

And, to cite a final example, Lee Bennett Hopkins became intrigued with the cinquain form of poetry originated by Adelaide Crapsey in the early 1900s and introduced the form to children living in both country and urban areas. These pupils, enjoying the simplicity and beauty of the style, created cinquains about a boy looking at a statue of Abe Lincoln, children romping on sidewalks or playing baseball in alleys, a child sitting by a slide, fireworks bursting forth in stars against a summer sky, and candles glowing at Christmas time. Hopkins compiled these cinquains, as well as many others on other subjects, in a little volume, *City Talk*, which is beautifully illustrated with Roy Arenella's sensitive black and white photographs.

In the process of compiling these books of children's verses, the authors were amazed at the great outpouring of poems that came from the pens of children from all over the United States, children who had been given the freedom to create by someone who cared to recognize their creative spark. It is hoped that each individual reading *Writing Aids Through the Grades* becomes someone, too, who cares about the written expression of children and young adolescents, who will see in it a way to communicate with the world of the young as well as a way to free children so they can communicate in turn.

Bibliography

BOOKS AND ARTICLES

Abbe, George. *The Incandescent Beast*. University Heights, Ohio: An American Weave Publication, 1957.

——. *You and Contemporary Poetry, An Aid-to-Appreciation*. Peterborough, N.H.: Richard R. Smith, Noone House, 1965.

Aesop's Fables. Drawings by Fritz Kredel. New York: Grosset & Dunlap, Inc., 1947.

Aliki. *The Wishworkers*. New York: Dial Press, Inc., 1962.

Arbuthnot, May Hill. *The Arbuthnot Anthology of Children's Literature*. Glenview, Ill.: Scott, Foresman & Company, 1961.

Asbjörnsen, Peter C., and Moe, Jörgen. *A Time for Trolls: Fairy Tales from Norway*. 3rd ed. Translated by Joan Roll-Hansen. Illustrated by Kai Övre. Oslo, Norway: Johan Grundt Tanum Forlag, 1964.

Barlin, Ann Lief. *The Magic Mountain, Little Duck, The Toy Tree, and The Brave Hunter*. New York: Ginn & Company, 1964.

Baron, Virginia Olsen, ed. *Here I Am! An Anthology of Poems Written by Young People in Some of America's Minority Groups*. Illustrated by Emily Arnold McCully. New York: E. P. Dutton & Company, Inc., 1969.

Behn, Harry, trans. *Cricket Songs: Japanese Haiku*. With pictures selected from Sesshu and other Japanese masters. New York: Harcourt, Brace & World, Inc., 1964.

Beilenson, Peter, trans. *A Haiku Garland: A Collection of Seventeen-Syllable Classic Poems by Basho, Buson, Issa, Shiki, Sokan, Kikaku, and Others*. With decorations by Jeff Hill. Mount Vernon, N.Y.: Peter Pauper Press, 1968.

Beilenson, Peter, and Behn, Harry, trans. *Haiku Harvest.* Japanese Haiku Series, vol. 4. With decorations by Jeff Hill. Mount Vernon, N.Y.: Peter Pauper Press, 1962.

Bemelmans, Ludwig. *Madeline.* New York: Viking Press, Inc., 1939.

———. *Madeline's Rescue.* New York: Viking Press, Inc., 1953.

Bethers, Ray. *Composition in Pictures.* 2nd ed. New York: Pitman Publishing Corporation, 1962.

Bodor, John. *Rubbings and Textures, A Graphic Technique.* New York: Reinhold Book Corporation, 1968.

Botkin, B. A. *The American Play-Party Song.* New York: Frederick Ungar Publishing Company, Inc., 1937.

Burton, Virginia Lee. *Mike Mulligan and His Steam Shovel.* Boston: Houghton Mifflin Co., 1957.

Carlson, Ruth Kearney. *Language Sparklers for the Intermediate Grades.* Berkeley: Wagner (2603 San Pablo Avenue, Berkeley, Calif., 94702), 1968.

———. *Sparkling Words: Two Hundred Practical and Creative Writing Ideas.* 3d ed. Berkeley: Wagner (2603 San Pablo Avenue, Berkeley, Calif., 94702), 1968.

Carroll, Lewis. *The Annotated Alice: Alice's Adventures in Wonderland and Through the Looking Glass.* With an introduction and notes by Martin Gardner. New York: Clarkson N. Potter, Inc., 1960.

Chiba, Reiko, ed. *Painted Fans of Japan: Fifteen Noh-Drama Masterpieces.* Rutland, Vt.: Charles E. Tuttle Company, 1962.

Child, Francis James. *English and Scottish Popular Ballads.* New York: Dover Publications, Inc., 1965.

Clark, Kenneth. *Looking at Pictures.* New York: Holt, Rinehart & Winston, Inc., 1960.

Clifford, Eth and David. *Your Face Is a Picture.* Indianapolis: E. C. Seale, 1963.

Cole, Natalie. *Arts in the Classroom.* New York: John Day Company, 1940.

Coolidge, Olivia. *Greek Myths, with Selected Episodes from the Trojan War.* Boston: Houghton Mifflin Co., 1949.

Creighton, Helen. *Songs and Ballads from Nova Scotia*. New York: Dover Publications, Inc., 1966.

Daniels, Guy, trans. *15 Fables of Krylov*. Illustrated by David Pascal. New York: Macmillan Company, 1965.

DeForest, Charlotte B. *The Prancing Pony, Nursery Rhymes from Japan*. Illustrated by Keoko Hida. New York and Tokyo: Walker & Company, 1967.

DeJong, Meindert. *Smoke Above the Lane*. Illustrated by Girard Goodenow. New York: Harper & Row, Publishers, Inc., 1951.

Deutsch, Babette. *Poetry Handbook: A Dictionary of Terms*. Rev. ed. New York: Funk & Wagnalls, 1962.

Earle, Vana. *The Busy Man and the Nighttime Noises*. New York: Lothrop, Lee & Shepard Co., 1954.

Emberley, Ed. *The Wing on a Flea: A Book About Shapes*. Boston: Little, Brown & Co., 1961.

Engel, Rose. *Language Motivating Experiences for Young Children*. Van Nuys, Calif.: D.F.A. Publications, 1969.

Friedman, Albert B., ed. *The Viking Book of Folk Ballads of the English-Speaking World*. New York: Viking Press, Inc., 1956.

Frost, Robert. *Complete Poems of Robert Frost*. New York: Holt, Rinehart & Winston, Inc., 1958.

Fussell, Paul, Jr. *Poetic Meter and Poetic Form*. New York: Random House, Inc., 1965.

Gag, Wanda. *The Funny Thing*. New York: Coward-McCann, Inc., 1920.

———. *Millions of Cats*. New York: Coward-McCann, Inc., 1938.

Gerould, Gordon Hall. *The Ballad of Tradition*. New York: Oxford University Press, Inc., Galaxy Books, 1957.

Gilbert, Elliot. *A Cat Story Told in Pictures*. New York: Holt, Rinehart & Winston, Inc., 1963.

Green, Lila. *Folk Tales and Fairy Tales of Africa*. Illustrated by Jerry Pinkney. Morristown, N.J.: Silver Burdette Company, 1967.

Greet, W. Cabell; Jenkins, William A.; and Schiller, Andrew. *In Other Words: A Beginning Thesaurus*. New York: Lothrop, Lee & Shepard Co., 1969.

Gummere, Francis B. *The Popular Ballad*. New York: Dover Publications, Inc., 1959.

Harris, Albert, and Clark, Mae Knight. *My Self-Help Dictionary*. New York: Macmillan Company, 1968.

———. *My Word-Clue Dictionary*. New York: Macmillan Company, 1967.

Henderson, Harold G. *Haiku in English*. Rutland, Vt.: Charles E. Tuttle Company, 1966.

Hiyama, Yoshio. *Gyotaku: The Art and Techniques of the Japanese Fish Print*. Seattle: University of Washington Press, 1965.

Holland, John, ed. *The Way It Is: Fifteen Boys Describe Life in Their Neglected Urban Neighborhood*. New York: Harcourt, Brace & World, Inc., 1969.

Hollander, John. *Types of Shapes*. New York: Atheneum Publishers, 1969.

Hopkins, Lee Bennett, ed. *City Talk*. With photographs by Roy Arenella. New York: Alfred A. Knopf, Inc., 1970.

Ishimoto, Tatsuo. *A Treasury of Japanese Flower Arrangements*. New York: Crown Publishers, Inc., 1959.

Japanese Haiku. Translated from the Masters of the Seventeen Syllable Poetic Form (Basho, Buson, Issa, Sheki, Sokan, Kikaku, Ransitsu, Joso, Yaha, Boncho, and others). Mount Vernon, N.Y.: Peter Pauper Press, 1955.

Johnson, Crockett. *Harold and the Purple Crayon*. New York: Harper & Row, Publishers, Inc., 1958.

———. *A Picture for Harold's Room*. New York: Harper & Row, Publishers, Inc., 1960.

Joseph, Stephen M., ed. *The Me Nobody Knows: Children's Voices from the Ghetto*. Cleveland: World Publishing Company, Meridian Books, 1969.

Kaula, Edna Mason. *African Village Folktales*. Cleveland: World Publishing Company, 1968.

Kirn, Ann. *Tale of a Crocodile: From a Congo Folktale*. New York: W. W. Norton & Company, Inc., 1968.

Kirtland, Elizabeth. *Write It Right: A Handbook of Homonyms*. New York: Golden Press, Inc., 1968.

Krutch, Joseph Wood. *The Most Wonderful Animals That Never Were*. Illustrated by Pauline Baynes. Boston: Houghton Mifflin Co., 1969.

Laliberté, Norman, and Mogelon, Alex. *Silhouettes, Shadows and Cutouts*. New York: Van Nostrand–Reinhold Books, 1968.

Latham, Jean Lee. *Anchor's Aweigh: The Story of David Glasgow Farragut*. Illustrated by Eros Keith. New York: Harper & Row, Publishers, Inc., 1968.

———. *Drake: The Man They Called a Pirate*. Illustrated by Frederick T. Chapman. New York: Harper & Row, Publishers, Inc., 1960.

———. *Carry On Mr. Bowditch*. Illustrated by J. O. Cosgrove. Boston: Houghton Miffllin Co., 1955.

———. *Trailblazer of the Seas*. Illustrated by V. Mays. Boston: Houghton Mifflin Co., 1956.

Lawson, Robert. *Rabbit Hill*. New York: Viking Press, Inc., 1944; Dell Publishing Company, Inc., 1968.

Leach, MacEdward. *Folk Ballads and Songs of the Lower Labrador Coast*. Ottawa: National Museum of Canada, Bulletin No. 201, 1965.

L'Engle, Madeleine. *Dance in the Desert*. Illustrated by Symeon Shimin. New York: Farrar, Straus & Giroux, Inc., 1969.

Leslau, Charlotte and Wolf. *African Proverbs*. Decorations by Jeff Hill. Mount Vernon, N.Y.: Peter Pauper Press, 1962.

Lester, Julius. *To Be a Slave*. Illustrated by Tom Feelings. New York: Dial Press, Inc., 1968.

Lewis, Claudia. *Poems of Earth and Space*. Illustrated by Symeon Shimin. New York: E. P. Dutton & Company, Inc., 1967.

Lewis, Norman. *The Comprehensive Word Guide*. New York: Doubleday & Company, Inc., 1958.

Lewis, Richard. *Of This World: A Poet's Life in Poetry*. With photographs by Helen Buttfield. New York: Dial Press, Inc., 1968.

Lewis, Richard, ed. *The Moment of Wonder: A Collection of Chinese and Japanese Poetry*. Illustrated with paintings by Chinese and Japanese masters. New York: Dial Press, Inc., 1964.

Lionni, Lee. *Tico and the Golden Wings.* New York: Pantheon Books, Inc., 1964.

Manning-Sanders, Ruth. *Stories from the English and Scottish Ballads.* Illustrated by T. Ridley. New York: E. P. Dutton & Company, Inc., 1968.

Manning-Sanders, Ruth, ed. *A Bundle of Ballads.* Illustrated by William Stobbs. Philadelphia: J. B. Lippincott & Company, 1959.

Mayne, William, ed. *William Mayne's Book of Heroes: Stories and Poems.* New York: E. P. Dutton & Company, Inc., 1968.

Meltzer, Milton. *In Their Own Words, a History of the American Negro.* Vols. 2 (1865–1916) and 3 (1916–1966). New York: Thomas Y. Crowell, 1967.

Mendoza, George, ed. *The World from My Window.* New York: Hawthorn Books, Inc., 1969.

Merriam, Eve. *It Doesn't Always Have to Rhyme.* New York: Atheneum Publishers, 1964.

Miller, Margaret J. *Knights, Beasts and Wonders: Tales and Legends from Mediaeval Britain.* Illustrated by Charles Keeping. New York: David White Company, 1969.

Moore, Lamont. *The First Book of Paintings: An Introduction to the Appreciation of Pictures.* New York: Franklin Watts, Inc., 1960.

Moore, Lilian. *The Golden Picture Dictionary.* Illustrated by Beth and Joe Krush. New York: Golden Press, Inc., 1954.

McCord, David. *Take Sky: More Rhymes of the Never Was and Always Is.* Boston: Little, Brown and Co., 1962.

McDowell, Jack, and Mikami, Takahiko. *The Art of Japanese Brush Painting.* New York: Crown Publishers, Inc., 1961.

McGovern, Ann. *Black Is Beautiful.* With photographs by Hope Wurmfeld. New York: Four Winds Press, 1969.

Nettl, Bruno. *Folk and Traditional Music of the Western Continents.* Englewood Cliffs, N.J.: Prentice-Hall, Inc., 1965.

Newell, William Wells. *Games and Songs of American Children.* New York: Dover Publications, Inc., 1963.

Niles, John Jacob, and Smith, Helen Louise. *Folk Ballads for Young Actors.* Illustrated by Lee Ames. New York: Holt, Rinehart & Winston, Inc., 1962.

Ocvirk, Otto G.; Bone, Robert O.; Stinson, Robert E.; and Wigg, Philip R. *Art Fundamentals, Theory and Practice*. Dubuque, Iowa: William C. Brown Company, 1968.

O'Neill, Mary. *Fingers Are Always Bringing Me News*. Illustrated by Don Bolognese. Garden City, N.Y.: Doubleday & Company, Inc., 1969.

——. *Hailstones and Halibut Bones*. Illustrated by Leonard Weisgard. New York: Doubleday & Company, Inc., 1961.

——. *Take a Number*. Illustrated by Al Nagy. Garden City, N.Y.: Doubleday & Company, Inc., 1968.

Perrine, Laurence. *Sound and Sense: An Introduction to Poetry*. 3d ed. New York: Harcourt, Brace & World, Inc., 1969.

Picard, Barbara Leonie. *Hero Tales from the British Isles*. New York: Criterion Books, Inc., 1963.

Politi, Leo. *Meiko*. San Carlos, Calif.: Golden Gate Junior Books, 1969.

Potter, Beatrix. *The Tale of Mrs. Tittlemouse*. New York: Frederick Warne and Company, Inc., 1910.

——. *The Tale of Peter Rabbit*. New York: Frederick Warne and Company, Inc., 1965.

Pratt, Davis, and Kula, Elsa. *Magic Animals of Japan*. Berkeley, Calif.: Parnassus Press, 1967.

Provensen, Alice and Martin. *What Is Color?* New York: Golden Press, Inc., 1967.

Rand, Ann, and Birnbaum, A. *Did a Bear Just Walk There?* New York: Harcourt, Brace & World, Inc., 1966.

Ransome, Arthur. *The Fool of the World and the Flying Ship*. Illustrated by Uri Shulevitz. New York: Farrar, Straus & Giroux, Inc., 1968.

Raths, Louis E.; Wassermann, Selma; Jones, Arthur; and Rothstein, Arnold M. *Teaching for Thinking: Theory and Application*. Columbus, Ohio: Charles E. Merrill Publishing Company, 1967.

Reps, Paul. *Gold and Fish Signatures*. Rutland, Vt.: Charles E. Tuttle Company, 1968.

——. *Square Sun Square Moon: A Collection of Prose Essays*. Rutland, Vt.: Charles E. Tuttle Company, 1967.

Robinson, Stuart and Patricia. *Exploring Puppetry.* New York: Taplinger Publishing Co., Inc., 1967.

Rowen, Betty. *Learning Through Movement.* New York: Teachers College Press, 1963.

Samson, Anne S. *Lines, Spines and Porcupines.* New York: Doubleday & Company, Inc., 1969.

Sanders, Thomas E. *The Discovery of Poetry.* Glenview, Ill.: Scott Foresman & Company, 1967.

Sato, Shozo. *The Art of Arranging Flowers: A Complete Guide to Japanese Ikebana.* New York: Harry N. Abrams, Inc., 1966.

Scott, John Anthony. *The Ballad of America: A History of the United States in Song and Story.* New York: Grosset & Dunlap, Inc., 1967.

Selfridge, Oliver G. *Fingers Come in Fives.* Illustrated by Murray Tinkelman. Boston: Houghton Mifflin Co., 1966.

Selsam, Millicent E. *The Language of Animals.* Illustrated by Kathleen Elgin. New York: William Morrow & Company, Inc., 1962.

Sendak, Maurice. *Where the Wild Things Are.* New York: Harper & Row, Publishers, Inc., 1963.

Solt, Mary Ellen, ed. *Concrete Poetry: A World View.* Bloomington: Indiana University Press, 1969.

Squire, James R. and Barbara L., eds. *Greek Myths and Legends as Retold by Eminent Mythologists.* New York: Macmillan Company, 1967.

Stegall, Carie. *The Adventures of Brown Sugar: Adventures in Creative Writing.* Champaign, Ill.: National Council of Teachers of English, 1967.

Stewart, Harold, trans. *A Net of Fireflies: Japanese Haiku and Haiku Painting.* Rutland, Vt.: Charles E. Tuttle Company, 1960.

Swift, Jonathan. *Gulliver's Travels.* Illustrated by Arthur Rackham. New York: E. P. Dutton & Company, Inc., 1952.

Tiedt, Iris M. "A New Poetry Form: The Diamonte." *Elementary English,* May 1969.

Traven, B. *The Creation of the Sun and the Moon.* Illustrated by Alberto Beltran. New York: Hill & Wang, Inc., 1968.

Twain, Mark. *Life on the Mississippi.* Holiday ed. New York: Harper & Row, Publishers, Inc.

Untermeyer, Louis. *The Forms of Poetry.* Rev. ed. New York: Harcourt, Brace & Company, 1926.

Vasiliu, Mircia. *The World Is Many Things.* New York: John Day Company, 1967.

Walker, Barbara. *The Dancing Palm Tree and Other Nigerian Folktales.* Illustrated by Helen Siegl. New York: Parents Magazine Press, 1968.

Weiner, Sandra. *It's Wings That Make Birds Fly: The Story of a Boy.* New York: Pantheon Books, Inc., 1968.

Westwood, Jennifer, ed. *Medieval Tales.* Illustrated by Pauline Baynes. New York: Coward-McCann, Inc., 1968.

Weygant, Sister Noemi. *It's Autumn!* Philadelphia: Westminster Press, 1968.

———. *It's Spring!* Philadelphia: Westminster Press, 1969.

Whiting, Bartlett Jere, ed. *Traditional British Ballads.* New York: Appleton-Century-Crofts, Inc., 1955.

Williams, Margery. *Velveteen Rabbit.* Illustrated by William Nicholson. New York: Doubleday & Company, Inc., 1958.

Windsor's Budding Poets. Vol. 4. Windsor, Ont.: Windsor Council, International Reading Association, Border Press, 1969.

Wood, Clement. *Wood's Unabridged Rhyming Dictionary.* Cleveland: World Publishing Company, 1964.

Wright, Wendell W. *The Rainbow Dictionary.* Rev. ed. Illustrated by Joseph Low. Cleveland: World Publishing Company, 1959.

Wrinn, Mary J. J. *The Hollow Reed.* New York: Harper & Brothers, 1935.

Yashima, Taro [pseud.]. *Crow Boy.* New York: Viking Press, Inc., 1955.

Yasuda, Kenneth. *The Japanese Haiku: Its Essential Nature, History, and Possibilities in English, with Selected Examples.* Rutland, Vt.: Charles E. Tuttle Company, 1966.

Zillman, Lawrence J. *The Art and Craft of Poetry: An Introduction.* New York: Macmillan Company, Collier Books, 1966.

INSTRUCTIONAL MATERIALS

Map

Uthaug, Jørleif. *A Folklore Map of Norway*. Text by Pat Shaw Iversen. Oslo: Johan Grundt Tanum Forlag, 1962.

Motion Pictures

Adventures of °. Contemporary Films. Animated color cartoon. 10 min. The story is an account of the life of an average contemporary human being, symbolized by the figure "°."

Creative Writing—Poems We Write. Grover Film Productions, Monterey, Calif. 93940. Film in sound and color, 16 mm. or super 8 mm. 15 min. The film is designed to stimulate interest in writing poetry about real experiences.

A Day Is Two Feet Long. Weston Woods Company. A film designed to encourage the viewer to express himself in writing or art. This company also issues *In a Spring Garden*, based on Richard Lewis, ed., *In a Spring Garden* (New York: Dial Press, Inc., 1965).

Dots. International Film Bureau. Color film. 3 min. This is an experimental film by Norman McLaren, made, without the use of camera or sound recording apparatus, by drawing directly upon movie film with ordinary pen and ink. The "dots," sparkling blue and white on a bright red background, explode and crash with the sound.

Fiddle De Dee. International Film Bureau. Color film. 6 min. To the tune of "Listen to the Mockingbird," this film employs abstract design, color, and rhythm to interpret the nuances of violin music.

Haiku: An Introduction to Poetry. Coronet Films. This film is a haiku experience. Beautiful scenes pass before the eyes of the viewer and one senses man's relationship to his environment. The film is effectively accompanied by *santour* music.

The Making of a River. Coronet Films. For secondary school pupils.

Poetry for Me. Grover Jennings, producer and distributor (Box 303, Monterey, California). Film in sound and color, 16 mm. 15 min. An introduction to rhythm, imagery, word sounds, and sound patterns. Many of the poems used for illustrative purposes are found in Barbara P. Geismer and Antoinette B. Suter, *Very Young Verses* (Boston: Houghton Mifflin Co., 1945).

Poetry to Grow On. Grover Jennings, producer and distributor (Box 303, Monterey, California). Motion picture in sound and color, 16 mm. or super 8 mm. 18½ min. An opportunity for the child to respond individually to each poem and show growth of understanding in poetry. Most of the poems used for illustrative purposes have been obtained from Isabel J. Peterson, ed., *The First Book of Poetry* (New York: Franklin Watts, Inc., 1954).

Filmstrips

Stories About Colors. Coronet Films. Filmstrips and recordings. "The Purple Flower," "The Orange Pumpkin," "The Yellow Bird," "The Green Caterpillar," "The Blue Balloon."

Stories About Shapes. Coronet Films. "A New Shape for Freddy," "Triangles Everywhere," "The Lost Rectangle," "A Circle in the Sky."

Recordings

Frank Sinatra Conducts Tone Poems of Color. Musical selections by different composers to accompany poetry, written by Norman Sickel, based on different colors. Capitol W735.

A Gathering of Great Poetry for Children (Vol. 4). Edited by Richard Lewis. Read by Julie Harris, Cyril Ritchard, David Wayne, and the poets themselves. Caedmon TC 1238.

Hi-Fi Hits. "Sabre Dance" (Khachaturian), "The Flight of the Bumble Bee" (Rimsky-Korsakoff), *Bolero* (Ravel), Rumanian Rhapsody No. 1 (Enesco), "William Tell Overture" (Rossini). Westminster Long Play Record XWN 18888 (33⅓ rpm).

Louis Untermeyer's Discovering Rhythm and Rhyme in Poetry. Read by Julie Harris and David Wayne. Directed by Howard Sackler. Caedmon TC 1156.

Miracles, Poems Written by Children. Collected by Richard Lewis. Read by Julie Harris and Roddy McDowall. Caedmon TC 1227.

Seeger, Peggy, and MacCall, Ewan. *The Long Harvest.* Series of ten long-playing records. Argo ZDA 66–75.

Singing History. Folk songs and books by Marty King (CBC-1A). Children's Book Council (175 Fifth Avenue, New York, N.Y. 10010). TV 23285.

CHAMBER
MUSIC

BY DORIS GRUMBACH

The Spoil of the Flowers
The Short Throat, the Tender Mouth
The Company She Kept

CHAMBER

A Henry Robbins Book HR

MUSIC

Doris Grumbach

E. P. DUTTON · NEW YORK

For information contact:
E.P. Dutton, 2 Park Avenue, New York, N.Y. 10016

Library of Congress Cataloging in Publication Data
Grumbach, Doris.
Chamber music.
"A Henry Robbins book."
I. Title.
PZ4.G887Ch [PS3557.R83] 813'.5'4 78-13033
ISBN: 0-525-07920-3

Published simultaneously in Canada by
Clarke, Irwin & Company Limited, Toronto and Vancouver

Production manager: Stuart Horowitz
Designed by The Etheredges

10 9 8 7 6 5 4 3 2 1

First Edition

For SHP

—sine qua non

ACKNOWLEDGMENTS

Chamber Music is fiction, not biography. Its three major characters are based, vaguely, upon persons who once were alive, but most of the details of their lives are conjecture and invention.

Some real persons, musicians, teachers, and actresses of the early twentieth century, appear in these pages in somewhat changed chronology. The Maclaren Community is imaginary and bears no relation to places it may resemble.

Two such real places, Yaddo and The MacDowell Colony, gave me working time and space for this book. I thank them both.

. . . Who may this singer be
Whose song about my heart is falling?
Know you by this, the lover's chant,
'Tis I that am your visitant.

JAMES JOYCE, *Chamber Music*

Part One

BEGINNINGS

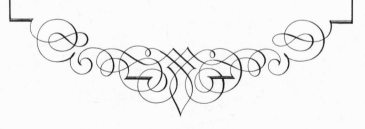

I HAVE DECIDED to write this account because, long as my life has been, it has given me no opportunity before this to say what I wish to put down here. Perhaps the time was not right to do it before.

When I was young, and even into my middle years, a scrim of silence surrounded what really happened in our lives. If there was talk, it was quiet conjecture about the little discreet adulteries, the attic madnesses, and the pantry drinking of our friends and neighbors. Rumor and gossip were conveyed in whispers. Secrets were surely no better kept than they are now, but they lived quietly, under the breath. They never appeared in public print or were reported by professional gossips on the air waves. They were confined to the inner coils of the private ear, a foot away, perhaps, no farther. We closeted our secrets, or forgot them. This we called decorum, and we lived securely under its warm protection.

But now the Maclaren Foundation, which I headed for so many years, almost fifty by now, wishes to have a permanent record of Robert's life, and mine. Ours together, to put it more exactly, and mine alone with the Community, after his death. The government has become interested, they tell me, in "the arts." There is a chance that, with its financial help, in some place, the Community will be restored to life.

My initial reluctance to accede to their request is a matter of personal habit, I suppose. I am an old woman born in the last quarter of the nineteenth century, with all that decent age's love of a calm surface to our society. It was then the custom to have a regular, uniform pattern to our lives, to present the historian with only those facts which would contribute to an orderly picture.

So I am not equipped to write a confession in the modern sense. Whether what I remember here will be useful as a record to the new Foundation I cannot say. I am of an age not to care, almost ninety. My hearing is defective, my bones seem to lie upon each other like dry kindling, my skin falls away in slack little pinches of flesh. I am dry and brittle, I strain and break easily. Rarely any more do I insert my two rows of teeth; few persons bother to visit.

I write this description of myself not because I want pity—who pities the very old?—but to explain my unaccustomed openness in this account. I have nothing to lose that extreme old age has not already taken from me, and no time to gain. The way the world thinks of me may well change, but even that, if it happens, I will not survive. The Foundation promises me that it will be some time before the history of the founding of the Community can be completely collated and that it has no plans to publish it. I will not be here to witness the astonishment of the reader. I am comforted by the realization that there is no one I know alive to be surprised at me.

For the representation of truth, old age is a freeing agent. No one should write of her life until all the witnesses and acquaintances, family and lovers, are dead. In addition, it helps to outlive the mode of one's time until it has changed beyond recognition. Then one is left alone with what was. The wrinkled, spotted hand writes of a time out of the memory of everyone alive but itself. So what one tells is unavailable to verification or correction.

I write this, then, because I am freed by my survival into extreme old age, and because I write in the air of freer times. Whether this air is entirely salutary, whether the old must of chests, of closets, bell jars, and horsehair sofas is not a better climate for the storage of the private life, I do not know. But I tire very quickly these days and must speak openly, for once. I am now free. Extraordinary for me, and for one of my time, I intend to put down extraordinary truths.

My birth coincided with the year of the Centennial Exposition in Philadelphia. In May my parents traveled for two days down from Boston to be present at the great crush when the Brazilian emperor Dom Pedro and General Grant opened the fair. Later in the week my father pushed my mother, who was seven months pregnant, in a wicker chair to see the Corliss engine, a gigantic 1,500-horsepower structure that seemed to him to represent the promise of the future. He took her past the English paintings and the Italian sculpture in the huge Agricultural Hall, remarking on what a strange name it was for a place housing such cultural treasures.

My mother remembered it all. Over and over she told me of the wonders she had seen. Later, in New York, she purchased a number of pieces of furniture made in the manner she had seen at the fair. They were of bent wood, rockers and a sofa of profoundly uncomfortable contours, as I remember. She told me about a gigantic grapevine, twelve thousand feet in all, which had been brought from southern California and replanted outside the Horticultural Hall. She and my father sat under one of the great arms of the vine, resting from the effort of traversing the long narrow halls of the art exhibit. They drank cold water from the Temperance Fountain and ate soda crackers given out at the Adam Exton of Trenton, New Jersey, exhibit. As a child, in bed at night, I heard so often about the two white whales that P. T. Barnum had placed in a tank forty feet high and wide and brought on a special train to the Exposition.

My childhood was composed of these stories of oversized glories. I believe that summer was the zenith of my mother's life, alone with my father, before I was born, in the presence of great marvels. My father at that time was full of plans for their future and mine. He thought it might be possible to apply the principle of the Corliss steam engine he had seen in Philadelphia to the automatic operation of knitting machines, which at present were worked by hand and by foot pedal in his small mill. But he died suddenly when I was nine without accomplishing that difficult reduction.

My mother was bereft. She sank down into a grief I have never since seen take such complete possession of anyone, the absolute despair of a mourner for a beloved husband. The Centennial became united in her mind with early love, her memory coalesced the Corliss engine with her proud, handsome, inventive husband. She paired my birth, I think, with the great umbrella of the Santa Barbara grapevine. Perhaps I, too, have symbolized that time, for the bentwood sofa is still downstairs in the music room, or at least it was the last time I was able to go there.

I grew up always living alone with my mother, regretting in a mild way the loss of my father but not mourning his absence as she did for the rest of her life. I remember his smells, of mustache wax, of the leather of his gloves and hatband. I can still smell his hands as he held me, the odor of acrid coke, the material with which he tried to power his experimental engine. He carried a cane topped with a silver knob. At my level, close to that knob, I could smell his hands and the oiled wood and the polished silver of the cane. He remains in me through the solid scents of his manhood. I cannot recall his voice. His face must have been too high and too often turned toward my mother and away from me for me to remember his eyes or the shape of his nose. His pictures show his mustache curling in a small thick arc around his upper lip, a waxed brush whose smell has followed me for eighty years: that, the bentwood sofa, and the memory of my mother's mortal loss of love.

After his death my mother's only interest was in my future. Left with a little money invested, through the advice of her brother, who was a clerk with J. P. Morgan in New York, in railroad stocks, she still dressed me well. She had educated herself in the fiction of romantic novelists and learned from them that a presentable-looking daughter was usually marriageable. I read her little collection of ladies' novels when I was fourteen, recognizing that the fanciful inventions about life they embodied were only wishful. All the same, I entered into them all. I cared very little about taffeta skirts and full-bodied, lace-edged shirtwaists, soft, high-buttoned kid shoes with small, high heels and felt at the tips, elaborate coiffures that required an hour's construction each morning and another hour of reconstruction in the evening. But I submitted to them all because my mother's interest and future were involved, as well as my own. I was her investment, the promise of her old age, and had I rebelled it would have meant the end to her hopes for our security.

My only rebellion was music. I had often watched and listened while a school friend practiced the piano. I pleaded with my mother for the use of a little of the money she had put aside each year for habiliments. I wanted to learn to play the piano, that noble, formidable instrument, to stroke those soft ivory strips, each with its slight lip, and the rounded edges of the black keys. The beauty of the piano bench which opened upon paper music collections, the fine, deep string-and-felt odor that came from the piano's interior as the harp-shaped cover was raised, the ease with which the stick fitted into its hole, the lovely, easy machinery of it: I loved it all.

Mother, who was tone-deaf and oblivious to every sensation but her grief, finally agreed. The lessons began in a tiny studio on Dartmouth Street, not far from Commonwealth Avenue where we had our rooms. I had no piano on which to practice, my mother being of the conviction that we had very little room in which to put one, "very little" being for her a relative term. She remembered clearly the wonderful Steinway pianos she had seen at the Centennial, where William Steinway had filled his exhibit with inlaid instruments, a piano decorated to represent the Parthenon, a delicate grand piano mirrored to look like the furniture at Versailles. She could not conceive of a piano that was small and upright and still able to perform properly. The large open spaces in the sitting room, almost devoid of furniture, for we owned very little, had to be kept free for breathing, she said. She believed that the fresh air in most rooms was consumed by the plush of sofas, the linen covers of chairs, the mahogany of side tables, and the porous, colored-glass panels of lamps.

I was delighted to go to my lessons, and to walk the long blocks every other day to practice there. I started when I was eleven and continued, almost without interruption, until I was seventeen. Mrs. Seton, my teacher, had been a Peabody, it was said by my mother to her acquaintances, as if to excuse by lineage her adult indulgence in harmony and composition. A *Peabody.* I never understood what that emphatic, raised-tone designation, which always followed Mrs. Seton's married title, always after a pause, implied. Was it a connection to the Salem family, or was there a connection to the Philadelphia musical persons? I never knew, or even heard from her, if that *was* her maiden name, for she was a woman given to gestures, not speech.

I remember that my lesson was at three on Friday afternoon. Mrs. Seton would open the door for me, bowing her head and smiling her slow and then quickly obliterated smile, wearing her hat. I don't remember ever seeing her bareheaded.

After she had smiled her greeting, she would lock the door behind me. I would start up her narrow brown varnished stairs, hearing as I went the sounds of the other two locks being turned. The last, a rolling bolt, took much doing and I was usually in the music room before she had managed it. Her floors always seemed freshly varnished and the leather of my soles stuck a bit to them, making a sucking sound. The room was small, windowless, and dusty—every beam and cornice of that room comes back to me even now

—just large enough for her upright piano, her wicker chair placed to the left of the piano seat, and a lamp, its squat gold base nudging the metronome that peered down at me like a tirelessly blinking eye.

At lessons she always sat, her face shaded by a large, broad-brimmed hat. The hat perched on her head evenly, as though she were balancing it, while she played passages in the pieces she was teaching me. She apparently never felt the desire to explain. Her method was to illustrate how notes should sound, her long, delicate fingers hardly lifting from the keys. Accompanied by the undeniable force of the square-set hat, her playing took on a didactic power that I could not withstand.

Mrs. Seton would gesture to me to be seated. When I was settled, a ceremony which, in the first years, involved arranging a stack of *Century* magazines under me to raise me to the proper height, she would point to the piece of music I was to begin playing. I was expected to extract it from the pile, open it, smooth it carefully, and wait. Using an ivory corset stay, Mrs. Seton would then point to the place where she wished me to begin. I would play. Her disapproval (very often it was disapproval that followed my efforts) would be indicated by a light tap on the back of my right hand (or the left: whichever was the greater offender) with the long, supple stay, not to hurt but to arrest. My hand would freeze—and lift. Hardly pausing, Mrs. Seton would then raise the stay to the music, pointing with the sharp tip to the mistaken staff. Wrong: one tap at the place, begin here, again. Two taps were hard to bear.

They signified despair at my repeated stupidity and begged for my close attention the next time I attempted the passage.

I was puzzled by her unbroken silence. Did it suggest a distrust of the spoken word, a faith in gesture and facial expression as more direct, less open to ambiguity than speech? As I think back, I assure myself that she must have spoken at times, perhaps to greet me when she let me in for my practice hours. Surely she had addressed my mother, but never that I can remember did she say a word to me during a lesson, or to fellow pupils whom I whispered to in a corner of the room at her teas. To each of us she gave thirty-five minutes of her expressive pantomime. We learned to play Schubert and Schumann correctly, or at least as well as her indicative fingers holding the stay, the dismayed bend of her head backward, could suggest to us. We heard no words of praise. She would nod yes two or three times, emphatically. For me that was almost enough.

I put all this down about Mrs. Seton of Dartmouth Street, her unbroken silence, her triple-bolted door, because it was in her sitting room that I first encountered Robert Glencoe Maclaren, to whose life I was for so long to join my own. I remember the occasion, perhaps because all of Mrs. Seton's gatherings were occasions. Twice a year she invited her pupils to visit her, to meet each other and a few of her musical friends. We came in response to tissue-thin, pink-paper invitations sent to us through the mail. Somewhere downstairs, I think, I still have one of them I saved. It measures about six inches square and is folded in half over her minuscule spidery writing. It reads:

Come at four. Tea. Biscuits. Friends.
                                    Amelia Seton

There was no provision for refusal. The delicate invitation had the weight and strength of a command. No address was included, on the theory, I'm sure, that only those who knew the way were invited, and the exact day seemed somehow to have been known to us.

Some years later, Robert, who was one of the "friends" she proposed to serve with tea and biscuits, told me that Mrs. Seton had never changed her dwelling. Her elderly parents had brought her as a young child with her upright piano to those rooms. Mr. Seton, of whom I knew nothing, had come to live there upon their marriage, I later learned, and had died soon after. Just before the Great War, my friend Elizabeth Pettigrew told me, Mrs. Seton died in her sitting room. She suffered a stroke when she was alone and lay there, it was conjectured, for three nights and three days unable to rise from the figured rug. Had she *then* used her voice? I wondered. Pupils who came to her door found it locked (three times?), there was no answer to their knocks, and so they went away. She was found by a neighbor who had grown curious about the continued darkness in the upstairs music room and broke a window to find her. Her body lay straightened like the stone effigies on tombs in Westminster Abbey, her eyes opened upon a final silence. Only her hat was misplaced. It lay some distance from her head, having been knocked away by her fall, I believe.

[13]

On that earlier afternoon of which I write, I arrived at Mrs. Seton's door at precisely five minutes before four, knowing well that she could indicate her displeasure at late arrival by keeping her heavy, red lids down over her eyes long after it would be expected she would raise them to look at you. I feared that canopied look and rarely came late. She herself opened the door for each guest. On feast days like this she wore her broad straw hat with a velvet band encircling the brim and ending in streamers down her back. She followed me up the stairs into the sitting room, her light step making me feel, in contrast, oafish and leaden.

Mrs. Seton disappeared into another room, presumably to get tea and biscuits for me. There were of course no introductions to the other persons already standing about. The young man standing next to me holding his cup carefully said, "You must be Caroline Newby."

"Yes."

"I'm glad to meet you at last. Mrs. Seton speaks often of you. My name is Maclaren. Robert Maclaren." He laughed a little. "Robert Glencoe Maclaren. My mother calls me Rob."

"Yes. How do you do?"

That is all I can remember we said to each other that day. I remember thinking: He must be very polite, or perhaps prevaricating. Surely Mrs. Seton had never *spoken* of me to him or to anyone. I watched him as he moved around the room, admiring his fine head, his russet hair, his thick brush of a mustache that sat upon his lip like—like my father's,

I thought. Yes, he looked very much as I remember my father looked, even to his ears, which seemed to pinch his head tight, his thin, almost arrogant nose ending so abruptly that it displayed the black dashes of his nostrils. He seemed foreign, somehow, perhaps because of the soft, low collar of his shirt. In those days men in Boston wore tall, stiff collars whose corners turned out neatly over their cravats. Perhaps it was the European look of his suit, which was made of a very heavy cloth.

I watched him put his cup down on the top of Mrs. Seton's glass-doored bookcase in which she kept small busts of Mozart and Meyerbeer. He opened his jacket and then unbuttoned his vest. I remember these actions so well because, watching him, I decided he must be a musician or perhaps an artist: his discomfort in his suit of clothes, his restlessness as he moved around from one side of the room to the other. Finally he sat down on the green settee and talked quietly to the man already comfortably settled there, to whom I was never introduced, only to rise again to greet a pupil standing awkwardly at the side of the piano. I recognized the pupil, a gangly, pimpled boy impelled, I decided, by his ambitious mother to wear the uniform of the prodigy: black silk tie, bowed extravagantly at the base of his collar, and velvet knickers. We had passed each other once or twice at the end of my lesson and the start of his, but we never spoke, Mrs. Seton's reluctance to express the simplest greeting having been communicated to her pupils. I remember comparing the pupil's awkwardness to Robert's grace, to the ease of his laugh, the tone of his low voice:

their *suitability* to the room, to the occasion, rising over the unappetizing dry soda biscuits and the blushing boy juggling his tea and his velvet tam.

I was seventeen that year. It must have been 1893, if indeed I am right in thinking I was seventeen. In the late summer Robert and I met again, walking in the Common. He tipped his hat to me and smiled. I felt an unaccustomed rush of pleasure in my face, in my breast. He said he enjoyed our meeting at Mrs. Seton's tea and then he laughed. At the memory of the tea? I wondered, flooded by the charm of his shy smile, as the leash on which he held his huge collie circled my long skirt, pulling it tight to my legs.

"What is his name?" I asked, unable to think of anything more intelligent to say, and untangling myself from the leash.

"Paderewski, I call him. After the pianist I very much admire."

"Have you been at his performances?"

"Once. In Stuttgart, when I was studying there."

"Piano?"

"Yes, and composition. I'm returning to Europe in a month or so, this time to Frankfurt, to continue my studies with Carl Heymann and Joachim Raff."

He smiled a beguiling, gentle, self-deprecating smile as though to indicate the vast gulf between him and the great teachers at the Hoch Conservatory. I could say nothing to this impressive itinerary, I whose musical horizons were limited to the windowless room on Dartmouth Street, to the hatted Mrs. Seton's mimic instruction. I remember staring at him: he seemed a paragon, almost supernatural, a man of the world with talent, free to travel, to study, to leave the little parks and tightly housed streets of Boston for the wide, ancient avenues and noble panoramas of Germany. I yearned for this conversation, full of revelations, to go on.

He took my arm. "May I walk along with you?" he asked, already in step with me, the collie marching slowly ahead of us both, at the end of his taut leash.

"Mr. Maclaren, do you ever think of conducting?"

"I would be pleased if you would call me Robert, or better, Rob."

"Thank you. I'll call you Robert."

"Thank you. I'd like to conduct, of course. I'd like to conduct my own work best of all."

"That seems to me the best one could hope to do, to compose music, and then to direct its performance."

"To me as well. Control, that is what one would achieve."

Our conversation on that occasion, as I recall, was formal and exploratory. He asked about my music and I told him, worrying as I did about the disparity between my small pianistic trials and errors and his great plans, that I hoped someday to accompany a singer, or perhaps to play duets, purely for my own enjoyment.

"Of course. Does your family support your ambitions?"

I told him about my dead father, and my mother whose life had closed too early, perhaps even as she sat, pregnant, enfolded in my father's love, at the foot of the great vine at the Centennial Exposition, my mother whose time was now lived in the twilight of that year, a light diminished with each disappointed day. "I'm afraid I am her only interest," I said. He smiled a concerned smile and shook his head. He said, "I recognize that condition. My own mother must resemble yours. She took me to Paris to study when I was fifteen, leaving my father and brothers behind in Boston. She told Professor Marmontel, when she had me play for him the first time, that she had recognized what she called my genius when I began to have lessons at eight. And so she has, you might say, invested herself in me ever since."

"Is she still in Europe? Waiting for you?"

"Yes," he said, "in Frankfurt."

We walked and talked together for more than an hour. It began to turn to dusk. I reminded him of my waiting mother, he said he would walk my way, we laughed together at Mrs. Seton's idiosyncrasies, he told me she had worn a hat during *his* few early lessons with her. By the time we arrived at my house I thought I knew a great deal about him. I felt he liked me, and I knew, without a single doubt or hesitation, that I loved him.

Three months later we sailed for Germany, leaving Paderewski with friends of Robert's, for the time being. Our engagement had been brief and somewhat perfunctory, only long enough to calm my mother's fears that I was rushing precipitously into the unknown, as she put it, when Robert asked her for permission to marry me before he returned to Germany.

"I will take good care of her," he said. "Some day I will have more money than I have now, I feel certain, and then Caroline will want for . . . very little." I think he started to say "nothing" but corrected himself, feeling no doubt that it was presumptuous to prophesy too much for his talent.

My mother agreed. She was willing to offer her aloneness to my success in marrying this charming and promising musician with an aura of foreign places clinging to his haircut and his unusual suit. She made no demands on us for the customary wedding. Indeed, she seemed too distracted and weary to plan and execute such an event. We were married before a city magistrate who was a friend of Robert's father. His brothers, Logan and Burns, were his best men, Elizabeth Pettigrew accompanied me, and Robert's father was a witness. But the titles were honorary, for the legal ceremony was very short. We took our guests to the Carlton for a late breakfast.

It was curious: my mother did not attend. It seemed to me she did not wish to leave, even for an hour, her abiding conviction that her life was at an end, especially for the predictable optimism of a wedding ceremony, especially for mine. So I took on a new person, and a new name, out of her presence. Not having witnessed the event, she appeared not to believe, or not to wish to believe, in the fact. Her letters to me in Frankfurt were always addressed: "Miss Caroline Newby." She spoke in her letters as though I were bearing the strangeness of a foreign country alone, warning me of the dangers in the streets at night for an unaccompanied young girl. She sent abroad small packages of Boston tea, and English biscuits in tins, even long leather gloves with buttons at the wrists against what she imagined to be the bitter cold of Germany's black forests.

My letters to her that year, I am sure, spoke of Robert, his hard work and long absences from home while he studied and practiced at the conservatory. I wrote to her about his great delight when he played his first concerto for William Mason, a favorite pupil of the great Franz Liszt, who praised him warmly and predicted a great success for him in the future.

My mother's replies to me, which came ever more infrequently in the first year abroad, gave no sign that she had received my news. She wrote of the terrible dampness of Boston that had begun to invade her bedroom. She was certain she detected mold in her shoes. If it grew there so easily it must certainly have fastened itself upon the lining of her lungs, which ached with every breath she took. She described the constant ringing in her left ear, which she believed had begun when a doctor had removed the wax from it and inserted in its place a tiny bell that rang whenever she moved her head.

Robert was amused by the fancies in her letters. "Poor woman," he said. "It comes of having too little to do in her life. Strange ideas take hold and grow in such emptiness."

I laughed with him, wishing at the same time that I had been able to fill her life more amply. Sixteen months after we sailed from the United States her letters ceased. I must confess I stopped writing to her. I felt no concern, thinking her silence a pique, or another aberration, like the mold, like the bell in her ear.

But it was not so. She had succumbed completely to her imaginings. A wire arrived from the Massachusetts General Hospital addressed to "Miss Caroline Newby care of Robt. Maclaren," informing me that my mother had died two weeks before, in hospital, of pneumonia. The details came later from Elizabeth: my mother had pulled her bed as far as it was possible to do into the closet, and gone to sleep with her head in what she hoped (I believe) would be a culture of mold. True or not, water had filled her lungs and killed her.

The city authorities wrote to tell me she had been buried, decently, they said, in a public field in Belmont. Robert was appalled and wanted to send money to have her moved to his family's plot. But somehow we never did it. There was not enough money at the time, and after a while it began to seem natural that she should rest, finally, as she had lived, among the anonymous of the city.

Elizabeth wrote to assure me that she had rescued some of my mother's furniture from the public sale. She had put it in the attic of her family's house. I was grateful that the bentwood sofa, particularly, had not gone to strangers.

It was accepted as reasonable that Virginia Maclaren,

Robert's mother, would not be present at the wedding. After all, she was abroad, the trip back would have been, to the Scots mind of her family, a needless expense, even a foolish one for so short a ceremony, so meager a celebration.

We met for the first time in Frankfurt in the rooms Robert and his mother had occupied in the Praunheimer Strasse before our marriage. Robert had wired her that he was bringing a wife. As we leaned against the ship's rail, or walked the deck of the *City of Paris* in the morning sun, he told me a little of her life dedicated so entirely to his welfare, of her constant worries for his health, her concern that he keep his feet dry and his hands soft.

I listened, watching the sea for whales or any sign of life in what seemed to me, at almost eighteen, a vast, anonymous, and ancient burial ground for armadas of ships. I had never crossed an ocean before. I had known of the Atlantic only from the Boston wharves where its grandeur was reduced to a series of brackish inways between piers, swirls of shallow water, full of the spill of ships.

I was frightened by the hugeness we were traveling over and, when it stormed, *into,* so frightened and sick that I was excessive in my relief and joy at landing and finally reaching Frankfurt alive. I remember, and still burn with shame when I do, that I threw myself into Virginia Maclaren's arms when we met, without waiting for evidence from her that she wished to engage in so intimate and enthusiastic a greeting. We parted almost at once: I felt a gentle but insistent pressure on my shoulder and withdrew my impulsive self from her arms. "What a surprise, Rob," she said.

"Why, Mama?" He accented the last syllable of that word in a way I had never heard in America. "I cabled. You knew I had married Caroline. The twelfth of November it was. You never answered the cable."

"Yes. I had the cable. *That* was the surprise, Rob. How long have you known . . . Caroline?"

"A few months. What difference does that make?"

While they talked, through, around, and over me, I stood between them and looked at my mother-in-law. She was a small, very tight woman with a solid, bosomless body, like a cork. Her bodice and skirt seemed pasted to her tubular trunk; her dress was wrinkle-free and taut. At the very top of her head her red-brown hair, the color of Robert's, was coiled like a spring, making her seem a little taller than she was. Still she did not come to Robert's chin. She had a way of directing her words into the far corner of a room, never looking at those to whom she spoke, not even her beloved son. This curious distance gave her statements, as well as her questions, the force of edicts. It did not matter that she spoke in English to German shopkeepers (she felt it unpatriotic, she once said, to learn a foreign language); they responded with alacrity to what they took to be her commands.

From that first day I knew that she considered Robert guilty of desertion in marrying me. She had left her home, her children, her husband, her beloved Boston, afternoon teas, evening socials and concerts, to live in a barbarous

[23]

country for the sake of his genius. Now, in his twenty-second year, a fully trained and maturing musician, he had deserted her. Her bitterness burned in the deep creases that crossed her forehead, kept perpetually red the lobes of her ears and the triangular tip of her small, furious nose. Only her eyes, which never lighted on any object, were gray and calm, like the horizon that they perpetually sought out, the color of haze or fog.

Robert did not seem to be disturbed by his mother's anger. "For a while, at least, until I can earn some money, Mama, we should like to stay with you."

His mother looked as if she had been asked to give lodging to the wife of Tom Thumb whom Barnum was at that time exhibiting in the capital cities of western Europe. "That is of course possible, if you wish, Rob," she said, looking into the distance. Robert went to bring in our cases and the trunk. She ushered me into a small hallway.

There is no other way to write of this. I must put it down directly. My mother-in-law pointed toward a huge room, almost the size of a Boston ballroom. Its ceiling was very high and beamed with what seemed to be half oak trees. At one end, mounted on a platform up three wide wooden steps, was a mammoth bed, as broad as four ordinary beds and covered with a yellowing lace spread. The canopy was of the same lace and draped down over the four posts, each one as thick and tall as a tree. I had never seen a bed of such proportions. It might have been a ship from a fairy-tale book—perhaps Timlin's *The Ship That Sailed to Mars*. It was the size of my entire bedroom in Boston.

I stared at it. "If you are staying here, this will be your room," she said. "Your bed."

Stupidly awed, I said, "But this must be your room. I wouldn't want to . . ."

"It was," she said, "mine and Robert's. Now it will be yours."

That night, huddled in a corner of the cold field of coverlets and comforters, I erred again. Young and badly frightened, I needed refutation of the strange vista of their lives that his mother had opened to me. "Did you share this . . . room with your mother before I came?" I asked him. I was afraid to say "bed."

At first he did not answer. His silence told me I had made a mistake to question him. He moved farther away from me and lay still, his arms folded under his head, his russet eyes taking light from the dying fire at the other end of the room. He stared at the canopy.

"Yes." Then he closed his eyes and slept or seemed to sleep. I lay awake, filled with fear of the great expanse of blackness outside the four posts, and inexplicable terror for the future.

So we three lived together. Mrs. Maclaren made the sewing room into a small bedroom. Robert left very early each morning for the conservatory and returned after seven in the evening for his supper. I spent my mornings trying to practice on the grand piano in the drawing room, feeling Virginia's resentment across the distance from the sewing room where she preferred to sit in the morning, staring at the barren tree outside her window, sometimes sewing or doing her needlepoint.

Often, in my cold misery (Germany in the winter is cold and dark and without hospitality even toward its native inhabitants, it seemed to me), I took walks along the formal, square blocks of the city, so different from the unpredictable curves of Boston. One could not get lost in Frankfurt. Its rectangles were too regular. After I had walked around one and come back to my starting point, I would have a hot chocolate and pastry in the Hotel du Nord, I think it was, and then walk around the rectangle in the other direction.

In those two years my days were filled with music and silences, transplanted, I would often think, from Mrs. Seton and her music room. I stayed away from our flat as much as possible, walking the streets of the city, visiting its museums, going to afternoon concerts. I made no friends and missed Elizabeth and the few I had in Boston. In those years —I don't know how it is now—Frankfurt had beautiful parks and I would walk there on pleasant days, wishing we had brought Paderewski with us to accompany me.

Only once do I remember Robert walking with me. He was very quiet, his head bent slightly to one side as though he were listening to sounds pitched so that only he could catch them. He seemed happy, he seemed to be enjoying the absolute peace of those woods. Later in that year he wrote a pianoforte piece called *From a German Forest.* Then I knew something of what it was he had heard in the silence of the woods that day: the grave low sounds of the wind as it stirs leaves and twigs, moving around amid the Indian pipes and mosses at the foot of great trees, and its high, rhythmic whirrings in the top branches, interrupted at irregular intervals by the cries and pipings of birds.

We were short of money, but I wanted very much to find rooms of our own. So Robert acquired two pupils, whom he preferred to instruct in the practice rooms of the conservatory. One wet afternoon (did it rain every afternoon in Germany or do I only remember it so?) I took the long walk to the school, thinking Robert and I might walk home together, at seven, his usual hour. The matron in a front room somewhat reluctantly directed me to the practice room on the second floor where he was giving a lesson. I went up. The door of the room I had been sent to was ajar, and I looked in. I saw Robert bent earnestly over a young woman seated at the piano, one of his hands lightly on her shoulder, the other poking at a place in the music before them both. She nodded and began to play. He stepped back, bending his head in his customary way, to listen.

Then I saw, standing in the shadow in a corner of the room, a slight young man whose extraordinarily white face was luminous in the dark space. He seemed to be listening intently, but his eyes were on Robert, not on the young lady who was playing. He watched Robert so closely that his whole body seemed pointed toward him.

I don't remember why it so disturbed me to see Robert doing what he said he had to do so that we might be able to afford separate quarters, and the young man (another pupil?) watching him from the shadows. There was surely nothing improper in what I saw. But my discomfort kept me from staying there to wait for him that evening or from inquiring about the young man in the corner. Never again did I return to the conservatory except for the night of the farewell party for Robert. Now I took walks in other directions, resting on the aged wood benches in the parks, on the stone slabs in the art galleries. I learned a little café German so I could speak, hesitantly, to waiters and to the amiable guards in the rooms of the museums. I can hardly remember the pictures I studied day after day, but I remember well my loneliness, my sense of being held in the solitary confinement of stone buildings, surrounded by unpeopled forests and empty oceans, always, everywhere, alone.

Robert would take his mother and me out to dine on Saturday evenings, every Saturday evening. I remember the heavy dinners in the restaurant we frequented in the Jahnstrasse, the blood-thick brown gravies over slabs of brown meat, the heavy, dark beer, the weightlessness of the fine strudel held onto the plate by full-bodied apples. I would leave the restaurant almost anchored to the sidewalk by the food. Robert would suggest we "walk it off," and we would: he two or three steps ahead, walking lightly and fast, my mother-in-law and I following a little behind, all three of us silent and shielded from each other by our resentments and the leaden sediment of the long dinner.

Sometimes now, in wakeful moments in the long nights of my ninetieth year, I go back to read in a small black leather notebook I kept during our time in Frankfurt.

[28]

There was no one for me to converse with so I occupied myself with putting down my thoughts, what I heard talked about, what I noticed:

October 18

Yesterday the rain slanted so oddly that, as it entered the gutters, it made no splash, merely met and joined the waters already there—is this called confluence?—as though flowing downward from another, higher stream.

November 2

Robert says that the piano's wondrous limitations ought to impel the composer to write for full orchestra. In those effects, the strings of the piano have been plucked out and mounted on panels to be bowed. The hammers have been amplified into percussion. Only the winds are not derived from the eviscerated innards of the pianoforte.

November 9

Robert is a handsome man. His thick red hair is parted carefully in the center, making him look freshly barbered, mother-tended, neat. He has all the graces of a young, confident, and talented man. His quiet humor is always turned first upon himself. The red of his irises seems a ruddy reflection of a glowing mind, stirred not by persons but by determination to know more. Why, then, does he not seem loving?

December 7

V McI—hers is a maternity which freezes from love and burns with hate, which consumes what it hungers for, not food but the nearby spirits of family and other persons, which dies slowly when deprived of the bed of its son.

December 18

Europe seems elderly to me, covered with hoar, learned, sly, selfish, an octogenarian who resents the sight of his American great-grandson who is youthful, vigorous, vital, and full of boundless hope.

January 9

Where is natural music, the real music of the world, to be found? In woods, among low banks of ferns, at the spindly tops of birches, in reeds at the edge of ponds, under the lift of ocean waves, and around the edges of its spume. Below one's feet passing on ancient bricks laid for roads. Between the folds of organdy curtains blowing into sun-rooms in a light wind. Under the eaves of an old house during a storm which dispossesses the swallows.

January 14

A story Robert told last evening: in Paris in the conservatory in 1887 there was a pupil named Claude Debussy. His elderly professor, Antoine Marmontel, was stiff and severe, rigid and Prussian. He preferred the smooth, effortless playing of Robert to Claude's abrupt and choppy perfor-

mances. Claude was somewhat younger than his fellow pupil. He breathed raucously when he played difficult passages so that his nasal noises intertwined themselves with the harmonies. He panted loudly in order to emphasize strong beats. When he performed at the conservatory he resembled a snorting steam engine, so everyone, including Professor Marmontel, despaired of him, predicting a dim platform future for the clangorous young pianist.

February 5

Robert recalls the time when his teacher, Carl Heymann, returned from a successful tournée *of Paris, London, Copenhagen. He seemed to his students no longer a teacher now but a performer, an elevated personage, an example of the polish and assurance such a journey and such acclaim give to a man. He seemed mysteriously now to be capable of anything. Robert said he played the classics as though they had been written by men with blood in their veins.*

March 9

Robert's red mustache has grown. It droops at its corners. Gravity is pulling it down, it fills the whole area of his face between his nose and lower lip, burying his upper lip, crossing his face with color. Now he brushes his hair upward in the imperial German fashion. But his pink and white skin is of the American type. Professor Joachim Raff calls him "the handsome American."

April 1

The Maclarens are proud of their Scots ancestry. They talk of it as though they had never made the oceanic migration to New England. They still salt their American speech with dialect from Scotland; their true patriotism is to the older country.

May 14

The death of Raff, the death of Liszt a few years ago. Robert wonders why he stays in Europe any longer. He has discovered there are no appointments for an American in Europe. Würzburg has turned him down, the conservatory here considers him too young for Heymann's post. That redoubtable old man has begun to lose his mind and is to be made to retire. Poor Heymann—often he plays the same piece again and again and again, sometimes for an entire day, and always the theme from Spontini's Olympia Overture. *A few days ago he sat seemingly fastened to the piano and the piano bench. He has to be lifted up and led away to his bed each evening.*

I reflect now on what I wrote in those long-distant German years, my interior dialogue, my rehearsal of what I heard Robert say, of what I thought. Sometimes I wrote in an effort to understand Virginia Maclaren's quiet decline, or to record my desperate, lonely reflections, my talk to myself alone.

Virginia Maclaren began to grow visibly thinner. The

solid cork of her body lost its firmness, her neck, a peg that had held her block-like head erect on her rigid shoulders, became ragged, bent forward, her chin often almost resting upon her chest as she sat in a chair in the evening working at her embroidery hoop. A strange weakness of her spine was diagnosed by doctors in Berlin. I never believed she was physically ill. I thought she wanted her eyes to sink down from the distances they once sought, to the floor. The strength in her neck and in her spirit began to weaken from the day I came to live in Europe. Everything gave way in her: the almost youthful, well-corseted stocky body, the sure posture of her head, her will to stay alive to witness her son's success.

Once, coming home early on a rain-drenched afternoon —I had been caught in the sudden downpour and was wet through my cape to my dress so that it clung unbecomingly to my legs—I stopped in the entranceway to remove my sodden shoes and cape, trying to make no noise, as my mother-in-law often rested in the afternoon hours. For some reason I remember my hat that afternoon: the black feathers, dyed egret, I think, that covered it like birds in flight, smelled dank, like crows submerged in a cistern. There was no sound of life anywhere in the long string of rooms in which we lived. I went to my room to change, passing the closed door of the sewing room.

The door to our room, too, was shut. Odd, I thought, because my New Englander's concern for the proper airing of bedchambers during the day always compelled me to leave it open. Opening it, I saw my mother-in-law stretched out on the bed, her face buried in Robert's pillow, her shoulders shaking although no sound could be heard. One of her hands seemed to be under her lower body, which moved convulsively, up and down, up and down over the hand. Her thin, violet-colored morning dress showed me the outline of her moving back, her legs, her shoulders, her knees dug into the softness of the bed. She looked as I imagined Christ might have looked from the back of the cross, still alive and moving, a woman in an agony of grief and sexual passion, crucified upon a coverlet.

I tried to back away. She heard me, sat up, saw me, and brushed her wet eyes with her sleeve. "And now you spy upon me," she said, her voice hoarse.

"Oh, no, I did not know you were here."

"I know, I know. There is no place left for me. You heartless Caroline Newby. You have taken it all." She climbed down from the bed's great height, down the steps to the floor, looking like a toy, a dwarf beside the treelike posts. Her eyes blank and unseeing, she went past me into the hall. I wanted to follow her, to take her head in my hands and kiss her suffering face and tell her that I had taken *nothing*, that her son gave almost nothing to me and surely seemed to desire nothing from me. I wanted to tell her what I had learned, that he belonged only to the secret music in his head, or perhaps to his young lady pupils or to his watching friend, but not to me. In the enormous bed in the great bedchamber she had had as much of him as I, or more than I because she had had him at the beginning and, I still believe, had taught him the arts of maternal love and mature passion, had loved him as only a mother, hardly ever a wife or a mistress, can love, with the hands that caressed his infancy, the lips and tongue that tasted the sweat and new odors of his puberty, the avid eyes that knew his contours from their first appearance, watched the curl about the ear turn to sideburns and reach down to become beard.

I wanted to tell her how deeply I envied the love between her and her son, how I had never learned to love my recently deceased mother in this way, how my mother had never loved me, my mother who, like Virginia Maclaren, had not come to our wedding, to whom, too, I had always been Caroline Newby.

But the long hall lay between her room and mine. Her heavy door was shut, the words she had spoken still hung like smoke in the air. Her beloved son, who was also my husband: all that stood in the way. I stayed where I was in the bedroom and closed the door. We never spoke directly to each other again.

How do I put down on this paper my feeling of inadequacy, so profound that it began early in my marriage to Robert and lasted until his death downstairs? I felt there was no way to charm a man so charming himself, or to interest a genius who heard only the higher treble notations of significance, while I stumbled about on the low notes of the bass clef. Or to console his mother, a woman bereft of her lover.

The night Robert and I first made love (of this subject I do not enjoy writing, yet I have set out to be open, so I must put down what I have felt, or not felt, not alone what I have seen and overheard) in the berth of a stateroom aboard the *City of Paris*, the act, which I had virginally dreaded, was over quickly. Robert was listless and tired, he told me what he was about to do to me as though he were a physician calming the fears of a child with a description of surgical procedures. I felt nothing under his demonstration but sharp pain and hot blood on my inner thighs. He fell asleep heavily while I tried to dry the blood from myself and the sheets of the berth without waking him. A week later—we made love again. This time it was my suggestion that we do so. I was curious to know if I had healed. I wanted to feel the rush of pleasure I had been led to believe (from the occasional confessions of my Boston friends) was customary.

I did not. This time, and in the growingly infrequent sexual encounters Robert and I had in the next two years, I felt nothing except mild satisfaction in serving what I considered to be his need. Never did I think of my lack of ardor as a failure in him. Always it was I who seemed deficient and inadequate, without beauty and charm, ignorant of the subtle guiles that awaken and sustain masculine desire. And then, after those two unsatisfying years, we rarely made love again.

I have often speculated: Why did Robert look upon me so kindly in the Commons that day and decide to marry me, I who looked mouselike, murine, perhaps even birdlike? "You are such a *little* girl," my mother had said hopelessly, in that age of proudly buxom women equally endowed in the bustle area. "You remind me of a starved heron," my friend Elizabeth once said, meaning it to be a purely descriptive phrase, not cruel, I am sure. My hair was, as it is still, without definable color, as though it had very early begun to rehearse for its inevitable whiteness: a thin, weak-brown shade. True, my hands and feet were small, and that was fashionable and called, often, aristocratic, but my reach at the piano keys suffered from this. Robert once said that my hands were not practical.

Why, then, did he choose to turn Miss Caroline Newby into Mrs. Robert Glencoe Maclaren? Because it was suitable, practical, for a young composer to have a wife? A man who hoped some day to have a chair of music at a university or a post as principal of a conservatory: should he not have a wife?

Or, I wondered, could it be that Robert was seeking to unlock the maternal prison? With a wife beside him he would be free at last, and yet hardly, at it turned out, tied to me. Once Robert's natal bonds were cut, he floated free, wary, careful not to form another emotional attachment as exhausting and lengthy. We two were bound to each other by law. But beyond that, we were bound by air, we lived in the common ozone of his indifference, his eternal politeness and charm, his passion to write music, perform it, listen to it, and, as it was to be later in Boston, to walk companionably in the parks in the evening with me on his arm and Paderewski, now growing heavy, walking beside him on a slack leash.

Inadequate as I felt to his needs and to the larger realization that he needed far less of me than I of him, still, often, he wanted me present. I may have served his desire to establish himself as a family man, trustworthy and solid, in the world's eyes. I suited his arm, I occupied a chair in his sitting room. I learned from his mother to keep an orderly, clean, and attractive house. I had, he often said, a way with servants. I *knew* food and was rapidly learning about wine. I took up very little room, being birdlike. The Steinway grand, newly arrived from Hamburg, was a larger, more decorative and significant addition to the display of his life than I.

We had been living in Germany for more than two years when Robert decided it was time to return to America. His musical future was there, he now felt. He said his education was over, smiling as he spoke, saying he hardly *felt* educated, in his self-deprecating way—and still, think of what the favorite pupil of Liszt had said of him! It was time to leave the world of student trials for the proof, to move beyond his tutors and masters in order to carry out their instructions.

We made our plans to depart, booked three passages on the *Servia* and arranged for the shipping of our household and the careful crating of the new piano and the great bed. In the first flush of optimism about his future, Robert thought of buying another piano to be sent to America but was restrained by the cost and by the reminder that William Steinway now had offices and showrooms for his instruments in New York.

But at the very last, Virginia Maclaren would not come

with us. She would not leave Germany. Robert tried to reason with her. I said, "You are so far from people, from your family." She shrugged, saying they did not need her. "My husband is dead, my sons are grown." I spoke of her friends. "I have friends no longer," she said, "here or there."

"Robert," I said, playing what I thought to be the strongest card. To that she said nothing, searching the floor with her eyes, looking up at Robert only briefly. He seemed to have grown taller as she shrank. "You would not wish to live so far from us, would you, Mama?" he asked. I remember clearly the strange tense he used: indefinite, conditional.

Again she raised her eyes from the floor to look into the distance. "Yes, I do. As far as it is possible to be. I no longer wish to live near anyone. Not even you, my beloved Rob. I wish to be alone, to live alone, without reminders of the past."

"But the shipping. The packing. We've arranged to have all this furniture sent back."

Her eyes strained into the distance of the hallway that led to her sewing room. She gestured with a sweep of her arm that took in the whole series of rooms. "I want none of this, to live or die among. I will acquire new objects of my own. Don't be concerned about that."

Even though I heard what I took to be theatrical coloration in her sentences, it was a dreadful time for me. But Robert seemed unaffected. He said nothing more, considering the matter peaceably, satisfactorily, settled. He helped his mother find a flat on Neuleystrasse which was already furnished. He supervised all the packing of her personal belongings.

From all the furnishings she had brought with her from America, and the others she had gathered in Paris, in Stuttgart, in Frankfurt in the years she and Robert had lived together in those cities, she took with her only a small needlepoint-covered pouf on which she had rested her feet in the sewing room. Its area was the size of a lady's handkerchief, its pattern that of two mourning doves, their heads tucked into each other's breasts, their feet a pattern of entwined twiglike toes.

On the last day before our sailing, Robert took his mother's arm and guided her toward the door, carrying her coat and parasol, for the short walk to her new home. I could not bear to watch. It was like being present at a human sacrifice or forced to witness a hanging. She stopped, reaching to peck at my chin, because Robert said as she walked silently to the door, "Aren't you going to bid Caroline *bon voyage?*" Her kiss was as dry as dust, her lips too parched, I thought, to feel my burning skin. I was consumed with embarrassment and pity. I know she hardly saw me as she bade me farewell. I was not present when she said good-bye to her son.

We came home in June of '96. I can see us still, standing at the rail in the wind, watching the tugboats pull at the

Servia, edging it with their great hawsers toward the pier. With one hand Robert held the high felt crown of his hat. With his other he worried at a sore on his lip, trying in his nervousness to work off the scab with his nail.

A cool wind cut across New York harbor. I remember thinking it was a new-world air, brasher and fresher than the ancient heavy air of Frankfurt we had just left. We watched the miniature waves of the Hudson River lap the white sides of the ship. Robert put his hands down on the rail and bent over to listen, I suspected, to the suspirations of the water. I knew he was listening for a pattern, a melody, even a refrain. I heard none, only the irregular gasps and smacks of tame harbor water.

The ship made its slow bend to the right, seeming to lean into the wind, nudged into its docking position by four insistent tugboats on its left side. The wind died as the maneuver cut the ship off from the river. Almost at once it became very warm, with the hot breath of the shore and the land.

I knew Robert was absorbed and nervous, not from the intricate motions of bringing a great ship to berth, but by the uncertainty of his future, by his already forming nostalgia for the securities of his life abroad. For him the present never existed, which was perhaps why I never seemed to exist for him. I watched him pat his hat again, saw that the work of his nail on his lip had produced a small trickle of blood. "Good Lord, Robert. Your lip is bleeding. You've been picking at it again."

He licked his lip, smiling a little as though he were pleased at the taste. Perhaps he was making a small physical addition to the pain he was feeling, to the fear of coming home to America, to Boston, compounding dread with blood. "Will it take us long to come through customs, do you think, Robert?"

"I don't know. Burns took me through last time. Even so, it was two hours before I could start for the hotel."

I tried to think how I could make the passage from the ship to the hotel easy for him, in place of his brother, whom we had not informed of our arrival. Robert was unable to manage such journeys, often following crowds in the direction they flowed, forgetful of his own. Sometimes I wondered if he thought everyone was going to his destination.

The gangplanks were lowered. They resembled three parallel tongues reaching toward the shore. We followed the crowd to one of them. Once down and on the pier, I felt the first assault of the depression that was to afflict me all that first year back in Boston. Robert had come home to promise, I to more of my married life as it had been lived in Germany: a maker of late suppers, a duster of piano keys and the lowered lid in the off hours when they were not in use, a solitary visitor to galleries and concert halls in the afternoons.

Still, the moment of stepping ashore at the foot of New York's towers was exciting. There was the chance that much might change now that Virginia and the conservatory were left behind. Robert might turn his eyes toward me, *see* me, might erase my sense of insufficiency with his love and notice. Now that we were home in our own land, he might open a little of his handsome European surface to my deep American love for him.

A few steps from the end of the gangplank we were met by a strange young man who seemed to have been waiting for us. He introduced himself to us as a reporter from the *Boston Transcript,* come to New York, he said, to interview the returning native son back from his European success. He wore a straw hat with a wide red-and-white band, and a white-and-blue–striped jacket that had suffered in the June heat of New York. There were semicircles of dampness under his arms. His forehead was wet. I saw Robert draw back from him a little.

"Have you lived in Germany very long?"

"For some years," Robert said, in the clipped Germanic diction he had acquired abroad. He sounded precise and curt, as though the interview had already gone on too long.

"Study there, did you?"

"Yes, of course."

"Performed on the piana too, did you?"

Robert looked at me helplessly. The newfound patriotism of his return seemed to be slipping away in the presence of this reporter's callow American ignorance. I gestured toward the trunks and grips, now piled neatly under a cardboard sign that said *M.* "Perhaps we should get into our line for the customs inspector," I said.

"Just a few more questions here, sir. Knew some of the greats, did you, over there in Paree?"

"I was in Paris only a year. Debussy was a fellow student there. We both studied under Savard."

The reporter, I saw, wrote down *DEBOOSIE* carefully in his notebook and then asked, "Where did you go then? Vee-enna?"

"To Frankfurt, Germany, where I studied with Carl Heymann and Joachim Raff."

I spoke up quickly to fill what threatened to be a long silence while the young man struggled with the proper names. "Mr. Maclaren's compositions were highly praised and encouraged by William Mason, a protégé of Franz Liszt," I said, to prevent Robert's leaving rudely.

The straw-hatted young man wrote on his pad *LIST* and something else I could not read. "And now what are your plans, sir?"

"To compose and play, and perhaps to teach, in Boston."

"Well, good luck to you, sir. And to you, ma'am. Excuse my dumbness. I'm—this is not my regular beat. Know nothing about music myself. City side of the desk is my place. Just happened to be in New York, so they asked me to come by."

"Quite all right." We walked away, toward the letter *M* and our luggage.

An astonishing metamorphosis of this conversation appeared in the *Transcript,* signed by what I took to be the young man's name, E. P. Duckworth. It was full of rhetoric and an invention of which I had not thought him capable after hearing him speak. The news report said that "the composer and his wife, Caroline, had lived abroad for some

years, he studying and composing a great deal of music of
which the composer Franz Liszt had been very admiring.
A friend of Robert Maclaren's, interviewed in Frankfurt, said
of the couple that 'their union, perfect in sympathy and
closeness of comradeship, was nothing short of ideal.' "
He continued (I am quoting now from the newspaper account, which I still have in a scrapbook and which I will
lay here in this account): "Their life in Frankfurt was
characterized by an ideal serenity and detachment. It was
a time of rich productiveness for Maclaren, who is now
only twenty-four, and it is to be expected that his return
to his homeland will be marked by further steps toward the
great promise of his talent. His lodgings will be in Boston,
where he and Mrs. Maclaren will reside on Mount Vernon
Street. There he will accept private pupils. His *First Piano
Suite* will be performed in November in Chickering Hall."

A felicitous editor, I imagine, had turned Robert's
bluntness, a reporter's ignorance, and Weeks's friendly blindness into tribute. I do not wish to seem critical or ungrateful
when I say that this magical process, this kind of trans-
mutation, was to occur again and again in Robert's biography.
Admirers of his charm and his music created the myth of
him that has remained to this day. The descriptive mode
used for writing about him has always been euphemism—
until the very end, and after his death, when critics, conductors, and students began to be critical of what they
called his extreme romanticism. They were to comment upon
the small scope of his work, the sentimental impressionism
(I am using their terms, not mine) of his later compositions.

But not yet: at this time about which I am writing, only panegyrics were written about him. The *Transcript*'s article was the beginning.

The house we rented in Mount Vernon Street on Beacon Hill was narrow and three-storied. It looked out at back on a small, lovely shaded garden, and had a very large room suitable for a music room, two small sitting rooms, one for each of us, and two bedrooms. We reclaimed Paderewski from the friends who had boarded and overfed him in Robert's long absence. He had lost his lean look and become lazy and slow in his movements. He loved to lie in the garden and to be taken for short walks around the gardens on Commonwealth Avenue. Delighted to have him back, Robert took him out for airings every morning, and then returned him to his banishment in the garden when he went upstairs. Robert could not bear to work with any motion or breathing in the room. Paderewski disliked being put out, but he learned to be patient, to lie under the plane tree until Robert, finished with a long day of composing and lessons, would come for him again in the early evening. They walked together while I talked to our supper guests, if we had them, or supervised the food if we were to be alone. Only on weekends was the routine broken, when Robert went out to perform with the Symphony, or with the Kneissel Quartette, or to play at Chickering Hall in Boston.

Or, on Sunday evenings, we very often went to concerts, to hear Robert's work played, for it was beginning to have a vogue and could be heard quite often there and in other cities. I remember when *Lear and Cordelia* was played for the first time by the Symphony Orchestra. Artur Nikisch was to conduct it. He came by to call for us that evening. We took a hansom cab together to the Music Hall, it must have been, since I don't think the orchestra had as yet moved into its new Symphony Hall. Nikisch, Robert, and I had met in Leipzig; Robert and he had become good friends. This evening was the first time in a long time, almost since the farewell party, that I had seen Robert so animated. It was not because the Boston Symphony was going to play his work but because someone from the past—a friend from his beloved Germany—was there in his Beacon Hill sitting room.

I doubt if either Robert or Nikisch knew I was present. We entered the old Music Hall through the back door, I somewhat behind the two of them, and they in a transport of delight in being together again. Robert had his arm around Nikisch's shoulder. It was much like a reunion of fellow army officers who had once been stationed on the same foreign post, or college classmates come together after a long absence.

I went to my seat, and Robert joined me there. When Nikisch came to the podium I noticed how much alike he and Robert looked, with the similarity that seemed to characterize most men of their age and European training and class. Except for his beard (Robert never adopted the European habit), Nikisch had the same short, middle-parted hair, the same thick, curving mustache, the same absorbed look.

They belonged to a close fraternity of artists—of men—which I had learned about in Frankfurt and from which, because I was a woman and a very minor musician, I felt eternally excluded. There *were* women musicians we had known in Europe—Teresa Carreño, who played Robert's *Second Piano Suite* in Wiesbaden, and a Miss Adele Margolis in London who performed two movements from his first suite. Robert wrote grateful notes to the two pianists, but he made no efforts to meet them: in the fraternity there was room only at a distance for women.

I had always thought that a *perfect union* (so the *Transcript* happily termed it) was the result of spiritual and intuitive harmonies, an intellectual fidelity, so to speak. If this were achieved, one could then enter into the highest harmony, which was physical love. In this day it is thought to be the other way around, but I have never believed that. Robert and I had almost no physical love, and never, it seemed to me, had it come at the culmination of the other unities, always as a sudden thought, a remembrance of conjugal duty. For neither of us do I think it was a great pleasure, certainly never for me. Indeed, I was not to know the joy of that pleasure of which so many speak and write until much later and in another way. . . .

Robert occasionally performed his duty as meticulously as he walked his dog, parted his hair, trimmed his mustache. But at the end of a long day, I knew his energy was very low, his interest elsewhere, his physical prowess used up. We lay in the great bed, which we had transported safely and crammed into an upper chamber of our thin New

England town house. We rarely touched; he slept stretched out straight on his side, unwilling to lose his rest by contact, as solitary in his sleep as he was in his waking hours, a man who lived almost entirely within himself. Every month when I had my female visitor, as we used to call it, he would move to the couch in his studio, offended, I think, by the unmistakable odor, which the strips of rag I wore could not disguise. His nights and days were designed to shield himself and his art.

Or so I then thought.

I have mentioned the farewell party given Robert by his fellow students and his pupils before he left the Hoch Conservatory, two evenings before, as I recall. None of the women students came, perhaps because of the lateness of the hour. It was at nine o'clock. I was the only lady among twelve or thirteen solemnly suited men standing about the room, wineglasses in their hands, talking together, Robert in the center, laughing often. I was introduced to a number of persons I had not met before. Professor Heymann came over to speak to me when I seemed to be pushed to the very edge of the animated groups. He took my arm and moved me over to speak to a pale-faced young man who was also standing alone. I remembered him at once as the young man I had seen in the shadows of Robert's lesson that day. "Mrs. Maclaren, may I present Churchill Weeks," the professor said. "A very good pianist. This is Robert's wife, Caroline."

Churchill Weeks stared at me. His brows were so heavy over his deep-set eyes it was difficult to see them clearly. His face seemed almost sickly in that studio light. He took my hand, raised it a little, and bent stiffly over it, in the German way, without kissing it. "I am honored, Frau Maclaren. Your husband is my very dear friend. I shall miss him very much."

I was astonished: tears streamed down his face. I was startled, for I had not seen his eyes, I did not know he was crying. That was all he said for a long moment, and then he went on, "You must pardon my display of feeling. I am an American—my home is in Milwaukee—and it is hard to stay on here—alone." He turned and left the room.

Walking back toward the Praunheimer Strasse, I asked Robert about Churchill Weeks. "Is he always—so emotional?" Robert seemed reluctant to talk about him. "He's—a musician, a composer. Very sensitive."

"Have you been friends long?"

"We have known each other since we came to Frankfurt at almost the same time."

"More than two years, then?"

"Yes, it must have been. Somehow it does not seem that long."

"Why did I never meet him before? Why did you never bring him home?"

Robert made no reply. We walked for some time in silence, the usual climate of our walks. Silence was more characteristic of him when we were together than the sound of his voice, low and pleasant as I remember it being to friends. After a while he said, "I enjoyed the party. It was good of them all to have it for me. They're very kind friends."

I managed to bury the memory of Churchill Weeks's pale, wet face until the letters began to arrive, not long after we had settled into Mount Vernon Street. One morning the postman handed me three thin letters in blue envelopes as I walked out to do the day's shopping. Robert was cloistered in his studio upstairs where he had breakfasted alone in order to begin work early. All the letters were from abroad, and in the left-hand corners read: *Weeks/Jahn-strasse 76/Frankfurt/Deutschland.* I went back into the house and climbed the stairs to deliver the letters. I first knocked on Robert's door and then went in. He was standing beside the piano, his head bent over a manuscript page of music, both hands resting on the lid. He had not heard me enter.

I did not want to interrupt, knowing how intently he was listening to the sounds in his head as he often did, even in company, and always when he was alone with me. I went out, closing the door quietly behind me, and left the letters for him on the reception table near the downstairs entry. On the way to his walk later, with Paderewski, he will find them, I thought.

That night we were to sup late. Robert was still in his studio, engrossed in his new *Woodland Songs,* which he had told me he hoped Carl Faelton would play in his recital in New York next season. Robert came to supper and ate in silence, wiped his mustache carefully with his napkin, folded it, and then for the first time turned his eyes on me, with that weary look he always had at the end of a long day of work, close to the end of his patience with himself and with me, for some unknown reason. "I found my mail very late this afternoon. Does it not usually come earlier?"

"Yes, about nine-thirty, usually."

"Why didn't you bring it up to me?"

"I did, Robert. You were working. I didn't wish to disturb you."

"You might have offered me a choice," he said in a small, angry voice.

I was aghast. No household crisis or sudden personal disability, nothing, had ever before been sufficient cause for Robert to be interrupted. But Weeks's letters . . .

I must now write frankly, perhaps more frankly than I am sure the Foundation wishes me to. For the fact was, those letters from Churchill Weeks were love letters. I must be pardoned for the venial sin I committed: I read them. It happened this way. A few days later another thin blue envelope from Germany arrived. This time I carried it at once to the music room. Robert took it, smiled his quick, charming smile, thanked me, and turned away to read it. I remember thinking how his smile had shrunk, from the wide grin I first noticed at our meeting in the park until now: it had become abbreviated, a token, a quick gesture like a handshake, the remains of a smile. Then it was gone and one was left, *I* was left, that is, frozen rather than warmed by it.

That afternoon Robert went to a rehearsal. I watched him from an upper window as he turned the corner into the avenue and then I went quickly into the music room. With me I took a duster as pretense. The room was meticulously neat—Robert could not work unless it was—but the surfaces were somewhat dusty and I began to stir the dust about. Under a pile of music paper near the back of the piano I saw a light blue color. And while only Paderewski watched my shameful act, I read Weeks's letters.

What shall I say of them? They were written in an agony of love such as I had never in my life been witness to. Weeks told Robert of the pain his departure had caused him, of the illness he had suffered for two months afterward, of his slow recovery during which his only thought was to see Robert again, to hold his beloved head in his hands once again, to take strength from *his* strength. Was it at all possible that Robert was planning a summer return to the Continent, since he, Weeks, would not be free to come to Boston? In a cribbed, uneven script that seemed visible evidence of his distraught state, he asked:

When shall we two be together again, my beloved friend? For the old talk, the old making of music together, four hands at the same keyboard, four hands and two mouths and our whole beings engaged in the same loving act.

These words, as I have here put them down, were etched into my memory and are still there. Often now I do not remember what day it is, or what dinner was served to me last night, but the words of Churchill's letter I have never forgotten. Other parts of the letters were sprinkled with Scots phrases, for Weeks claimed his ancestry was like Robert's and seemed to affect the Scots language as part of his own. He called Robert an *auld farran,* he blamed himself for being a *bluntie,* sometimes a *blunker.* He felt alone and melancholy—*leefulane* and *ourie*—he sent his *lock o' loo* to his fellow *pingler.* Some I did not know and had to look up in the large Webster; I had never heard Robert, the proud descendant of Scots, use one of them. It must have been their private language of love, kept for those burning letters.

I returned the letters to the place I had found them, feeling deep guilt for having allowed myself to be driven to such an act. Of course I know nothing of Robert's answers to those *cris du coeur;* were they, too, sprinkled with loving dialect? But Robert wrote, I know. Once I saw a letter, addressed to Weeks, before Robert carried it himself to the postbox on the corner during one of his walks with Paderewski. In the late evenings I would see him writing, I seated across the room knitting or reading (never writing: to whom would I have written? surely not to my mother-in-law, who would not have responded, I felt sure), Robert holding his writing desk on his lap.

As he wrote he would rub his lower lip thoughtfully. The sore I had first noticed tended to heal and then to appear again because, I always thought, in his nervousness and unease, he would rub his lip, returning the little eruption to life.

What was I to do with this discovery, except to recognize what I thought at the time might be one explanation: there was a deep, unfathomable alliance among men of talent which involved them wholly, making it impossible for women to enter their consciousness except in a curiously negative way. Remove our services, our presence as help-meets, and our absence is remarked upon. Our physical support restored, we sink back to the outer limits of their awareness.

But admission to the alliance? I have never seen it granted, except as a chivalric courtesy uttered for the moment—Shall we join the ladies?—after ample brandy and smoking and the serious talk was exhausted. The next half hour would be spared us for polite small talk, women's subjects.

Perhaps, I tried to tell myself, the letters were an extension of all this, with the added exaggerations and emotional excess natural to creative persons who thought and wrote in the romantic tradition. In one of Weeks's letters there were quotations from Heine and Goethe. My imagination supplied mottoes from Tennyson and Victor Hugo in the replies Robert must have sent to his friend. Once I came upon Robert standing with his foot on the grill in front of the fireplace, his face reddened by the flames, reading Tennyson's poems, saying a line or two aloud, to himself.

Our life went along evenly. The only change was Robert's increasing success and recognition. Those were good years to be in Boston, to be a young American composer. We began to read, in the musical columns of the newspapers and in the journals, praise for Robert's compositions, which were played with increasing frequency by pianists in New York, in Philadelphia, in San Francisco. The Symphony Orchestra in Boston, now under a new conductor named Emil Paur, played his work often. Poor Nikisch had gone back to Hungary after three years in Boston, a disappointed man who told us one evening at dinner that he had tried without success to come to terms with the men of the orchestra. But they had resented his demands for rehearsals over and above the ones they felt reasonable. Nikisch had invited Robert often as a soloist; Paur did, too, even increasing the number of appearances he offered him in a year.

Robert traveled to other cities on the invitation of conductors, one of whom, Anton Seidl, I think it was, told the *Evening Post* that he considered Maclaren the first great American composer. Robert returned from that trip glowing at the phrase, almost a prophet in his own time and country, he quoted Seidl as having said, with his tight shy smile to Elizabeth Pettigrew, who had been visiting with me while he was gone those weeks. Later, Philip Hale was to say almost the same thing in the magazine *Music*.

Elizabeth congratulated him. She had always admired him. Now, from the distance of her spinsterhood, I was able to tell, she regarded him with awe. She had a way of rising whenever he entered the sitting room, as though he were of a priestly caste. I think she found it very difficult to sit in his presence. But I don't think he noticed, or noticed her at all, thinking of her, I felt sure, as an occupant of my spare time who did not, fortunately, impinge upon his.

The unaccustomed glow in his face after that tour turned into a fever almost immediately upon his return. At first he denied its presence. Finally he was too sick to insist upon its absence and took to his bed, lying inert and hot, refusing to allow me to call a physician. "It's the body's way," he said. For three days he slept, long and feverishly. I brought him meals and sat on the edge of the great bed while he tried and failed to eat. He said his throat was too sore.

"Shall I read to you, Robert?"

"I think not, Caroline. I don't mind the silence. Sometimes it's a pleasure to hear nothing but what comes into my head from the temperature, can you believe it?"

I tried to be playful. "Would you care to hear some early Maclaren, like *Petits Morceaux pour Piano?*" In the dressing room off the bedroom was an upright piano on which I used to play a little now and then, quietly, so as not to disturb Robert.

"Thank you, but I think not."

"Some Liszt, perhaps?"

"No, no, thank you. It will sound odd, but I think I have begun to avoid listening to music, except my own when I must, so that I won't be in danger of using it when I begin to write."

I remember his weakness during that time but, more, his new, acquiescent agreeableness. We seemed close to each other, because illness brings the nurse and the patient into an anxious union and because, as it does many men, his illness frightened him. He seemed willing to be nursed and tended to. But not doctored. The rash that covered his body worried me—could it be scarlet fever? But after a while it receded. I was converted to his view that home care and bed rest were adequate doctors. In two weeks the fever and the rash disappeared. Even the little red shiny herpes on his lower lip healed finally and never returned.

Our closeness in that September: I cannot forget it. Robert would allow no visitors, wanted to hear no music. We talked together, as always, very little. But I felt pleasure in being able to spend my days in his company, crocheting, I recall, the large afghan for the couch in his music room, stopping now and then to fetch tea or soup for him, or watching his face as he slept. I slept on the little couch in the guest room so that I would not disturb his nights. When the afghan was half finished he recovered enough to walk about the room, and into the dressing room, where he would play small pieces, sometimes only fragments, on the piano, first humming gently, and then following the sound of his voice with music on the piano from the store in his head he had apparently collected during the fever.

At the end of the third week he dressed slowly and went downstairs. I could hear the fresh snap of long sheets of staff paper as he turned them impatiently, the runs of trial notes on the piano. For a few days he allowed Paderewski to lie in the room with him during the morning as he worked, an admittance that delighted the loving old dog, who worshiped him in somewhat the same way Elizabeth did. But the slap of his tail and his occasional strolls about the room between naps began to irritate Robert. He was expelled to the garden and never again, in the time of his life that remained, was he granted that privilege.

I took heart from that interlude. It made me hopeful that we could find paths to each other that might wipe out my loneliness. The year that followed was near the end of our time in Boston. One day in October—a beautiful fall full of cool sunlight and the little gusts of air that made life on the old Hill and along the paths of the Public Gardens so pleasant—Churchill Weeks knocked on our door at teatime.

Settled in the sitting room, munching on cookies and drinking cup after cup of tea, he told us of his plans. He had come home to begin his American career as Robert had done before him. You will remember that in those days European training was thought to be essential for an American musician. He said he was on his way to Milwaukee, where his parents lived. We spent the time of dinner and the early evening hearing tales of life at the Hoch Conservatory, of the students Robert and he had taught, of their teachers, some now dead, others about to retire.

I was content to sit on the edge of those hours of talk that night, providing the coffee and schnapps they both liked, listening to the talk that moved so easily between the two old friends. I was content because I had realized at their first moment of meeting that time and distance had transformed Weeks's feelings: the strength and passion of his professed love for Robert, in the letters, had weakened or died out entirely. They sat at a distance from each other, having seemed to choose chairs to effect this, and their voices were loud and forced, as though they were giving instructions to a class or lecturing to a club.

Weeks was attentive to me, ascertaining my comfort in the small chair I had chosen, twice offering to surrender his upholstered armchair to me. I began to like him, to forget about the anguish his person, even at a distance of three thousand miles, had caused me. I asked him if he would care to stay the night and he accepted gracefully, with no hesitation. "It is very good of you to think of it."

"Not at all. You're an old friend. We're both pleased to see you again."

But Robert said nothing. He seemed nervous, rubbing on his lower lip in his old way. After his illness of September his energies were low in the evenings. He excused himself to go early to bed. Weeks seemed disappointed but showed no surprise at his departure. "He looks very tired. It must have been a severe illness."

"It was. And as usual he refused to have anything done for him, anything professional, that is. He waited it out, as he likes to say. But he's much recovered now."

"I see, yes. And you're looking very well."

"Thank you. And you." It was true. His pale skin had been colored by his ocean voyage, he looked sturdy, healthy, and, somehow, American. The Berlin cut of his coat could not disguise his country look.

"I am about to be married," he said. "I wanted to tell you both, but Robert went up before I was able to."

I took a deep breath and relaxed in my hard chair, almost unable to say anything to this news. "You can tell him in the morning. I'm so pleased for you. To someone from the conservatory?"

"No. The daughter of my mother's close friend. The three of them visited me in Germany last year. We've been in correspondence ever since. The wedding is to be at Christmas in Milwaukee. Do you think you and Robert could come?"

"Surely," I said, very quickly, and then checked myself. "That is, yes, of course we would both love to, but I must consult Robert about his schedule."

"I'll send you an invitation in plenty of time to arrange for it."

I showed Weeks his room. On my way to ours I felt light-headed, almost giddy, uplifted by his news. Now I believed it all to be a sick fancy. The letters did not exist or they were merely literary exercises, romantic jokes exchanged by the two men. Robert was asleep when I came to bed. I lay awake for some time thinking of how time, by means of its simple accumulation, had wiped out the apprehensiveness that had lasted so long. Weeks left the next morning before Robert was awake.

Robert worked very hard in the next month, to catch up,

he said. Because money was still a problem for us, he took on a third pupil, a boy of eleven named Paul Brewster whose self-taught prowess was almost miraculous, said Robert. Now three pupils occupied his afternoons, always the best hours of his day. He kept his mornings, in which he was usually very slow to start, for composition, and in those hours he worked with such concentration that he abandoned his walk with the collie, taking him out only in the late afternoon. Paderewski had grown very old since our return from Europe; his still stately gait was now very slow and deliberate. This satisfied Robert, who was weary from working for nine hours before the walk. I would sometimes come upon the two old companions ambling along the paths of the park, Robert dazed and self-absorbed, Paderewski looking back at him every now and then.

We made our plans to take a Pullman room on the *Twentieth Century* train to Chicago and then on to Milwaukee for Churchill Weeks's wedding. I had persuaded Robert he ought to go. But in the end we did not do so. In early December Robert had a letter from his mother. It was a stiff, formal, strange letter:

I wish to tell you, Rob, that I feel very close to the end of my days. I am now almost always bedridden with what my physician has called a disease of the heart. My feet and ankles swell badly at times so that I am unable to walk at all. I would not concern you with this but my physician has issued a warning to me, advising me to communicate with

*my relations in America so that I will not be alone in a last
illness which, he says, may well be imminent. I am not
writing as he suggested, for I wish no company now, having
had none in the last years. But it seems wise to convey to
you the warning he has given me so that you will have had
notice.*

*Your mother,
Virginia Maclaren*

Much disturbed, Robert booked passage for himself on
the first ship sailing to Wilhelmshaven, the *Kaiser Wilhelm
der Grosse,* I think it was. We were not in a position to
afford two passages, he said. I agreed: Virginia Maclaren
needed Robert unaccompanied by his wife. Two days before
he was to sail, a cable came for Robert from the coroner of
the city of Frankfurt informing him of his mother's death.
Sometime later a long letter arrived from an attorney-at-
law describing the contents of Virginia Maclaren's will. Her
husband having predeceased her, she left her small estate
from him to her sons Burns and Logan. To her youngest
son, Robert, and wife, Caroline, were to be given her personal effects and her clothing. To the Hoch Conservatory,
with her gratitude for the fine training it had given to her
son, the composer Robert Glencoe Maclaren, she gave all
her books and the manuscripts in her possession of his early
works, including the one most dear to her, Opus 3, *Bar-
carolle pour pianoforte,* dedicated *A ma chère maman.*

Boston was growing too much for Robert. He talked often
of finding a quiet place in the country in which to live and
work. I still loved the city, having renewed acquaintance
with some of my school friends, visiting the Museum of
Fine Arts with them and with Elizabeth, lunching often in
the downtown shops. I went each week to the Boston Public
Library, where there were afternoon lectures on the most
recent books. Sunday mornings Elizabeth and I went to the
Unitarian church together.

But Robert was restless because of the demands upon
his time. He became increasingly short with his pupils,
especially with young Paul Brewster, who was advancing
so fast that it seemed to me to be in direct disproportion to
Robert's patience with him. Robert always referred to him
as Master Brewster, suggesting by the designation that he
was far too young for opinions, of an age only to listen and
then do as he was told.

I must tell you more about him. Paul had been coming
to Robert for some months when we decided to find a place
in the country. Working as hard as he did, Robert had lost
weight. In the first three months of that year he had gone
on tour, performing, lecturing, conducting his work and
the music of his admired European masters, Liszt, Mozart,
Beethoven. He came home exhausted from these trips. On
lesson days he would lie on his couch through most of the
morning, write almost nothing, storing up his meager supply
of energy against the arrival of the precocious Master Brewster.

Paul Brewster at eleven still dressed as a young boy, in dark knickers, a silk shirt, a black silk tie. Twice each week, accompanied by his mother, he came to our door. When I opened the door to their ring, his mother would dip into a small curtsy, as I had not seen it done since the peasant women in Germany, greet me in a language I did not understand, and then disappear.

Robert told me she was Hungarian. Paul was her only child. In her eyes she and her son were sentenced to exile, living in the United States until the time came for Mr. Brewster's firm to send him back to Budapest, where they had met and where Paul was born. To her, Boston was a tomb, a cell, a cage, she had told Robert, who understood enough Hungarian for those words. Having arranged for Paul's lessons, and unburdening herself of these few details of autobiography, she made no other explanations. Her sole function became the delivery of the small genius, her son, to our house, and his retrieval an hour later.

In that year, because of Paul's avidity and skill, Robert sometimes instructed him far longer than his allotted hour. The boy seemed to consume the music he was given. His small, thin, tense, accomplished fingers were capable of performing extraordinary feats for one so young, his memory was perfect, his understanding of what he was doing almost that of a mature musician. I worried, not about him, for I hardly encountered him at all and knew all this only through Robert's weary reports of him at our late suppers, but about Robert, whose fatigue grew with the boy's virtuosity. No longer did he stand to give his lessons but had moved a wicker chair from another room into the music room, a chair that reminded me, when first I saw it there, of Mrs. Seton's.

Many afternoons, through the closed door of the music room, I heard Robert's sharp, angry voice, reproaching Paul for a mistake, I surmised, since I was not able to hear the words. His voice would maintain the same tone after the repetition of the long passage, which to my ear was played brilliantly. Robert would find some small matter to carp about, the boy would play the music again with verve, with greater accuracy, although, not having discerned the initial error, I cannot be sure of this. Again Robert's voice would cut across the last notes. Often I went downstairs and out into the garden so that I did not have to listen to Paul replaying the same passage, the same rejected perfection followed by the same unreasonable anger.

After all this time I no longer can remember how prepared I was for what happened. But I did wonder: Would the boy complain to his mother so that she would take him away from Robert's lessons? Would Robert completely lose control of himself at the boy's undeniable talent and send his pupil away?

It was not to be either of these suppositions. In the spring of that year, and just after Robert had returned home exhausted from his tour, Paul arrived alone for his lesson. He had been caught in a sudden rainstorm. His eyes red, his nose running, he stood, coughing, on the landing. His coat dripped water, his thin face was apologetic, his shoes full of water. The boy seemed afraid to go to Robert in this state, and yet there was little I could do for him except to insist he remove his shoes. I gave him a pair of Robert's old slippers, many sizes too large. Coughing and shuffling in the slippers, he knocked on the music room door and went in.

I took the sodden shoes down to the kitchen to try to dry them. So I missed the explosion. Paul had been ill with a cold, he had apparently told Robert: "I did not practice yesterday. I hope you will understand that . . ."

The ceiling above me shook. Something heavy had been—thrown? dropped?—to the floor. I heard a crash, and then a desperate, thin, child's voice cry: *"Stop!"* I went up the stairs as quickly as I could, hiking up my skirts to facilitate the climb. The door was ajar. In a fury such as I had never thought him capable of, Robert, in his shirt sleeves, stood in the center of the room, holding the fire poker above his head. Paul was crouched on the window seat, his face drawn and white, his mouth open in a mad, terrorized grimace. All his small, even, sharp teeth showed. "Robert, what *is* it? What are you doing? Stop that. Put it down." Commands and entreaties poured out of me in one long line of sound.

Robert looked at me, dazed. Then he sat down, almost as if he had collapsed, onto the piano bench, dropping the poker at his feet. He put his head into his hands. I started over to him, but I was too slow. The boy had jumped toward Robert from his crouched position on the window seat, like a small spring released into the air. Before I could stop him he had crossed the room, stooped down, opened his mouth, and dug his teeth into the flesh of Robert's upper arm.

Robert sprang to his feet. "My God! Let *go!*"

Paul Brewster appeared for a few seconds to hang by his teeth from Robert's raised arm, the cloth of Robert's shirt bunched into his mouth. Robert went on screaming, the high, thin sound flowing from his mouth like sickness. His other hand slapped at the boy, trying to make him let go. I held Paul's mad head in my hands and tried to pry open his teeth, which were like small pointed stones. His mouth was lined with foam. I felt it wet my hands.

Finally, it seemed an incredibly long time, but finally he let go when Robert's blood filled his mouth. He coughed, gagged, turned his head away, and vomited into the cave of the piano. Robert sat down heavily on the sofa, holding his bloody wound. I knelt down beside him. Robert had stopped screaming. The only sound in the room was Paul, spitting and retching. "Don't move, Robert. I'll send the maid for the doctor. You must have a doctor."

Behind me I could hear Paul staggering toward the door. He mumbled something but I could not make out what it was. I had no desire to stop him, I wanted him out of the house. At that moment I never wanted to see the beastly little boy again.

That day and night hang like bats in my memory, black and unmoving. Robert stretched out, inert on his sofa. The doctor I sent for came at once, inspected the wound, looked troubled. Robert's whole upper arm was now a furious blue-black color, with red teeth marks outlining the edges of the gash.

"May I have a look at the dog that did this?"

"It was not a dog."

"*Not* a dog?"

"No," I said. "A boy."

"Good Lord!" The doctor examined the wound again. He gave Robert several white papers of powder to take with warm water at intervals through the next days, washed the area again with alcohol, and shook his head. "There may be infection. One never can know. We will watch it. Rest," he said sternly to Robert. "I'll be back in the early morning."

Rest! Robert was so shocked that I could not persuade him even to leave his sofa for his bed that evening. His eyes closed, his wounded arm resting on a pillow at his side, he lay without stirring, refusing dinner, refusing to move at all to another room. He had been assaulted in every corner of his being, I believe, his whole system was affected, the insult was to his spirit as well as to his arm. For he told me the next day that all of his body ached, his head, his back, his knees and ankles. He was very thirsty, he said, his tongue felt burned, his throat cut and raw, but swallowing cool water hurt. The second night he moved painfully to our bed. He would not allow me to lower the lamps or to close the shutters and drapes. He seemed to be afraid he might be attacked again in the dark. Did he think the mad boy still crouched in a corner of the room? And the wonder of it! He wanted me to sit beside him while he slept.

His sleep was stony. He never moved, he breathed so lightly that once I bent over to see if he was still alive. By morning I was exhausted. Robert still slept his torpid, motionless sleep. I sent the maid to Elizabeth to ask her to come to relieve me, after the doctor had been there and assured me there was no fever and no infection: "It's healing very well," he said. "I'll look in at him again this evening." Because I did not wish to disturb Robert, I went to sleep in my sitting room, feeling somewhat of an exile, on my mother's bentwood sofa, covered with the afghan I had just completed.

The days that followed: Elizabeth and I and the doctor, together and separately watching over Robert, entreating him to return to his work if only for an hour or so a day, to see a pupil for a short lesson, to come to the dining room for dinner, to take a walk with the dog. And he, refusing, lying collapsed, white, as if wrapped in bonds of unforgivingness, hardly speaking, his sickness not of the wound (which healed quickly) but of the mind, the whole organism. He lost weight, his nightshirt hung upon him, his energy, almost his will to live, seemed gone.

The doctor came every morning to dress the wound. At the end of a week he whispered to me that he was no longer needed, that I could do what he was doing for a few more days and then the bandage would no longer be necessary. "No reason for me to come again, unless there is a change, and then you can send for me."

I hoped the doctor's permanent departure would persuade Robert of his recovery, but I remember that his invalidism went on long after that. He refused to leave his bed. I had his music room completely rearranged, the ceiling painted, the paper redone, and the piano taken apart on the premises, without moving it, and cleaned by two men from the Steinway plant. I kept him informed of each stage in the transformation and the cleaning, but it did no good. At last he confessed to me, it was not the room, but the boy, the *boy*. Whenever he thought of returning to the room he saw Master Brewster crouched there, waiting to spring at him. He could not bring himself to go back into that room. I realized then that we had to find other lodgings.

Elizabeth and I visited agents in the area and spoke to them about a farmhouse to rent for the summer. I was given lists of houses to visit in New Hampshire, in northern Massachusetts, and in the upper part of New York State. We hired a touring car for the day and visited the places closest to us, without success. Some of the houses offered were in bad disrepair, others too expensive, and still others inaccessible for a couple without a motorcar. Only at the end of our search did we venture to New York.

The day we found Highland Farm, as it was later to be called, is still vivid to me. Elizabeth and I set out in the early morning to take an omnibus to the train depot, Robert being cared for by our maid in the few days I planned to be away. A block from our lodgings we almost collided with Mrs. Brewster. She looked discomposed. In her poor English, which I barely understood, she explained that she had been on her way to call on Robert and me, to tell us how mortified she was at what had happened between her son and Maestro Maclaren. From her random, rambling words, some of which were in Hungarian, I gathered that

Paul had told her only that there had been a bad argument, so serious that he could not return for lessons. "Terrible. Terrible, I am so sorry for it. He too, he will not now touch the piano. He gives it up now, he tells me, never again to study. Can you believe?"

Her eyes filled with tears; she clutched at my arm for understanding. I nodded, and at last brought myself to ask, "How is Paul? Has he recovered from his cold?"

"His cold? Yes, from that, but from his other sickness, no. That will never go."

"His other sickness?"

"The fits, the grand mal, the seizures. Since he was a small baby, and always now, the doctor says."

Shaken, I bade her good-bye and said I hoped she would find another teacher for her talented son. I mentioned that his shoes were still in my kitchen, but she did not seem to hear. On the train to Saratoga Springs I thought of the two musicians, the thin, epileptic boy and the weary, sick maestro who fought with each other, locked together in a mortal madness born of the passion and the weariness of making music.

Part Two

THE FARM

THERE WAS no transition.
From the first day, Robert loved the house I had leased.
He settled into his quarters at one end of the rambling farmhouse and began at once to work. Some of his best music
was to be written here. The house stood at the edge of a
large farm property, seventy acres of lovely woods and
meadows. The original fields, which had once been culti-
vated, now were almost returned to high weedy places
where insects and bees lived and where new birches and
maples were beginning a wild reclamation. Our privacy was
absolute, the quiet, after Boston, so *loud* that at first we both
had to grow used to it.

Everywhere there were fine walks into our own woods.

Yet we were not isolated, for the village of Saratoga Springs lay at the foot of our property. Often we would walk into it in the evenings, stopping at the fountain to sip the ugly-tasting, sulfurous, healthy waters. At the center of the village were two large, quite splendid hotels and many small shops which filled to overflowing with visitors in the summer. In August another wave of visitors occupied the great houses on the outskirts. Then the streets were filled with motorcars and horse-drawn carriages as these late arrivals, the fashionable families from Newport and New York, Philadelphia and Baltimore, Charleston and Boston, visited and dined with each other, went to the races, gambled, took the baths, and drank the curative waters.

We had moved to the Farm in May. Our first summer was a delight. We enjoyed the bustle and confusion in the streets after the silence of our Farm, the cosmopolitan air the little village took on instantly with the warm weather. Mingled with well-dressed and sporting persons were strange, black-suited, long-haired, ringleted Jews from the East Side of New York who lived for the summer in the boarding houses near the baths. They came, we were told, to drink the sulfur waters they regarded as a valuable diuretic for washing away the winter's accumulated interior impurities.

In August the racetrack became the center of the village. Everyone, except the Jews, whom I never saw near the track, traveled up Union Avenue for the afternoon sessions. From our veranda (we never went to the races) we could hear the roar of people in the stands as they cheered the takeoff of the horses. And afterward, the paths near us were crowded with persons on foot, on bicycles, on horses, in their new open motorcars, coming away from the race grounds, returning to their hotels, their rented houses, their elaborate homes. It was a colorful, exciting, and somehow open and free place to be after the formal confines of Frankfurt and then Boston.

When the summer was over, we asked the agent to renew our lease for the next full year. In October, Robert wondered if we could afford to buy the property, if indeed it were available for purchase. I made inquiries and found to my delight that it was. "But all this property, Robert. How will we care for it?" I had been remembering the neglected state of our tiny backyard square of grass and shrubs on Mount Vernon Street.

"More to the point," he said, "how will we pay for it all?" His concern for money was theoretical, general. It was I who kept the bank records, the family accounts, saved what I could, recorded the payments for his compositions from orchestras and choral groups, paid the month's bills. He was right to be concerned, however, because now, alas, there were no pupils whose fees might have helped the year's income.

I visited the Saratoga Springs Savings Bank and found its president eager to lend the well-known composer and his wife money to acquire property near his village. Everything we had saved went toward the purchase of Highland Farm. I resolved, as Robert and I signed the ownership deed, that I would find a way to buy the property outright for

Robert's protection and security, to pay off the huge mortgage somehow.

After one long winter at the farm, I came to realize that I had romanticized the village from its summer pleasures. Its vitality and interest departed with the summer visitors. Most of the shops closed, and the park band, the bathers, racing enthusiasts, and solemn, pale Jews departed for the cities, taking the life of the village with them. The paths and roads were deserted. Highland Farm was engulfed in oppressive, almost ominous quiet. The silence of the red woods and the yellowing fields was extended into our own almost soundless house.

I found myself alone, more alone, it seemed, than I had ever before been in my life, in a strange place, a large, quiet house, with Robert estranged from everyone by his music. He had resumed his usual schedule. Rarely did I see him before evening, except to take him his late-morning coffee and roll, and his tea in the afternoon. Then, as it had been in Boston, he sat with me at dinner still in the grip of the music he had written during the day, a silent audience to it, his head on one side in its customary listening position. He ate everything served to him, automatically, without seeing or tasting it, I think. Often I would chat desperately to fill the void. He listened politely but rarely responded. He was not rude, I would not wish anyone to think that, he was merely not present.

Guests came from Boston, from New York, even from the Continent, to call upon Robert. I always invited them to stay to dinner, often to stay the night, for the trains to New York and Boston were hard to reach in the evenings. We still did not own a motorcar: Robert felt that we would spend too much time motoring guests if we acquired one. At company dinner, Robert would rally briefly, speak of the world of music as it filtered through to us in the papers, and of his own work. But always, near the end of the meal, his small store of goodwill exhausted, he would sink back into apathy.

It was too late for me to regret the move to the Farm. We had the house and the large acreage. Robert seemed content. I resolved to try to build upon the long silences by going back to my own music. Fortunately, I thought, the house was large, I could practice at one end without disturbing him.

I can now clearly recall the pure, heady pleasure of that return to serious study. An incentive presented itself, by accident. I discovered one day, when I stopped at the town library to borrow my week's reading, that the librarian had, briefly, sung with an oratorio society in New York. "I am Miss Milly Martino," she said, for that was how she always referred to herself. She learned I was Robert Maclaren's wife, and then she said, "I know so well who your husband is." She told me about her meager musical training, she apologized for it: "I studied voice with a lady in Glens Falls," she said, "a lady who sang at one time in the chorus of La Scala Opera. I left there to go to New York for a while, and then came to work in Saratoga Springs.

Since then I have worked alone, at the piano—I do not play very well—with whatever music I can find in the library collection. There is not much."

I see Miss Milly Martino as I write, although it is more than half a century since those winter evenings we played and sang together. She was a strangely shaped, buxom little person, made of two great balls of flesh, one upon the other, almost like the snowmen children used to love to erect in the front yards. Her warm, soft-fleshed, well-corseted form I was to see reincarnated, I imagined, many years later in the person of the great soprano Rosa Ponselle, whom I met only once. Miss Milly Martino was much like Ponselle in her rounded contours, her heavy arms and legs, her full red lips and black bright eyes, her shiny black hair. Often I think how close her voice might have come to Ponselle's: ripe, controlled, supple, lovely. Her back, too, was so fleshy it made her look almost humped, a sadly prescient shape, for in later years she had to retire from her post as town librarian because of a disease she had which was later named for its discoverer, Parkinson.

But not yet. I worked hard at the piano after I met Miss Milly. My fingers slowly began to regain their old dexterity, and my love of the piano as a sensual, satisfying instrument, soft and pliable to the touch, returned. Suddenly there seemed not enough time to accomplish all I wanted to do. I walked down into the village to tell Miss Milly Martino I thought we might try an evening together. "It must be at your house," she said. "I unfortunately have no piano now."

"Of course. At our house. Tonight?"

"Delightful. I shall be there at eight."

"A singer from town is coming here tonight. I will try to accompany her," I told Robert at dinner. "Fine. Fine," he said, absently. I don't think he heard what I'd said, for his custom was always to respond to the announcement of a plan with words like that: "Good, good. Fine, fine."

We worked well together, Miss Milly Martino and I. Her soprano was expressive and superbly controlled. Pressed, it could achieve extraordinary power and heights. It seemed to grow, expand, and rise without losing the delicate grain and texture of her middle range. She said she loved above all else to sing Mozart, so that first evening we began with *Così fan tutte*, Dorabella's recitative and aria. My confidence in being able to accompany her increased when I realized her grasp of the subtleties of the music, the firmness with which she attacked the little runs and slips of "Ah, scostati! paventa il tristo effetto." Since moments during my final year with Mrs. Seton I do not remember feeling such delight at being able to achieve with my fingers what my mind told me should be done, at falling back, acknowledging by my diminuendo, by the quiet tones, her right to soar out and over them, as though her voice had triumphed over my accompaniment as well as its own origins and limitations.

At nine o'clock Miss Milly gathered together the music we had been doing. "I must start back before it gets too late. It is quite some distance from here."

"Where do you live?"

"On Phila Street. You go down the hill, and then two

squares over from Union Avenue. I board with the Seeleys."

"You have a beautiful voice. I so much enjoyed what we did tonight."

"And I. You play very well."

I walked with her to the door, urging on Paderewski, who had reluctantly agreed to come along, with my knee. The ailing old dog hated to be told to leave the house or the hearth. His trips to the outdoors to perform his bodily needs were always at my prompting. Indeed, at times I remember lifting him over the sill of the front door to help him out.

Miss Milly Martino admired the dog. She asked how old he was, and I told her not so old, really, but he seemed to have gone into middle age when Robert left him behind to return to Europe, and then moved into premature senility upon his return. She thanked me for allowing her to borrow the Mozart score. We arranged to have another time together on Wednesday of the next week. I waited at the open door, watching her start off down the Farm road, the road the town was later to name and register as Maclaren Road, and then I pulled Paderewski back into the house. I held his thick hair at his neck; he was so big, I so small, that my arm almost rested on his back. I was happy, with a new music-filled happiness, and the feeling of pleasure at having found a congenial, talented friend to share it with.

I remember another thought on that evening in November in the year that marked the start of a new century: it was possible to commune with the slow-breathing, warm, soft-haired body of an animal like Paderewski, even to feel his response to one's own contentment. I have had dogs since but none who so perfectly accepted my state of mind as compatible to his, perhaps because his age had made him patient and slow. I wanted the pleasure of that evening to remain, to dally in my head as he lay beside me. I was still able to feel the physical thrill that always rises in me as I listen to the perfect placement of a soprano voice.

When I closed the door behind me, I found Robert in his velvet house coat standing in the hallway, his fists clenched at his sides, his usually pale face red with fury.

"Never again, do you hear?"

"What is it, Robert?"

"The noise. That . . . that screeching. I could not think. I could hardly hear my own playing. There is to be no more of that in this house, Caroline."

He seemed overwrought, on the verge of tears. I took his hand. "Come to bed, Robert. It's late. I had no idea we were so—loud. Next time we'll be quieter. I thought you had finished your work long since."

The next Wednesday was cold and rainy. The fall had turned abruptly to winter, the ground was white and treacherous with the first freezing rain. Much of that day I worried that Miss Milly Martino would not make it across her two squares to Union Avenue and then up the hill to our road.

But she came, the score under her arm wrapped in a piece of oilskin and with it another score from the library, so that we would each be able to read, she said. Her broad felt hat and her coat dripped with rain, her men's overshoes were buckled tightly to her heavy feet. She seemed to be delighted to be back at the Farm. As she took off her wet clothing she told me she had practiced all week and thought she "had" the scene we had started "by heart."

On our way through the house to my sitting room I said, "Tonight we must try to keep our sounds low. Sometimes my husband works late and he is easily disturbed by any sound when he is composing."

"Of course, *of course.*" I remember that her high sweet voice almost squeaked with awe. "I've never met him or even seen him. But once I played some of the short pieces of the *Woodland Songs.* Everyone in the village thinks it is a great honor to have him living near by."

We settled ourselves. I began to play the first bars of the aria "Smanie implacabili" . . . softly. Miss Millie started her "che m'agitate entro quest' anima" in a light, subdued tone. Then, apparently transported by the aria she loved, by the lovely absurdity of Dorabella planning to go mad for the rest of her life, she struck the high G flat, showing the Eumenides how to scream with all the force of her absorption with the music. My admonition was forgotten. Accurately, elevated, she carried the aria along in that intensity, the music demanding another G flat and then a third. She was note-perfect: her flights between were triumphant, she sang with her whole voice, gaining in power and lyricism, showing me by the movement of her sparkling black eyes how much she had learned during her week of practice.

Robert flung open my door so hard it hit the sideboard with a crackling sound and swung back almost into his face. He waved it away. His voice was shrill.

"Out. Out. Get out. No more of that . . . noise. Out." His finger pointed at Miss Milly Martino's shoulder, then prodded it as she tried to move across the room out of his way to where her overshoes stood. I was afraid he was going to strike her, but still I could not move. I sat frozen on the bench. Never do I remember feeling so angry and so impotent. I wanted to shield her from this undeserved indignity, to assure the uncertain, frightened woman who was stumbling into her damp india-rubber galoshes and now struggling to put on her coat, that her voice was beautiful, her high notes pure joy to listen to as well as her effortless movement from one phrase to the next. But I could say nothing. Her mouth was clamped tight with terror. She scurried about the room, frantically gathering up her things. Immobilized by embarrassment, I could not intervene for her with Robert.

He stood to the side to let her out of the door. She pushed past him, saying nothing. Seated still, I felt as though I were leaving with her, accompanying the heavy, rubbery, clumping sounds as she padded the long length of the halls to the front door, fumbling with the lock—I don't think there was any light in the front hall in those days. Then the snap, the sharp clasp of the door closing behind her, the little click of the lock: I heard it all from the piano bench.

Robert had gone when I returned from my motionless trip to the door with Miss Milly Martino. He had turned down the gas lamp over the piano. I listened again, now to *his* slippered feet crossing the hall to the stairs that went to our room. I remember I sat for some time by that darkened piano, crying from frustration and chagrin. I closed the cover to the keys, thinking how stern and rigid those ivory keys appeared which in my girlhood had seemed soft, endearing, pliable.

The expulsion of Miss Milly Martino was never spoken of by me or by Robert. Of course she never returned: I believe she was badly hurt by Robert's treatment. I wanted to invite her to come again while he was away on tour, but somehow I never did. Sometimes I would encounter her behind the oak counter at the library when I called for my week's reading matter. But we never referred to that evening, not even on the afternoon two weeks later when I gathered my courage to return the library copy of *Così fan tutte* she had left behind. Both of us, I suspect, were embarrassed by our memories of that terrible evening and preferred to stay safely on the subject of the weather, the latest indignities to library copies by schoolchildren, and summer visitors, whom she always called riffraff.

A few years later I saw that she tried to disguise the growing palsy of her hand by holding her right wrist with her left hand as she stamped the date on a library card. But often she could not manage to insert the card into its tight little pocket at the back of the book. The townspeople, who had grown fond of the quiet, cheerful, fat little woman, would reach out quickly to perform the task for her. The library's withdrawal records became illegible. Dates were stamped at perilous slants one on top of the other. Friends of the library took up a collection to help Miss Milly retire. I recall that I requested the Maclaren Foundation to send a contribution.

But I never heard Miss Milly sing again, and after her retirement I never saw her. In a few years, she went to stay at a boardinghouse for the sick where, a friend, Sarah Watkins, reported to me, she was a sensible, cheerful patient. Even after her faltering head had to be held at the chin by a broad scarf attached to the uprights of the chair in which she always sat, she could be heard, on occasion, singing snatches of what my informant said she took to be opera.

The first five years of this century: I must tell you about them in summary, because I confess the details have amalgamated in my memory into one continuous year. Robert wrote much, and well, in those years. He was awarded honorary degrees, his music was praised in the columns of *Music*, the *Courier*, in the English *Musical Times*, and in the large city newspapers. He was away often in the spring and the fall, playing and conducting his work with orchestras in New York, in Boston, in Charleston, and as far west as Cleveland. He would return tired out by the long railway trips between cities, for he was unable to sleep in the Pullman cars. Twice he went abroad, but I did not accompany him: the fees offered him for concerts were not sufficient to allow both of us to travel.

But during the long, hard New York State winters at the Farm we were alone together, except for the dog and the groundsman, Edward Collins, who kept our paths and roads clear, and the maid from the village, Ida, who came to do the household chores. Robert followed his usual routine rigorously, seven days a week. I "kept" the house, as we used to say, and prepared a lunch (Robert ate no breakfast and made his own cup of chocolate at six in the morning when he started his work), which I left at his closed study door. After my own lunch I rested and then walked into the village, to the greengrocer's or the butcher shop, which remained open in the winter, and sometimes to the bake shop if Ida had not made enough sweet rolls and cakes to satisfy Robert's passion for such things.

Yes, the days I was able to fill. I made a friend, by chance, the wife of a retired Hamilton College professor. She was about thirty, I think, fashionable, alert, and charming to look at. She loved to talk. I must confess I had grown hungry for talk. In our long conversations in her house in the afternoons over tea, I felt a comfortable connection to the trivial, friendly world I had thought I had lost during my life with Robert. I enjoyed listening to Sarah Watkins, for that was the name of the second wife of Professor Gordon Lyman Watkins. I felt ill at ease only when I became aware of my own lack of contribution to the talk.

Sarah would rattle on in her light-headed way, often humorous and sometimes wry and regretful, about her days —and her nights—with the Professor, as she usually referred to him. My days and nights, indeed, years, were composed of solitude and stillness. I had little I could add to her absorbing narratives. Awake, Robert and I lived at opposite ends of a large house, so that the sounds of my housekeeping, my "puttering," as Robert called it, would not carry into his study. He could not bear to hear talk before he began his day of composing. He said it sent him off in the wrong direction, colliding with and dispelling the usable silence of the early morning. In that silence, he said, he found the beginnings of melodies.

Sarah's confidences were about her husband's habits and practices, his failings and wrongs to her. She had no discretion; she never seemed to feel she owed him any loyalty, and perhaps I was wrong in so openly relishing her revelations about him. But I was lonely. I needed her chatter and her friendship, so I listened, feeling that her strange stories filled the void of my life.

As I came to think of him (seldom was he present in the afternoon room when I was there; usually he was in the shed at his woodworking bench), he was a fool, a figure of fun who, I imagined, fumblingly tried to love his younger wife and to live with her peacefully despite his elderly habits. He hoped to content her with mild caresses, with the bristling, wet brush of his heavy gray mustache on her cheek. Holding her teacup in one hand, she would lean across to me, making circles in the air with her slender fingers:

"The Professor likes me to come to bed in my chemise. He plays endlessly with the ribbons, he rubs them and fondles them. He touches my . . . my . . . bosom through the cloth. Never underneath, isn't that odd? His hands are roughened now from all the woodworking he does. His nails are so long they curl over the edges of his fingers. I can feel them through the cloth."

I would listen, wondering why she brought these details of the private bed into the sunny room, while I . . .

"The Professor likes to stroke me with his tongue. He uses it in the dark as we lie together, in all the chambers of my ears, and in other places which I cannot mention."

I would wait, adding nothing, having nothing to add. Then, perhaps feeling that she had gone too far, revealed too much, she would change the subject and tell me about his hobby, which was carving birdhouses for the gardens and the lawn.

"I understand about the birdhouses with small openings for wrens and little cups for hummingbirds. And the roofed, gabled residences he makes for orioles and cardinals. And the special apartments which he says mourning doves and even owls prefer. But now I think he's gone quite queer: he's made an enormous wheel, the size of a wagon wheel. He made our gardener mount it flat on the roof, for storks. Storks!" she would scream in her light, charming voice. " 'Pelicans, too, and flamingos will be made to feel welcome there,' he tells me, 'and anhingas.'

"He lectures me about birds. 'Do you know,' he tells me, 'that some birds migrate a thousand miles and others only a few hundred feet? So,' he says, 'we must be prepared for the long-distance traveler, like the stork, as well as our friends from Watertown, Lake Champlain, and Bellview Street in Saratoga Springs.' "

All the trees around the Watkins' house, every gable and portico and porch, were hung with accommodations for birds. Professor Watkins, who taught classics before his retirement, had turned his entire attention to a concern for such housing. He told Sarah that often he lay awake thinking of the homeless bird, forced to sleep standing up on its fragile, twiglike legs for lack of a proper resting place. He mourned the apparent homelessness of the grouse: "Think of the grouse, with its heavy feathered feet. It must need a specially soft floor for its domicile." And so he built an elegant, ground-level cabin, lined with plush to spare the grouse further·pain.

Professor Watkins' hands had hardened and split at the finger tips. His palms were crossed with healed cuts and rubbed places. The same capable hands that provided for the hotelling of birds turned feeble and foolish when they approached the lightly clad body of Sarah in their conjugal bed.

I write of this not because of Sarah. What, after all, is Sarah (and her curious husband who gave his whole time to the happiness of birds) to the point of my narrative? I write of this because it was to gossip, to such confessional afternoons, that I turned to escape the soundlessness of Highland Farm. Intimately involved in this way with the curiosities of Sarah's life with her husband, I could, for the afternoon, with tea and little cakes on the table before us, escape the blank pages, the empty saga, of my own existence.

Sarah did not always chatter on so, indifferent to her listener. Many times, I am sure, she must have asked how

Robert behaved toward me. She waited for admissions from me about my satisfactions, shall we say, the "transports of delight" as they were termed in the fiction of my day. But I could not bring myself to describe the void, the great bed in which Robert and I lay like strangers, his exhausted back to me, his skin seeming to shrink from any contact with me. My life touched his only through the food I prepared and we ate together in the evening, through the accounts and records I kept of his earnings and our expenses, in the hundreds of letters from his admirers and musical friends to which I responded at his direction.

It might be thought—indeed, I have seen it written somewhere—that the woman who is unawakened to the pleasures of the body, for which she has only uninstructed hopes, feels no physical need or lack. She is said to live in peace with her ignorance and her unfulfillment because she does not know what fulfillment is; nuns in convents are said to be endowed with such good fortune. I know this not to be so. Even Sarah's indelicate little disclosures to me about the Professor's small, feckless, ineffectual doings in their bed awakened warm rushes of feeling in me. There were regions in my body, bird-thin to the eye, arid and meager, that seemed to come alive when I heard about the Professor's fumbling with Sarah's ribbons. Just as, reading of the passionate embraces of men and women in the lending library's novels, of heroines' heaving bosoms as they felt the arms of their lovers around their shoulders, the touch of their fingers, I would respond hotly. My heart would pound. In my thighs, in my chest, at the small of my back there would be sensations I could not explain: warm, exciting, secretly wet.

Why do I write this foolishness? Why do I break now the reserve of three-quarters of a century, except perhaps to insert into the recounting of the history of that five-year span a few of the unspoken and unrecorded details of the heart and the spirit? It is hardly enough to know that a woman was born and lived and married and, in time, died. It seems somehow important to record, beyond the vital statistics, what she yearned for and was refused, what she imagined and did not realize.

And while I am writing of Sarah, and her one-sided confidences in those static, holding years: how many truths of the secret lives of women are lost to history in the still, social afternoon air that hovers between two women as they reveal the small singlenesses of their sex, the behavior of their husbands as lords, as lovers? Quickly said, revealed in a breath, in low tones, even whispers, such special truths are quickly buried and forgotten. And yet they hold more valuable human reality for the searcher after truth than the dates of history and the narratives of the lives and deaths of kings.

I may have told Sarah that I longed for children when she told me she did, but none had come. But I'm certain I never revealed that, since the time of his first serious illness in Saratoga, Robert had no capacity for the conjugal act. We had believed that illness to be a kind of pox, because of the terrible rash. When the scaly patches formed on his back and legs, I finally persuaded him to have the doctor inspect it.

Robert saw him alone in his offices: it was not the pox. The Saratoga Springs physician, Dr. Holmes, did not really know what it could be, Robert reported to me after the examination, but he prescribed a smoothed lump of sulfate of copper to be applied to the afflicted areas. I rubbed them carefully (painfully for poor Robert), but it did no good. Some of the areas became ulcerated and oozed a rank yellow pus. The doctor instructed me to apply a yeast poultice. On the worst places I placed, again at his instruction, a pack of crystals of acetate of soda. Robert would cry out in pain at these applications.

"What is it?" I asked the doctor on the one occasion I was in the examining room with Robert, who had grown weak and nervous under the ailment and could hardly walk alone.

I noticed he looked at Robert speculatively. Robert shut his eyes, and then the doctor said, "It is very hard to say." But the strange rash receded, taking with it his old, occasional desire for me and some of his thick, dark-red hair, which came out on his pillow and his shoulders in broom-like segments. It seemed to me he showed more concern for his loss of hair than for his connubial failure.

None of this did I tell Sarah. Even to myself I have not rehearsed these elements of my marital life, until now. Because to the musical world Robert was a much beloved figure. But this public man, this famous man, was important also to me, who needed private love so much. His indifference and discontent with me seemed at the time of no great moment beside his fame. He was renowned, a talented musician, "a composer of genius," many critics had already written. My contributory existence and auxiliary services, like my small, thin physique, were of no account in his light. History must be full of such alliances between famous men and their satellite, serving wives. Their true persons and their inner lives are rarely known or described in the painful and almost faithless detail I have given here.

And Sarah would go on and on with her logorrheic talk: "He spent this morning making special food for his warblers (although, he said, peregrines were said to be fond of it, too), roasting bread crumbs in the baking oven, and then mixing in the seeds of pumpkins. When I tried to enter the kitchen he told me I would confuse his recipe, so I left him alone. I'm sure he prefers his birds to me. I think he would like to live in a house under the eaves with them if only he could construct one large enough to hold them all.

"One died early this morning. Apparently its neck was broken as it flew head-on into the multiple apartment dwelling that hangs from the back roof. It lay on its side on the floor of the veranda. It was a finch, I think (I don't know the birds well, and I was afraid to ask Gordon). Its purple head was turned entirely backward as though (Gordon said) it had been examining its past in its last moments: a classical bird. Its beak was red with its own blood. The Professor wept and sat still on the veranda all morning looking at it and would not pick it up to dispose of it, and its blood sank into the wood. I sent the maid to him and he told her, politely, mournfully, to go away. I think he's quite mad.

"Did I tell you that last summer he discovered there

were pigeons living in our attic above the maids' quarters? The maids said they would not stay if they were not removed. But the Professor lectured them, told them the pigeons had come there to find a shelter against the neglect and cruel treatment by the villagers, who find them dirty and offensive and try to poison them. Once I found him on the stairs climbing to the attic carrying a loaf of freshly baked bread and one of my down pillows. He said, 'They are nesting.'

"They are still there, although in the winter they seem quieter. One maid left in August, saying birds over her head frightened her. The other two, I think, have grown used to the rush of wings and the scratchings of feet and beaks on the boards above their heads.

"Flight. That is all he now talks to me about. *Mad!* Only organisms capable of flight are entirely alive, he believes. Walking creatures, weighted to the earth, are half dead, their feet turned and moving one after the other down into the full, dry dirt of the grave. 'Flight,' he says, 'is life, the climate and reminder of eternity, of ascent, not deathly descent, of triumph over the Fall. Not until men fly,' he says, 'will they be immortal. Some insects and birds are without mortal restraints. I have studied them, day and night. I know.'

"Nastily, I asked him about the dead finch, despising him and his madness and wanting, I suppose, to hurt him, to strike at his crazy creed.

"He never listens to me, he never hears me. He doesn't answer."

I go on too long about Sarah. But her stories about the Professor (who died peacefully in his sleep, I remember, at the age of eighty-six, long after Sarah had drowned in Lake George, thrown from a boat during a storm, they said) occupied and entertained me in those years. She introduced me to the life of the town, and through her I made friends with a few wealthy summer residents who came for the races: Anne Rhinelander, Cecily Lorillard, the Leland sisters, Emily Chisolm. They were later to form the core of the Maclaren Foundation, from which the Community grew. I have always been grateful to poor Sarah for that, and pitied her for her ripe, charming middle age wasted upon an aging, obsessed husband. I have always held to the private belief that she drowned herself, went downward into the cold blue water of Lake George to escape the Professor, or to provide him with further proof of his aeronautical metaphysics. But of course I do not know.

On the thirtieth day of August, 1904, Paderewski died. I will never be able to eradicate the memory of that day.

He was twelve years old, but for him it was extreme old age. He seemed to have come to it long before his appointed canine span. His sight had almost gone under the weight of cataracts in both eyes, we were told. His last months were noisy. His body was subject to attacks of ague. During them his trunk would shake, and his tail, independently agitated, would thump hard against the bare floor where he always lay because he hated the heat and texture of our oriental rugs. Most of the day he slept, breathing heavily, each long, hard breath ending with a penetrating snort, often so loud that it could be heard in the rooms at the other side of the house.

His nights were sleepless. We were never able to discover what disease it was that aged him so early and drove him so inexorably into senility and sickness. Sometimes in his deep internal distress, he would hoist himself painfully onto his thin legs and withered paws and move about the dark house, walking almost blindly, stumbling into chiffoniers and chairs, sideboards, and piano legs.

What was he searching for in those black rooms among the lifeless dark furniture, down at the edges of the tasseled heavy drapes? Was it Robert, the young, brisk, charming man with loving hands and bright smile, the soft, cocked way of listening, the gentle, amorous voice? I do go on here unpardonably, but I, too, remember Robert in this way. He had long ago exiled the aged dog to my quarters because his heavy, long-haired pelt gave off an odor not unlike mold and was offensive to him. Paderewski's pounding tail and snores during the day were disturbing to his work.

I have said it was late August, a very hot summer noon. The air was heavy, oppressive, with the promise of rain. My rooms, so close to the eaves over the south end of the house, were warm; it was hard to breathe the thick, still air. I thought I would walk out into the woods that stretched behind the house. Deep within them were cool, pine-walled, and needle-carpeted pockets, almost small rooms, where I used to sit in the months of the heat to read.

Paderewski was asleep, as usual, on the stone floor before the hearth. I remember starting out, and then returning for a shawl to sit upon. I don't remember, but yes, I must have done so: I left the side door ajar. Robert was certain that I had. He told me I had become forgetful, and perhaps he was right. It was from being alone so much, I came to believe, and having no markers, no hitching posts, in the long silences for my memory to fasten upon. But I do remember I was gone two hours during the hottest part of the noon and after. When I returned to my room, Paderewski was not in his sleeping place.

I searched the downstairs, knowing he could not have climbed the stairs. Desperate to find him, I disturbed Robert in the only place I had not been, the music room. Robert was resting on his couch at that hour, his eyes closed. But he was not asleep.

"Of course he is not here," he said, sounding irritated. I knew he hated to be disturbed during the day. He once told me he listened in his head, during his afternoon rest, to what he had written that morning. But he was upset enough at Paderewski's disappearance to come outside in his shirt sleeves to help me search.

We walked around the house, calling his name. Never, until that day, had that tributary name seemed so unsuitable for a dog. To be calling for a renowned, middle-aged pianist in the steaming Saratoga woods: I felt foolish. But he was nowhere near the house. We started to walk down the long, dusty Farm road—the road that was later to be given Robert's surname by an edict of the town council. But I think I may have already written this.

We rounded the bend in the road from which it is possible to see the avenue beyond. Coming toward us were two men, carrying on a board between them what we could tell at once was the bloodied fur and crushed head of Paderewski. They were evidently summer visitors. Their straw boaters, white duck trousers, and striped linen jackets marked them apart from the native men who rarely dressed this way in midafternoon. Robert ran ahead to them.

"What happened?"

"Is this your dog?" one man asked.

"Yes. Yes."

The man—we were later to learn his name was Henry Huddleston Rogers—his face troubled and solemn, said, "It was entirely my fault. Entirely. I did not see him standing in the road until the horses were almost upon him. I shouted. I tried to rein them in, but it was too late. I am entirely to blame. What can I say?"

Robert seemed stunned, yet ready to agree with the poor contrite fellow, I thought. I intervened: "No. Don't think that. He never leaves the house. He must have wakened and been confused by a dream, or something like that. He's never done this before. Usually I've had to half carry him out." I knew I was rattling on foolishly.

"Oh, be still, Caroline."

Robert pushed me aside. He lifted the dead dog from

the board into his arms, staggering under the weight. Somehow he managed to turn and walk back to the house, bearing Paderewski in his arms.

The man who had not spoken tipped his hat to me and started back down the road to the avenue, carrying the blood-stained board.

Mr. Rogers said, "This is terrible. I wish I could do something."

In the distance we could hear the roar of the crowd. Down the hill at the track the first race of the afternoon must have started.

"I'm Mrs. Maclaren."

"The composer's wife?"

"Yes."

"Oh, I'm so terribly sorry for this. That must have been the . . . your husband. This is terrible. Will you tell him again how sorry I am?"

"I will. But don't blame yourself. The dog was old and almost blind." I put my hand out. "Good-bye, Mr. . . ."

"Rogers."

"Mr. Rogers. Good-bye."

I almost ran back. Robert had taken the massive burden into the house: the front door was open and there was a light smear of blood on the middle panel where he must have brushed against it. I found them in the music room. Robert had put the dog down on the top of the closed piano, where he lay, already stiffened, his blind eyes opened to a new dark, his once-handsome coat suffused and beaded with blood and dust. Around him the piano cover, at that time, I remember, a fringed shawl I had brought back from Frankfurt, lay in contrasting splendor to the mangled Paderewski. Already he seemed to have shrunken, a mass of confused hair, paws, ears. Only his fine long narrow aristocratic muzzle remained intact.

Robert insisted on keeping him there for one whole day. I was reminded of Professor Watkins and his finch. Uncharitably, I thought of how anachronistic his attention to the dead dog was: for several years he had not allowed the animal in that room. Robert did not work the rest of that day but walked about the room, his hands behind his back, circling the piano, his eyes often on the now redolent carcass. I mourned Paderewski alone in my room, remembering all the haptic pleasures of that silken fur, the firm softness of his long, sleek, sensitive head and ears and nose.

Robert was more silent than ever at dinner that evening, and I suppose I, too, was absorbed in my own grief. I was full of it, ready to break down at the thought of losing the companion of my solitude, my walks and rests, in all those years since Germany.

On the second day Robert called our groundsman, Edward Collins, to remove the dog. Edward had dug a grave on a grassy little hill at the far end of the property. He brought a wooden box he had made to convey the body in. Robert would not watch the removal and conveyance. He refused to see Paderewski buried. I followed the farm wagon to the grave and stood at the side of the small, deep trench as Edward put the box into it, covered it with dirt and placed squares of sod over the raw spot.

"Will we want a marker for it, ma'am?"

"I'll ask Mr. Maclaren tonight what he wishes done."

"Very good."

But somehow Robert and I never mentioned Paderewski to each other again. Ida told me she had been unable to remove the bloodstains from Robert's shirt even after three washings, so I gave the shirt to Edward, who seemed very glad to have it. Robert did not ask after it. The piano shawl had to be disposed of.

The grave was never marked. I walked often to the place after that. From it there was a lovely view of the Adirondacks to the west, and the wooded hills of Highland Farm on the other side. I thought Robert had forgotten the place—he rarely walked that way alone that I was aware of, and surely never with me. But he must have remembered it. For later, in a cubbyhole in his desk, Anna Baehr found a small piece of staff paper on which he had written:

Bury me on the knoll near my dog,
Paderewski

We did. Robert lies there now. We did not disturb the small box Edward uncovered when he dug Robert's grave. The granite marker, elaborate and imposing, was put in place by the Maclaren Foundation in the years when it had the money to do that sort of thing. It is imposing, with Robert's name and dates, and my name and birth date. Only the final date is missing. Soon it, too, will be chiseled into the stone. Then we shall both lie beside our dog.

The letter said:

> *The trustees and the President of Columbia University are pleased to inform you that the University wishes to bestow upon you the honorary degree of Doctor of Humane Letters at the Commencement on June 5, 1905,*

and went on to give the details of the time and the arrangements that would be made for the comfort of those to be honored.

Robert showed it to me at dinner one evening and wondered if he ought to go. "Of course you must go. It is a great honor. You will enjoy yourself, and it's been so long since we have been to the city."

"But, Caroline, so long a trip? How will we travel? How much time will we have to spend in New York?" He was full of anxiety, his voice so low I could hardly hear him.

"A week, perhaps. Oh, Robert, you will enjoy it, I'm sure. We can hear some music and visit the galleries. Some of your former pupils live there, and your friends, friends from Hoch and Boston. Churchill teaches at Columbia. We can see him. Oh, Robert, let's go."

I watched him struggle to decide. He seemed worn out and very tired: The dog's death has diminished him, I thought. His work, all the copying it required, seemed to

take him longer and longer, he stopped earlier than he used
to. More and more often when I came to call him to dinner
I would find him stretched out on his couch, exhausted.
Lately, he said, he would lie down to rest at three. When
I came at six, he was still there, inert and half-asleep.

How old and frail he looked to me now! His hair was
more gray than russet, and very sparse. After that strange
illness it had never returned to its full, thick, youthful
growth. No trace of the old, charming smile remained, for
he never smiled now. Looking at him, I was reminded of
Paderewski, for Robert was like him: prematurely old at
thirty-three, spent and lusterless, a used-up man.

Our preparations for the trip took almost a week, the
packing of the grips, the arrangements made for a landau
to convey us to the railroad depot in Saratoga Springs, the
purchase of our tickets. For Robert it would have been a
wearying series of chores, so I spared him everything but
his actual presence at the departure. For me it was a great
delight.

The season was just beginning. The arriving trains were
full of stylish-looking visitors. Outside the depot the roads
were crowded with omnibuses, dogcarts, and phaetons waiting to take travelers to the Grand Union and the United
States hotels. I remember that the bells in the depot cupola
rang as a train approached or departed. Robert disliked the
racket and cringed against the terrible noise, but I enjoyed
it all: the bells, the sounds of cars and horses, the shouts of
Negro porters, train whistles, all making a fine cacophony
of active, alive sounds.

We took a Pullman room. But Robert hardly slept. I stayed awake with him while he went over and over his short acceptance speech. He was trying to commit the ten or so sentences to memory, but he seemed unable to do it. I felt an uneasy surprise at this, at Robert who, a few years ago, could conduct the Brahms *Fourth* and the Beethoven *Seventh* symphonies together in one evening's program without the scores.

In those agonizingly long hours, traveling through the dark state along the Hudson River, past the dim, sleeping river towns (for Robert would not permit me to draw the shades over the windows: he said he felt very confined in the small room allotted to us), I realized for the first time how much he had failed. In our house at the Farm surrounded by familiar objects and secluded by the custom and routine of our quiet lives, I had not noticed, or perhaps I had not looked closely. My own days and nights were of an unchanging sameness which I must have extended to his. Now in this unfamiliar, moving place I could see how far down he had gone. Can I be blamed for my blindness? When he was sick he would not tell me until it was unavoidable, as though there was a shame in admitting to bodily weakness. And even then, he resisted having a physician called to see him. He must have hidden his symptoms and his debility to have grown so old, so quickly, so soon.

I had written ahead. In the morning, among the crowds of persons milling around the Grand Central Station, we found Churchill Weeks and his wife, Catherine. They were at the barrier to meet us, to arrange with the porters for our baggage, to take us to our hotel, which on that occasion was the Chelsea. Catherine, whom we knew only slightly, said nothing. It seemed to me she found our arrival a trial, as though she were not accustomed to such heavy responsibilities. She was a thin, neurasthenic, almost flat woman whose body seemed concave at the front. Her brown hair was pulled tightly back from her thin face and fastened at the nape of her neck in the style of those days. She had the look of someone waiting always for something unpleasant to happen, always expecting a repellent flavor as she looked at her food. When she spoke to her husband her voice was sharp and impatient as though his very presence were an annoyance to her. Try as I might for Churchill's sake and Robert's, I could not like her.

In our rooms at the hotel Churchill said, "We'll leave you now. You must be tired from the long journey. Is there anything we can do to make you more comfortable before we go?"

"We are expected to lunch with the faculty at twelve sharp, Churchill," said Catherine, in her rough, edgy midwestern voice.

"Nothing. Nothing at all, thank you," said Robert. "You are very good." He spoke as though he had not heard the asperity in Catherine's voice, and perhaps he had not. His own voice was distant and weary. He smiled at Churchill his half-smile, his eyes lighting up as he looked at his friend. "We will rest and perhaps take a walk and wait for you to come."

Churchill had looked at Catherine as though he were

preparing to strike her, but when Robert spoke, he smiled at him. For one moment, I thought, the old ineffable love seemed to hover in the air between them. Neither sharp Catherine nor birdlike Caroline was present to them.

Catherine stared stonily at her husband. I thought, What a strange marriage this is, without even the pretense of civility before others. Or perhaps I was oversensitive to the import of the looks they exchanged and to the overtones of her words, because my own marriage had no resonances except for the echoes of wordlessness. It must have been that.

They left us. Robert lay down on the bed and slept almost at once. I lay beside him, careful not to disturb him by my motion, listening to his almost silent breathing and hearing beyond the hotel windows (we were on the second floor, we never stayed above the second floor, because Robert was afraid of fire and so feared to sleep in a room on a higher floor) the continuous roiling sound of traffic on the street below, and the shouting, and the clanging of wagons and motorcars. I felt exhilarated to be in a city.

At six o'clock the Weekses returned, but Robert had decided he would prefer not to venture out for the promised dinner. So Churchill arranged with the hotel to bring to our room a lavish set of covered dishes on a moving table, a service I had never before seen provided for guests in America. I enjoyed it all hugely, as did Churchill, who talked a great deal to Robert of the pleasures of living in New York, of teaching piano and harmony and composition in a university where an academic department devoted to the study of music had just been established. Robert smiled, nodded assent, but spoke very little. I listened. Catherine, as I recall, said nothing.

The morning of Commencement Day was beautiful, cool, and clear. We traveled by trolley car along Broadway to Morningside Heights and walked through the great gates to the new Seth Low Library to meet the president, Mr. Nicholas Murray Butler. Weeks was there with other faculty members from the department of music. I was given a ticket to the chairs set up at the foot of the library steps. When I found my place, there was Catherine Weeks. I sat beside her. She asked after Robert's condition and seemed to wish to explore the subject of his apparent ill health (it is uncharitable of me, but I felt she was the kind of sour woman who enjoyed the spectacle of other people's misfortunes). But before I was required to say very much, the music— trumpets and horns—started. We rose to our feet to attend the glittering procession of garbed professors and students. Walking near the head was Robert, looking pallid and gaunt in his black academic mortarboard with a gold tassel falling before his eyes. He wore a handsome blue robe decorated with the crowns of King's College, for so this university had been named at its inception, I read in the engraved program handed to me when I entered. Robert's forehead was wet with perspiration; I was sorry he had insisted on dressing in his old but still fine German suit. He was going to be very warm up there, I thought.

I sat through the opening of the ceremony feeling very hot, too, for the sun was beating down on us at that hour. I felt uneasy for Robert. Always before, as I had waited in audiences for him to perform or conduct, I was confident, knowing well his perfect control, his quiet command of all his powers. But after the night in the railway car my confidence was shaken. How would he *do*?

At last—it seemed to me a very long wait in that hot sun—President Butler rose to read the awards of honorary degrees. I was delighted that Robert's was read first. The citation was glowing and effusive. "Robert Glencoe Maclaren is one of America's great composers. He has turned his excellent European training to the service of American music, American themes and subject matter. America's Orpheus, he has been called by one critic, and his future," read President Butler from a parchment scroll, "promises to be as distinguished as have been the short years of his already eminent career. He is a man whose thirty-three years of life are studded with world-recognized accomplishments."

I watched Robert, seated in the front row on the platform, as the president read. He was looking straight ahead into the audience, listening perhaps, but somehow I felt he did not hear what the president was reading. The president stopped, there was applause. Mr. Butler looked over at Robert, expecting him to rise and come forward. The audience applauded loudly, but Robert did not rise. I saw a professor seated behind him lean over to shake his arm and whisper something. Robert seemed to awaken, looked back at the red-gowned man behind him, nodded his head slightly, and stood up. Then, to my horror, he turned and walked away from where President Butler stood, making his way carefully toward the steps at the opposite end of the platform.

A murmur went through the audience. I could feel myself covered by a red flood of embarrassment and heat. What could I do? Nothing but sit on my camp chair and watch my poor confused husband wander in the wrong direction, away from his honor, in front of hundreds of graduates and parents, professors, and the president of the university.

President Butler was quick-witted. A vigorous man in his early forties, he had only recently taken over his eminent position. At that terrible moment he seemed capable of dealing efficiently with anything, even so eccentric a situation as this. He strode briskly the length of the platform, while everyone else sat, frozen. He reached Robert and took his arm just as he was about to descend the steps and leave the platform. He pulled him back, turned him around, and, with wonderful tact that made what he was doing seem normal ceremonial procedure, pushed him gently ahead, in the right direction, inching him toward the podium.

Robert then seemed to remember what it was he had to do. He reached into the inner pocket of his hot woolen suit and brought out the sheet of paper on which I had printed for him in large block letters the words of his speech. While the president discreetly sat down behind him, Robert began to read in his low, musical voice.

I relaxed a little, although by now my dress was suffused with perspiration and my handkerchief could no longer contain the moisture from my forehead and hands. No, I thought, it will be all right. Beside me, Catherine shifted in her seat. In my apprehensive state I took her movement to be a tart comment of some kind on what had just taken place on the platform.

Robert came to the last line. He read it slowly, distinctly. A low swell of applause began to grow on the platform and in the audience, but it died abruptly when Robert's voice went on. Dear God! I realized he had begun at the opening sentence and was reading the whole first paragraph again! I was overcome with horror, hearing the low murmur around me. I wanted to rush up to the platform and rescue him, stop the solemn proceedings and take Robert home to the Farm where he would be safe from the world's knowledge.

But again the clever president assessed the situation quickly. He half rose from his seat as Robert once again came to his final sentence of gratitude, and when it was horrifyingly clear that he was about to begin a third reading, President Butler was at his elbow, taking his hand firmly in his two hands and shaking it, saying something to him very low that I could not hear. Robert stopped reading and turned to the president in confusion, seeming not to recognize him. But he was silent, at last. The audience was now enthusiastically applauding my poor oblivious husband, as the president led him back to his seat while appearing merely to be politely escorting him. How grateful I was, sitting below in a bath of fright and heat, for the president's intelligence and his quick thinking.

The rest of the afternoon I remember quite clearly, for much of it I was now able to enjoy. Luncheon was served in wicker baskets to us and to the graduates and their parents and friends. Numbers of persons shook Robert's hand and asked him if he remembered them. To each he nodded, said "Yes," and smiled his weak, gentle half-smile. But I could tell he remembered none of them. He held my arm, or Churchill's, during the hour that followed the luncheon, acknowledging the faculty members who spoke to him of their admiration for his music. He nodded, giving them each a wordless, childlike smile, sweet and vacant.

No mention was made by anyone of the debacle on the platform. It seemed to have been accepted and forgotten, reegarded as the eccentric, absentminded behavior of a genius. Only I knew better.

The Weekses had arranged tickets for us for a music-hall entertainment that evening. The variety show was a theatrical experience Robert had loved since a boy. Often he had spoken to Churchill when they were studying in Germany, and later to me, of a variety star he had seen in Boston, Della Fox, a wonderfully beautiful, plump, girlish singer, as he described her to me. By fortunate chance it happened that she had decided to return to the vaudeville stage, which was now very popular, during the weekend we were to be in New York. Churchill was kindness itself. He had obtained four tickets for Della Fox's third appearance, on Sunday evening, the evening of the Columbia Commencement, after her scheduled opening on Friday.

Robert was excited, awakened from the trancelike state he had been in during the ceremony by the prospect of seeing and hearing Della Fox again. We sat in midafternoon under the great elms on the campus, cooler now, with Churchill and Catherine. Robert was better. He talked more than he had since we left the Farm.

"I simply cannot wait. I remember, it must have been when I came back on a visit almost twenty years ago—could it have been that long ago, Church?"

"I think so, Rob. The newspaper account said she had been retired for almost twenty years."

"Twenty years! She was my idol, my dream, my ideal woman when I was, what was I? Fourteen? I must have been. She sang in a small but pure soprano. The *Police Gazette* called her 'la petite Fox.' Do you remember ever seeing her, Church?"

Catherine stared at her husband. He blushed, and then admitted gallantly, I thought, to Robert, that yes, he remembered hearing about Della Fox.

Robert went on: "I removed her picture from the *Gazette*. And my mother found it in my room and destroyed it. But I see Della Fox in my mind's eye so clearly. She is small and blond, very blond, with small blond curls. She dressed differently from the other musical stars of those days. They wore spangles, and pinched-in stays and tights. But Della wore a white satin man's suit—trousers and vest and jacket and cravat, even a white yachting cap with a small visor that sat jauntily on her curls. Her eyes were deep, sparkling blue, and she was delicate, very delicate, yet—yet full-bodied, do you know? Do you know what I'm trying to say, Church?"

Churchill smiled at him, ignoring what I took to be his wife's evident displeasure at Robert's nostalgic flights, for she was looking sternly, unsmiling, at her husband.

"She is magnificent, Rob, I'm sure. I cannot wait to see her."

Robert continued: "And I remember, as clearly as if it were yesterday, the song she always sang as she lounged against a table, with her leg thrown over it so the audience could see her ankle. Something like . . . shady brook? Yes—'Shady brook, babbling brook, and now serenely mellow,' " he sang in his fine, low tenor.

Churchill joined in. The two men sang the verses of the foolish little song to the end. People seated near us on the grass applauded and laughed, and the two men looked dismayed at having been so carried away. Churchill gracefully acknowledged the gentle applause by tipping his straw hat. Robert, flushed, looked away, but I could tell he was pleased. It had been so long since he had come out of himself, enjoyed himself in that way.

Then Churchill said, "One caution, Rob. I read in the *Sun* last evening that Della Fox's first two performances had to be canceled because she was ill. I'm hoping that won't be the case tonight, but we won't know until we get downtown to the theater and see if the bills are posted out front. But there are six other acts if she doesn't appear."

Robert was still transported into his past and did not seem to hear Churchill's warning. "She smoked, onstage! I can see her now, leaning back, reaching into her white jacket pocket for her little silver case, opening it, putting a cigarette into her mouth and lighting it. She breathed out a ring of smoke and looked at us all in the audience with those deep blue eyes, as though she dared us to disapprove. Never have I seen so—so seductive an act. She was charming, performing what was forbidden in full view.

"I see her still, standing there, her leg swung across the edge of the table—another charmingly illicit act—all that delicious femininity encased in that white suit, blowing smoke rings at the audience and singing. Della Fox . . ."

We all laughed at Robert—all but Catherine, who stared at the table during his elegiac reminiscence. In that moment he looked almost young and eager. I could imagine him reaching out with his hot boy's hand toward a mythic goddess of incredible allure. It was so good to see him like this again. I was impatient for the evening's entertainment.

We dined with the Weekses in their apartment on Fifty-seventh Street, a long, dull meal with too many hot rolls and heavy brown gravy for the beef. We finished with pie made, it seemed, of leaden apples. (How is one able to remember the details of unmemorable meals such as this one? It must have been the happenings of the evening that fastened these trivial matters forever in my mind.) At dinner Robert was quiet but pleasant. He watched Churchill carve the roast most capably and pour the Médoc, admiring, I could tell, his skill with the knife and the cork. At one point, I remember, he hummed "Shady Brook," and we all listened, and then laughed.

There was much talk of the old days, in Paris and in Frankfurt. Only once was there a break in the pleasant tenor of the supper. When Churchill mentioned their beloved teacher Joachim Raff, rehearsing the details of his sudden death, Robert's eyes filled with tears that ran down his cheeks. Catherine looked away while Robert searched his pockets for a handkerchief. When he could not find it, Churchill passed his. We all waited for Robert to regain control.

Churchill said it was time. We walked down Broadway to the Lyceum Theatre. For me it was exciting to see the city in the evening light, spread, unbelievably, upward, and glistening in the clear air. I held Robert's arm and felt almost gay and young again, wishing we could preserve the exhilaration of that evening, wishing we could recapture the pleasures of the early days when we walked together on the Common, with Paderewski encircling us with his leash and drawing us together. . . .

The marquee that jutted out over the sidewalk was lighted. A small crowd of persons gathered under it. Churchill smiled with pleasure when he saw the bills posted on both sides of the door:

Under the corner of the bill on the right side of the entrance was a picture of Della Fox in her famous white suit, looking much as Robert had described her: a small, plump, pink and white, full-breasted young woman, jaunty and fresh-faced.

Our seats were close to the front of the orchestra, in recognition, I guessed, of what Churchill had remembered of Robert's boyish passion. I wondered if we were not too close. We seemed to be seated almost directly above three shabby-looking musicians in the orchestra pit, now trying out their instruments in a peculiar cacophony.

"No. We'll see well here," said Robert. He was in a state of high excitement. All his morning's weariness and disorientation had vanished. Like a child, he seemed hardly able to wait for the curtain to rise. He applauded when the musicians, now somewhat more together, began the notes of "Shady Brook." The rest of the audience was quiet. Unself-consciously, Robert clapped alone.

After a long introduction, which consisted of a medley, I assumed, of Della Fox's "hits," the theater was darkened and a spotlight opened upon the left side of the stage. The curtain went up on a set vaguely designed to resemble the interior of a dilapidated cabaret. The spotlight hovered uncertainly around the wings, the music repeated its themes, the pause, in which nothing happened, seemed to stretch interminably. And then she entered.

I can recount what I saw that evening, for my memory of it is still very clear. The white suit, the white cap, yes, they were still there. But stuffed into them, straining every seam and thread, was a monstrously fat little woman. Her great girth made her seem abnormally short. Once onstage, she hesitated uncertainly, dazed by the bright light. Then she wandered toward the center of the stage, her small feet appearing too slight to bear all that gross weight. She smiled at the audience, a foolish, idiot-child smile with her red bowed lips minute in her huge powdered face, and patted the white button at the top of her cap as though to be sure it was still there. Then she waved to the musicians in the pit that she was ready to begin. That gesture, grand and silly, gave away her state: she was profoundly, completely drunk.

After two false starts, during which either Della Fox or the little orchestra was out of step, she began to sing. Her voice was tiny. She sounded as though it were being squeezed out of her mammoth chest, issuing from between her bubble-like cheeks. She forgot the words, sang "la la de la de la" in their place, grimaced, fluttered her little fat fingers in the dim air in front of her, and then tottered over to the cabaret table at the right of the stage.

Now the famous act, I thought. But it was not to be. Della Fox made a gallant effort to raise one great leg, packed tight into the trouser, over the corner of the table, but failed. Instead, still singing in her little high-pitched tuneless voice, a measure behind the pianist in the pit, she crossed her ankles and fumbled for the famous cigarette. The silver box gleamed in the spotlight. Trying gamely to open it, she dropped it and it struck the steps a distance from her. The little dance she did, half-bent from the waist, made it clear that she would not be able to pick it up.

I glanced across at Catherine Weeks. For the first time all day she was smiling. Robert's eyes were closed.

"Let's get out of here," Churchill whispered, leaning across both of them. We walked up the aisle. I could hear the boos, the whistles, laughter, and shouts of insults from the gallery. People were already ahead of us in the aisle, on their way to the box office, I was sure, to have their admittance money returned to them.

Robert stopped outside to look at the picture of Della Fox on the poster, at the tiny dimpled creature whose young innocent eyes sparkled even in the old, poor photograph. In her shining man's suit, smoke curling about her piquant face, she was indeed, as she had been all those years in Robert's memory, a lovely creature.

"We should have known. I should have known," said Robert. "How could it have been otherwise? All those years."

Churchill, looking as though he were responsible for the

whole fiasco, felt he had to lighten Robert's spirits. "Well, Rob, look at us. We're not what we were, either, if you examine us closely."

Robert put his hand on Churchill's still black hair and ruffled it a little. "Perhaps so," he said in the absent way he had of talking of the past, "but I think you look very well, Church." He hesitated, and I wondered if he might be thinking of his lapse of the morning. "I'm more like poor Della Fox. Old. Forgetful. Decayed. All too soon." He paused. Then he took my arm in his accustomed way when he was tired, and said in a whisper that I'm certain only I heard, "Lost."

That was almost the last, perhaps even the last, of the good times, for him. In our few remaining days in New York we heard the Aeolian String Quartette at Carnegie Hall play one of Robert's early quartets, the third, Opus 12, I think it must have been. We walked about in Central Park, we dined at Rumpelmayer's with Adolph Burmeister and his wife. Adolph and Robert had been in Frankfurt together. Now Adolph played in the string section of the New York Symphony Society.

From that dinner we came back early to the hotel because Robert complained of an odd unpleasantness: "I could not eat my dinner because it is hard to move my tongue," he said. "It feels heavy, wooden." I believed this to be an excuse for the dull silence he had maintained with the Burmeisters at dinner, but I said nothing. We left New York the next morning, two days before we had intended. It was Robert's last visit to the city, his last trip any distance from the Farm, and, it turned out, the start of the last year of his life.

The trip home in the railway car was longer and more tedious than the one down. Robert was very silent, persisting in his claim to a sore, cumbersome tongue. I read a little, sampled the chocolates from Maillard's Candy Store that Churchill had given us upon our departure, and slept well in the berth above Robert. In the early morning I tried to distract him by reading to him from the *Sun* newspaper I had brought with me from the city. It was on the theatrical page of this newspaper that I learned that Della Fox had made no further appearances at the Lyceum after the one we had witnessed. She had been taken to Bellevue Hospital, the same night we saw her sorry performance, suffering from the delirium tremens of acute alcoholism. I did not convey this information to Robert, preferring to read the comments on a musical affair at Carnegie Hall on the same page. But nothing could take his mind away from his troubling, strange new affliction.

"My tongue burns," he insisted on that morning of our arrival at the Saratoga Springs depot. We came back at last to the Farm, tired out from travel, dusty and disheartened. I remember the heat of that summer, I remember the persons who called and were turned away because, I told them,

Robert was working, or tired, or temporarily indisposed. I was able to visit with Sarah Watkins only occasionally when I could get away from the care of the house, the garden, and Robert.

If now I will seem to dwell too much on the unpleasant details of that last year, you must forgive me: but they continue to live in my mind, vivid as fire. Now more than ever I see that they seem to be an integral part of the story I have determined to tell.

I do not remember exactly when it was that I knew Robert and Dr. Holmes were not acquainting me with the nature of Robert's illness. I confess to feminine foolishness or, perhaps, human blindness. But I think that, more than these, it was ignorance. For his increasingly horrifying symptoms meant nothing to me until the Christmas Anna Baehr came to help me nurse him, when his care had grown too heavy for me. She was to inform me; until then I knew only that strange and pitiable things were happening to him.

In late September, Robert agreed at last to go into the village to see Dr. Holmes. The racing season was over, and the lines of vehicles: the touring cars and phaetons, omnibuses and barouches that had conveyed visitors back and forth from the hotels to the track and to the Club-house for gambling had all vanished, and with them the pickpockets and touts, the politicians from New York City, and the theater actors and actresses who played in Saratoga. I always enjoyed reading all the details of that high life in the local paper. The *Saratoga Union* reported that the village was al-

most back to its normal population; only a few of the fashionable and wealthy families lingered on for some weeks of the
baths and for the cure of the waters.

It was widely believed in those days that the hot dis-
sipations of the summer, the "pace that kills," as the *Union*
put it, could be cleansed from the system by sufficient doses
of the mineral waters of the Congress Spring. In the late
mornings, well-dressed men and women walked in leisurely
fashion from their hotels toward Congress Park to drink
agate cups full of heavy, sulfurous water. Often the men
were portly and red-faced: one knew that rich food and fine
French wines from the United States Hotel and the Grand
Union Hotel dining rooms, the late suppers at the Club-house,
had been taken heavily into their distended stomachs five
times each day. Even at the racing clubhouse they ate and
drank as they watched the races. In those years their wives
never accompanied them to the races or to the gambling
casino—such attendance was thought risqué and *fast*—but
still, the ladies, too, seemed to grow heavy in the season.
They resorted to the same purgative treatment as their husbands in the Saratoga springs before they moved on to Wiesbaden or Vichy in the fall.

The morning we drove to the village to see Dr. Holmes
we were stopped by a little procession of strollers on their
way to the Congress waters to take the cure. Our hired
motorcar waited for them to pass before turning into Broadway. But then I saw the carriage behind the walkers, driven
by the famous woman.

"Look, Robert. Do you know who that is?"

"Who? Where?" he asked. Then he said, "No. Who is it?"

The woman driving her carriage alone was what we used to call a spectacle. Almost larger than life, she was crossing the broad avenue slowly, a great peacock of a woman in a white carriage, a lavender parasol in one hand, the other holding white doeskin reins to her all-white horse. Her hips, ample and stately, completely occupied the whole seat of the carriage, as though it took that breadth to bear the broad, snow-white, almost fully displayed bosom above them. She was dressed (*swathed* was the word we used to hear for this) entirely in lavender. Her huge, large-brimmed silk hat was lavender, too, except for the brilliantly red roses on its brim, and she smiled from side to side of her carriage, the smile of a confident, famous, massive, but still lovely face.

"That's Lillian Russell, the actress, Robert. She's grown fat, but isn't she still beautiful, in her way? She looks— majestic."

Robert looked at her and did not reply. Perhaps he was thinking of Della Fox, wondering if obesity was the fate of all boyhood visions, of all great beauties. "Let's move on," he said to the driver.

"We can't pass. The driver can't pass. Everyone ahead has stopped to see her."

Lillian Russell's carriage was trimmed with solid silver. On her lap, erect and small, lean and haughty, sat her Japanese spaniel, his diamond collar, the *Saratoga Union* reported, having cost eighteen hundred dollars. It was altogether a wonderful sight to see. I have never forgotten it. The *Union* reporter wrote that Lillian Russell had grown grossly fat from gluttony. She was said to eat three whole chickens at dinner, to drink three bottles of French wine during an evening, and to finish with six cream desserts. But I forgot that as I looked at her, lordly and elegant, her enormous stays lifting her great bosom far into the space before her, shading the little dog in her lap. She passed the corner where we sat still waiting and came to the corner of the Grand Union piazza. Every man seated there, resting after the strenuous season, I suppose, rose to his feet as she passed, removing his hat, as though to acknowledge the progress of a queen or a goddess.

She had passed the Grand Union Hotel and was driving up Broadway when our driver was able to move our vehicle. I was still full of the vision:

"Robert, do you know, she refuses to stay at the Grand Union Hotel. I read that in the newspaper. Despite all its elegance."

"Why?" he asked thickly. His tongue was again troubling him, and I could tell he inquired only out of politeness.

"I think it's because of that sign."

On the registry desk of the Grand Union Hotel a notice read:

No Dogs or Jews Allowed

"She has that spaniel she is so devoted to. So, of course she stays at the Crumb House instead."

Dr. Holmes examined Robert. Then he came into the waiting room with him. "I want him to be seen by a colleague of mine, a doctor in New York. Dr. Keyes, Edward Lawrence Keyes, at the Bellevue Hospital in New York."

"I will *not* go there," said Robert to neither of us, into the air of the waiting room. "I will not go back to that city."

"You must, Mr. Maclaren. You must be seen. I am not certain of the new treatment for your—ailment. Keyes is a specialist, an expert. He is writing a book on—such matters. You must go to see him."

Robert refused. Soon after, it must have been a month or so later, fortune came our way. Dr. Keyes, visiting friends in Saratoga Springs for the famous fall display of color in the leaves, called upon us. There had been no change in the condition of Robert's mouth and tongue. If anything, it had grown worse. The one view I had of them made my heart pound with fear. He could eat almost nothing, he said, everything stuck to his tongue and in his throat. Now it was impossible to keep his desperate state hidden any longer. "Look, Caroline."

He opened his mouth. I looked. Clinging to the normal dark-red lining of the roof of his mouth were white mucous patches, ugly and dead-looking. His tongue was coated on all sides with thick, viscid saliva. Before he closed his mouth again quickly, sensing my horror at the hideous sight, I caught a foul, acrid odor and turned away without thinking, to escape the unpleasantness of it. I felt nauseated.

"Dear God, Robert. What *is* it?"

He shook his head. His eyes looked wild and terrified. Rarely in the days that followed did he speak, for his difficulty in moving his swollen, covered tongue and the pain in his cheeks and mouth made him avoid the slightest effort. Once again, on the evening before Dr. Keyes's arrival at the Farm (Dr. Holmes had sent word with the mail carrier of the imminent visit), I caught sight of the terrible thing he kept shut away in the diseased cavity of his mouth. At dinner, eating the warm milk toast I had prepared for him, he tried to cough and choked. I started to go to him, thinking to help him by pounding his back, but he gestured me away. Then (Lord, how clear that moment is still to me!) he thrust his fingers into his mouth and pulled out a rancid, ropy mass of thick, oily, copper-colored saliva. It clung to his fingers, he could not shake it off, he groaned helplessly. I rushed to him with my dinner napkin, wrapping his foul-smelling hand in it. It was the beginning of my witness to his long and terrible dying.

The next morning Dr. Keyes was with him in his bedroom for almost an hour. I waited downstairs at his request. When he came down he asked me to be seated. He took the settee at the side of the hearth.

"Mrs. Maclaren, I must be open with you. Your husband is gravely ill. There is treatment, of course. We can assuage his symptoms, we can make him more comfortable in this—

affliction. But, I must be direct with you, we cannot cure him. It is, sadly, too late. He should have been treated when this first appeared, perhaps ten or more years ago. I do not know that exactly—he will not say. But even then we could not have been sure. We knew very little about the treatment then. Now our method works often, not always. At all events, it is too late to apply it to him now. It would do no good."

"What is it, Doctor? What does he have? Does it have a name?"

I thought Dr. Keyes looked uneasily at me. "It has a number of names. Some have called it a blood disease, a disorder of the red corpuscles. Others see it as a disturbance of the nervous system, a brain disease. But whatever it is named, it starts and then recedes, appears and then rests a long while before it finally reappears with terrible virulence, as you now see it in Mr. Maclaren."

"I understand. Can you tell me if other . . . what else will happen?"

"That, too, varies with the patient. The liver may be involved—there may be the jaundice that comes of that. His tongue may ulcerate, then harden, and finally become almost useless. That will cause a great deal of salivation, almost constant drooling which he will not be able to control. You must—uh, prepare in some way for that, with towels and large napkins, perhaps even a capacious bib of some kind. There may be bad swelling and splitting of the lips from all the water, but we can help that with mercurial ointment."

"Yes. Is there more?"

"His gums are now spongy, almost like a soft cheese. There are large patches of fungus on them, what we call noma: they are very infected. So we may expect his teeth to—be lost quite soon. Even now there is much bleeding from the gums. The blood tends to be caught in that thick saliva you may have seen. His throat is similarly afflicted now, and it will be worse. It will swell and cause him much trouble swallowing. He may try constantly to cough, or to vomit, with no results. This condition we can lessen: we cannot stop it entirely."

"Dear Lord! How can this be? How long . . . ?"

"The worst part will be over in a few months, I think. After that there will be inevitable weakness in all the limbs —and, I must tell you, for most loved ones find this hardest to bear, diminution of the mental faculties. He will be bed-ridden, but must be helped into a chair each day for a short time to prevent liquid from forming in the lungs. He will require feeding and his bodily functions will have to be cared for, for he will lose control of them. Often he will be irritable and sometimes irrational in his demands and complaints. You must be patient."

I stared at him, I'm sure, all the time he was reciting these terrible expectations. "Can nothing be done? Something, there must be something to do for this—nerve or blood disease, whatever it is. . . ."

"I do not believe so, Mrs. Maclaren. But of course there are other doctors you might wish to consult. There is a Dr. William Gottheil in Boston who has written impressively on this subject. You could—"

"No, no, that is not what I meant. I trust your experience, your knowledge, Dr. Keyes. But to know, so surely, that it is incurable . . ."

"I wish it were otherwise, with all my heart. But it is not. I can only say that . . ."

"Robert will die?"

"Well, yes." He stood up. He turned a wry smile toward me, but I understood from what followed that it was directed more at himself: "A fatal termination, we say. But he will die, and soon. Yes."

I find it hard to remember if I responded aloud to this frightful finality. I do recall the curious mixture of my feelings: profound pity for my poor sick husband who had still so much more suffering to endure, and pity for myself at the prospect of having to witness his torment. But grief? The stricken and furious grief of the wife about to be a widow? I felt none of that, for wife I was only in a sense, and woman I had not yet learned to be.

I saw him to the door. His chauffeur waited outside in his motorcar. Dr. Keyes turned to me and took my hand in his.

"My dear madam. This is a very hard thing for you to bear. I am keenly aware of that. But I will instruct Dr. Holmes, who is very capable, in all the procedures I am familiar with and he will be able to care for Mr. Maclaren well. Upstairs I have left on his table some prescriptions for treatment of the mouth—tincture of benzoin, another compound for his throat. Dr. Holmes will know what to do, whatever happens, you may be sure."

"Thank you. I will call upon him, of course."

"One final matter. If it is at all possible, I suggest you employ a nurse to assist you, very soon. It will be increasingly arduous for you to move him alone—you are a very slight lady. And you will need to be relieved from the constant care, especially—ah, at the termination, when you will need professional assistance in many ways."

"Thank you. I will give serious consideration to that. Thank you again."

So Anna Baehr came to Highland Farm. Dr. Holmes knew of her when I inquired a few weeks later. He told me this young woman had nursed a dying old lady in Fort Edward, very capably and kindly, he told me, and if I desired he would see if she was still unemployed after the lady's death.

It happened that she was. I prepared a room for her near the pantry and kitchen. She arrived on Christmas Eve in the afternoon. We had never met—Dr. Holmes had made all the necessary arrangements. So I was unprepared for her youth. Somehow, her name sounded so Germanic, I pictured her as impassive, strong, stolid, somehow. But the girl who arrived at the Farm was twenty-five, she told me (I would have guessed twenty), and had been in nursing service in New York, in Albany and in Fort Edward, a small village north of us.

During the long evenings we spent together that winter of Robert's dying, while he slept, she told me a little about her life. I learned it only very slowly, for she was not communicative about herself. But I put it down here, all together, as I came to hear it over the years.

Anna Baehr's voice was delicate, low, and charming; her diction had the formal awkwardness of someone whose first language had been German. She told me her father was a doctor who emigrated to this country with his wife and two daughters; Anna was eight and Rosa eleven when they settled in New York City. He died soon after, while caring for the sick of the East Side during an epidemic of smallpox. His widow, leaving her young daughters with a friend, a Berliner who had settled in New York's Yorkville section, took his body back to Germany and never returned.

Anna told me, "Rosa and I never understood it. She wrote to Frau Mundlein, she sent money, but she never came back to this country. We waited, thinking, any day, but she never came. Even when Rosa sickened with diphtheria and then died. My mother wrote to me. She sent money to Frau Mundlein to pay for masses to be said, for proper burial in a Catholic cemetery in Queens after a low requiem mass.

"But she did not come.

"Five years ago, after I had been graduated from nursing school, I went to see her. I sailed on a ship, earning my passage by acting as ship's nurse. I found her living in a house just off the Kurfürstendamm under another name. She had been married again and had been afraid to write to me about it. Her husband was in the government. It was strange indeed: she never told him she had two daughters in America. She was afraid he would not marry her if he knew. For everything it was the same: she was afraid.

"Even when I came to Berlin she told me to meet her outside the house in a café. She did not want me to come to her house for fear her husband would come home unexpectedly. So I never met him. But after she and I had two meetings in that strange way I sailed back on the return passage of the same ship I had come on. She continues to write to me, but I do not answer. She is not afraid of letters, but I do not wish to be related to a mother through the mails."

The skin of Anna's face was tight and scrubbed, almost translucent. Her long hair, light and thin, shone with the luster of much washing. She wore it around her head in a pouf like a halo, the ends tucked away at the top of her head in a small bun. In the pictures I have of her that arrangement of hair now looks odd, but it was everywhere the fashion in those days.

The only strange thing about her looks was the color of her eyes. The irises were so pale they sometimes faded almost away into the white part. At other times, when she was distressed or ill or angry, they took on the color of slate. Her figure was full and ripe-looking, much like the young women I remembered seeing on the streets of Frankfurt who had full bosoms, slim waists, and then the opulence repeated in the hips. Next to her glowing youth, I felt old and withered. And so I was, in some ways. My body had never come to bloom. It was still pressed into the flat lines of my girlhood as though maturity, the rounded voluptuous flesh of a woman's fullness, was always to be denied to my sparrow's body.

By the New Year, Anna Baehr had settled in and assumed most of Robert's strenuous care. His sickness proceeded in all the terrible ways Dr. Keyes had predicted for it, as inexorable as a teacher following closely the syllabus for her subject. Anna had to make many trips by foot into the village to obtain the ointments and acids, the granules and powders for Robert's decaying mouth, the mercury in compound tincture of bark tonic for the lesions that had broken out at the edges of his eyes and at the back of his ears. She was always willing to take those long walks: she loved the out-of-doors and the exercise.

At her suggestion we had Edward dismantle the great bed, carry it piece by piece down the stairs, and reassemble it in the largest downstairs room, the drawing room. It became Robert's bedroom. Anna and I sat with him there or, when he slept, in the small morning room near the music room, which was now shut off to preserve the fireplace heat for Robert. She moved her bed into the breakfast room so that she could be close to him at night, and I slept on the sofa in my little sitting room on the other side of the drawing room.

All the old orderliness of the Farm, the musical calm and routines arranged to protect the composer's need for quiet and solitude, disappeared. Highland Farm had become a hospital with a single patient and four persons— Anna, Edward, Ida, the maid who came every day from the village, and I to care for him. All the rooms that had fires for heat were made into bedchambers. The whole downstairs became one vast dormitory.

There was no place to receive anyone, and no time. Callers hoping to see the noted American composer, as they put it, were turned away. Only Dr. Holmes stopped regularly at our house on his visits to his patients outside the village. Robert's extensive correspondence with persons all over the music world ceased entirely. The letter carrier rarely came now. We laid in stores against the expected heavy snows of February and March, the horse and sled being used for such trips to the village. Already the roads had become difficult, almost impassable. Edward brought ice, water, and wood to the house every morning and evening, and shoveled paths as best he could.

Most people now alive have never known the frightening isolation of those upstate New York winters. The snow piled against the ground-floor windows and the doors, and froze there, making caves of the rooms downstairs. I remember how delighted we were on those rare occasions when the warmth of the inside fires caused small spaces to melt outside the blocked windows. Then we could glimpse the dim, thin light of wintry February mornings. All day and in the evenings, fires were lit: even so, there were very cold pockets and corners in the house. We used the upstairs as little as possible. Lamps had to be lit in the early morning and they burned all day.

In those frozen days Anna and I were, as I have said, cave dwellers, the cold outside kept at a distance by our fires and our lamps, and by the ceaseless activity of caring for Robert. Our sense of enclosure and imprisonment was part of the very air of the house.

Without Anna I could not have managed, without her gentle, strong hands (the skin on them, as on her face, was pulled tight and shone with scrubbing) around Robert, putting him into his chair in the late mornings, changing his gowns, cleansing him many times a day with the prescribed powders obtained at the pharmacy: he could no longer bear water on his skin. The sores were everywhere, on his feet and hands, on the bridge of his nose so deep the bone was exposed, on his forehead and at the nape of his neck, on his palms and the red, diseased soles of his feet. Anna patiently applied the ointments everywhere, rubbing so gently that he did not flinch at the application of her fingers. Sometimes this procedure took almost an hour in the morning and again at night.

Anna sewed a thin, long shirt of gauze cloth for Robert to wear under his nightgown. This absorbed much of the odorous mercurial oxide and made the daily launderings of his bedclothes easier for Ida. And because the inunction had to be done to Robert's most private areas, Anna devised a flannel garment to serve as underwear, a large diaper-like structure. I see him still in those garments when I remember that winter: gaunt, weak, pale, his ulcerated head almost without hair, his gauze shirt hanging upon his bony shoulders, sitting in his armchair. He looked like a toothless, ancient Byzantine saint one sometimes sees in icons awaiting martyrdom. Edward and I would lift him a little from his chair, while Anna slipped the flannel diaper under him.

Then she would start the arduous application to his furious sores—in his parts. He cried while this was being done and tried to push her away, but she held his hand and went on with her task. By noon his treatment was finished. Anna would renew his bed—with this I could be of help to her— and then we would call Edward and return him to it.

Anna and I had our luncheon, which Ida prepared, in the kitchen. At three, after I had rested and Anna had lain down to read, she said, in her New Testament or her herbals (for she had chosen the place on the Farm in which she planned to plant a garden when the spring came), the relentless process started over again: the mouth-cleaning and tongue-scraping, the cleaning up, the unctions.

I remember only a few breaks in the routine. Once I thought Robert's long tristful hours of staring ahead of him as he sat in his chair, or lay open-eyed in his bed without seeming to see, might be made more pleasant with music. I opened the door to my bed-sitting-room and began to play, I think it was a small section from Schumann's *Country Suite,* a gentle, quiet work I thought might ease his nerves.

I had just started when I heard a sound. I stopped and went into his room. His head was sunk on his chest and he was crying. "Is it the music? Don't you want to hear the music, Robert?"

He shook his head no. Another time I played, very quietly, a little from his own music, the piano transcription of the "Maiden's Song" from the *Indian Suite #2.* I have always loved the graceful, melodic curves of that piece, the way in which the tenderness of the squaw toward her dying brave is expressed in the long, slow, ascending tones, followed by the despairing fall, the descent of an octave in gradual degrees into the total grief of the low notes.

But the sound of the song unnerved him, made him cry again. Voices in other rooms had the same effect: his eyes filled with tears when he could hear them. Only silence soothed him. We took to wearing carpet slippers in the house, even Edward, to spare Robert the sounds of our footfalls.

So we existed through the months of that long winter, the heavy silence inside (except for the small, so-welcome pockets of easy talk between Anna and me), the covered-over and frozen spaces outside intensifying it. Robert's illness took its ugly, painful course, until the blessed time in the early spring when most of the terrible symptoms disappeared. But, like a country from which a plague has been lifted, he was left wasted, a shell. As his body cleared of its open sores and ulcerations, his eyes emptied and his body stiffened, becoming almost paralyzed, so that his bones seemed locked together, frozen stiff. His mouth was a black cavity, all his teeth having come out.

He no longer knew me, I am sure. He could not tell who it was, I or Anna, who fed and bathed and changed him. The vision of him as he was then is still with me: seated in his chair, his knees and shoulders covered with blankets, and on his lap the book he always wanted there, a large picture-book copy of *Mother Goose*. He would stare at the pictures for a long time, and then blink his eyelids rapidly or gesture with his fingers to let us know he wanted the page turned. Coming to the end, we would start turning the pages backward. The pages of the book became frayed and torn with our constant turning, but he never wanted another.

I saved that book. It must be downstairs someplace, perhaps in the drawing room where many of his books are still. I remember that the book often got wet, for the excessive salivation continued. Pints of saliva poured over his bottom lip, requiring constant wiping by one of us. Sometimes we were careless or too late, and Robert had drooled upon the book he so loved.

Postponed often by late freezes and icy March rains and snows, the full spring came finally to us. The windows were washed of their winter ice-grime and opened, ashes were taken from the fireplaces. Outside, bedding hung on lines to be aired of its sour winter odors in the spring sun. Everyone, Anna, Ida, Edward, and I, took heart at the warmth, at the sight of rich brown earth and the suggestion of buds on trees and bushes.

Everyone but Robert. He sat in his chair knowing nothing, suffering nothing of which we were aware (Dr. Holmes said he was experiencing no pain), unable to celebrate with us the end of the wearisome winter. For him the freeze went on: he was always cold, always shivering as he sat wrapped in shawls and blankets. Inert, silent, almost paralyzed, he became the still, inevitable hub of our household, the unmoving center of all activity, his welfare the point of or communal existence, like the statue of a deity, a Buddha.

But he was not there. The endless gowns and robes,

blankets and shawls, shirts and towels that caught his ex-
cretions (by spring he could no longer contain his urine or
his feces) and his saliva attested to his presence, but he was
not there.

During the early spring evenings, Robert in bed in the
next room, Anna and I alone in the little bed-sitting-room of
mine, we played lotto. Anna taught me the game. When we
tired of it, I taught her to play chess and dominoes and
checkers. We usually played in silence. By that time in the
evening we were both too weary for talk. I was occupied
by the rules of the game and by the thought of Robert
asleep in the next room. I didn't know what it was Anna
was thinking, her almost colorless eyes fastened on the
pieces and counters, until the evening she pushed the game
away as we finished a round and said, "Where do you think,
Mrs. Maclaren, he came into contact with it?"

So absorbed in the game had I been that I did not at
once understand her.

"Contact with what, Anna?"

"His disease. This—luetic disease."

What was this word, *luetic*? I assumed it came from
her medical training, a technical adjective.

"I don't think anyone knows. How does one contract
blood disease or diseases of the nerves like this? Dr. Keyes
did not tell me anything about that."

Anna's eyes, I noticed, seemed to darken as she turned
them, now suddenly slate-colored and fierce, upon me. "Do
you then not know what it is, how it comes?"

"No, except for what I have said, what I have been

told, about the blood, the nerves. No. I don't know what else there is. What do you mean?"

Anna breathed deeply, and then with her expelled breath she said, "Syphilis. Syphilis is what I mean. Mr. Maclaren is dying of syphilis in its final, tertiary stage. Dr. Keyes is a very famous syphilologist. That is why Dr. Holmes sent him to see Mr. Maclaren. Surely you knew."

I was aghast. Did I know? Did I suspect and refuse to let myself know? It is all so long ago now it is hard to separate what I knew or was later told, what I looked away from in my fear or was unaware of in my discreet, feminine ignorance. It has always been my way: did I closet the truth to delude myself or others? . . . But now I knew. Anna was incredulous of my innocence. She went on: "There is another thing I wish to say, now that I have said so much already. It is not only a terrible disease for him, but it can be communicated when two people—come together. Often it is—given to the other person."

My heart pounded. My hands were wet with sudden terror. "Do you think—are you saying I might have caught —his syphilis?"

"Of course, I do not know. Only a doctor can tell you that. You must be tested, examined by a doctor to find out. Sometimes the first signs are so slight you do not notice them. A small, hard sore on the side of the lip or even— I knew a man in the hospital where I trained who had a little sore at the edge of his finger, almost under the nail. That was all, the only sign."

I thought of Robert. How could he not have known earlier about himself? In time to be helped?

Anna and I had begun, unconsciously, I am sure, in those evenings and even in Robert's presence during the days, to use the masculine pronoun for him, not his name, and to refer to him in the past tense. He was the subject of all our sentences and the object of our silent, mutual concern. Our alliance began, it seems to me, not with us but with him, his needs, his past, his terrible present.

"He may have known and not said anything to anyone, not even to a doctor. You cannot tell. Or he may have requested his doctors not to speak of it."

That was how it all came out, after a game of lotto. Now I knew. There were questions still in my mind: Where did he contract it? When? From whom? Why had he not sought treatment? Did he know? Anna told me of the two stages that preceded this final one which his shame or ignorance or secrecy must have disguised and ignored. The pox, I thought. . . .

I wanted to know so much. But there could be no questions from me, and no answers from him. He was no longer there. The talented son of ambitious Virginia Maclaren, the pride of Professor Raff, the beloved American composer, the respected conductor of symphonies, and the performer of great works as well as his own distinguished compositions, my husband: brought to this by bacteria, a spirochete (as Anna told me it was called), a minuscule germ of disease put into his blood by a sick person with whom he had—lain.

[143]

It was hard for me to believe: so much, brought at the last to so little. Paralyzed and demented, there he sat through the spring and summer, always smiling gently, his eyes fixed vacantly on the picture of a cow jumping over a moon.

Part Three

AFTERLIFE

ANNA WAS a devout Catholic.
Many winter mornings it was impossible for her to get to
Mass in the village. She accepted with equanimity what she
must have regarded as a deprivation. But when the spring
thaw arrived she started out at five every morning for the
hour's walk to the church in the village. She bundled against
the cold, wore heavy overshoes, and wrapped her head,
peasant-like, in a woolen shawl. She always managed to return before Robert woke and I had barely awakened. Her
cheeks glowing from the cold wind, her eyes bright, she
told me, in that low, charming voice that always caught
my attention, that the reception of the eucharist renewed
her spirits. I remember smiling at her rhetoric and thinking,

It is as much the walk, the wind, the out-of-doors that she so loves.

At once, after returning from her three hours outside, Anna bounded about her room, airing the bedding, and then made her bed, straightening everything in the small space allotted to her. By the time I was dressed and had come into the kitchen she had changed into her gray shirtwaist dress covered with a white bib apron, the "uniform," she called it, which she always wore for work, and was breakfasting with Ida.

Sometimes I joined them, more often I ate alone in my sitting room, feeling the need to continue the foolish distance between me and those in my employ. But Anna's open, vital presence started every day for me: she was the one healthy, fresh thing in that wretched house of sickness. Her liveliness enlivened me and made bearable the relentless daily routines.

In the evenings, the arduous procedures for Robert being over, and he in his bed for the night, we sat in my little room, adjacent to his bed-drawing-room. When the games we played began to pall we often read. Now the fires were smaller. It was April and a little warmer in the house, so our evenings together lengthened appropriately: in the little room it might be described as being cozy.

Anna's reading was in the New Testament or Thomas à Kempis' *Imitation of Christ,* or sometimes in her *Gardener's Complete Herbal.* I recall I was reading *Middlemarch.* Now and again we would interrupt each other's companionable silences to read something aloud. I loved her apologetic insinuations into my attention, the sound of her soft voice with its light echoes of her beginnings in the formalities of the German tongue. I learned she was particularly fond of old wives' wisdom about the weather, about growing things. "In the Decay of the Moon," she read aloud, "a Cloudy morning bodes a fair Afternoon."

I always laughed at these ancient superstitions, but she was very firm, very serious about them. "You will see. Frau Mundlein who raised me taught me these things. When our garden flourishes in the summer, they will be proven. You will see."

I in turn pursued the history of Dorothea Brooke, reading aloud to Anna the wonderful passage on her visit to Rome:

Our moods are apt to bring with them images which succeed each other like the magic-lantern pictures of a doze; and in certain states of dull forlornness Dorothea all her life continued to see the vastness of St. Peter's, the huge bronze canopy, the excited intention in the attitudes and garments of the prophets and evangelists in the mosaic above, and the red drapery which was being hung for Christmas spreading itself everywhere like a disease of the retina.

It grew later, the lamps burned low. It was almost ten o'clock. Anna countered my rolling literary sentences with her stepmother's wisdom about the best state in which to plant turnip seeds. "How?" I asked.

"You should be unclothed."

"Unclothed? Why ever so?"

I thought she smiled, her brief, quickly erased, charm-ing smile, but I could not be sure.

"It is quite sensible. If it is warm enough to be without any clothes it is then warm enough for the seed to be sown. I have heard it said that in one English county farmers sit naked upon the ground to plant their barley. This must be the same kind of test, don't you think?"

Naked. It was a word I had seldom heard spoken aloud in those days, let alone acted upon. Even my own body I rarely saw without clothes, for I was accustomed to dropping my nightgown over my loosened stays and chemise before removing them, from habit, I suppose, because my mother had shown me how the act was properly performed.

But when my gentle friend Anna said *naked,* I had a startling, unaccustomed vision: of *her,* stripped of her gray shirtwaist dress, her pointed black leather high shoes, her gray stockings—everything. In a manner I do not believe I ever thought possible for one woman to want of another, I wanted to see her so, *naked,* to see her breasts I could only sense from their deceptively bound contours under her dress. For in those days women were beginning to bind themselves as flat as possible if they were especially full in that area. Immediately I suppressed this desire, put it away from me, telling myself my emotion was curiosity. It had been so long since I had been close to live flesh. Like a child, I thought, I miss being held, warmed, comforted, and touched by the softness of another. This need, for a woman, I could in no way comprehend. Yet it was there, in that curious moment.

But always, the living-dead existence of Robert ruled every hour of my life. I felt the weight of emptiness at the center of my being that nothing and no one had filled— since when? When had the small spark of passion left to me from my girlhood, the reaching out, which I suppose is what passion is, died in me who had hoped so ardently for so much in life? I had placed my emotional faith in music, in love, in the handsome young composer who walked with me in Boston Common. When did it all disappear? When had love died in my marriage and the long loneliness begun? In Virginia Maclaren's cold, dark-paneled rooms in Frank-furt? In that practice room in the Hoch Conservatory of Music? In my surreptitious reading of Churchill Weeks's love letters from Germany? Somewhere. Because it *was* dead, or absent, or dormant, until the moment Anna Baehr said *naked* one evening and stirred in my heart a vision, a strange, ineffable hope.

After Edward plowed the garden for her, Anna did her planting. It was all accomplished according to her eclectic learning. At one end of the plot was an old stone wall. Against it she planted fruit trees, which she said might be espaliered some day when they were larger. Around the base of each newly planted tree she wound strands of horsehair, obtained from the track stables down the road from us. She lectured to me: "Out of season is when one must obtain them. The hairs are in great demand by upholsterers for sofas and chairs."

I was dubious about the efficacy of horsehair. My doubts
met with Anna's usual, serious conviction: "Believe me. It
will keep earwigs, slugs, and snails from the trees, because
as they go up the stems from the ground they must pass
over the points on the sharp hair. They will be mortally
wounded." I shuddered at the prospect of a border covered
with sick and dying insects. Anna smiled. "You will not
notice. Quickly their carcasses become part of the useful
soil."

In late April she waited, she said, for the waxing moon
in order to plant the vegetable seeds. "Why?" I wanted to
know. She was somewhat vague about her reasons but con
vinced it had to be so, that in the periods of a new moon
there is likely to be more rain. So, oddly enough, it happened.
It rained every other day until the first sprouts appeared.
She seemed pleased and smiled indulgently at my surprise.

One morning while we were changing Robert's great
bed I noticed that the small bun she had always worn at
the top of her head was gone, the ends of her long hair
being held in place with large combs.

"Have you been cutting your hair?"

"Well, yes. I needed it. This week I will be planting
beans."

"Oh?"

"Yes. If you place human hair in the trench you have
dug for the seeds it makes the bean stalks strong and tall."

These were the natural oddities, the lore I came to
accept as truth. I learned from Anna that ordinary refuse
was to be cherished and used. She saved banana skins to be

placed beneath the surface of the soil around our lilacs, which then, I must report, later flourished and bore flowers as never before in any year. Our tea leaves nourished the three climbing rose bushes at the side of the house. And stranger still: Robert's now unworn and outworn leather boots she would not allow me to put into the dustbin. I was permitted to throw away only the rubber soles and heels. "These you can have back. I will bury the uppers in the far end of the garden. When they rot they will enrich the soil."

The garden flourished as Robert declined. By summer all the flesh was gone from his bones. Now he was inert and almost always asleep, and caring for him was somewhat easier. Except to remain beside him when occasionally he awakened, and the thrice-daily changing of his bed linen, there was little we could do for him. He could not eat. He lay still, like a stone, in the center of that great bed, a burden for Edward to lift so that Anna and I could roll clean sheets under him. Even his opened eyes seemed fixed, staring, paralyzed in their sockets. His scanty hair had turned completely white. "Only his heart," said Dr. Holmes, who now came almost daily, "keeps him alive. It cannot be long now."

On August 31, 1906, in the cool of the late afternoon, while Anna weeded in her garden and I dozed in my chair beside him, he died. He made no sound, there was no rattle of protest in his throat, no gesture of his hand seeking help. He died in his sleep, the newspaper reports said. But his sleep had been almost a year long: he had died long before. On that afternoon in August his heart stopped.

Anna discovered it when she came in from the garden,

smelling of the tomato vines she had been tying up with scraps of our silk stockings. She woke me gently, pointing to the still form.

"He is—gone. You must send for Dr. Holmes. To certify."

She knelt down at the side of the bed, crossed herself, and dropped her head in her hands. For the first time in my life I too knelt. I tried to pray for Robert, to say the childhood words to God that my mother had taught me: *hallowed be Thy name . . . Thy will be done . . . and forgive us . . . and lead us not into temptation. . . .* But nothing more than this rote would come, for (I feel I must now be honest) I could feel nothing as I looked at the still, white face of my poor husband but pity for his lost life, for his meager remains. And when I began to feel something, I realized it was pleasure at the closeness, the sun-warmed heat of Anna's soft skin, her arm against mine as we knelt together, the joy at being, for the first time in so long, adjacent to a glowing life.

I watched her as her lips moved. She had taken from her pocket a string of wooden beads. At that moment I wanted very much to be able to join in her worship, to find the proper words to say with her, to be united in her devotions. . . . It was impossible for me. The deep emotional freeze in which I had lived for so long, the ice age of my heart, would take a long time to melt, even beside the glowing flesh and warm heart of Anna Baehr.

From where I knelt I could see, out of the long window of the drawing room, the edge of one of the climbing

rose bushes. I thought irreverently, I remember, how effica-
cious the tea leaves had been. The bush was bursting with
flowers which crowded each other against the panes of the
french door.

The funeral was simple, but still rather grand because of
the persons who came, so many eminent people from the
world of music. Many walked up from the village, and
others came long distances by motor and by train from New
York, from Albany, and from as far away as Philadelphia
and Washington. My old friend Elizabeth Pettigrew, now
married, whom I hadn't seen in many years although we often
corresponded with each other, traveled from Boston.

Robert was laid out in the music room, dressed in his
old performance jacket with brown velvet lapels which he
had not worn in a long time. The funeral service was conducted in our drawing room, now restored to its former
appearance, by the Reverend Edmund Whitehall, an Epis-
copal minister from Saratoga Springs, who had not known
my husband at all. Robert was strongly opposed to all
churches, even refused commissions to write liturgical music,
and would not have been happy with these high-church
arrangements. But Father Whitehall had offered his services
out of his long admiration, he claimed, for Robert's music,
so I accepted his church's established service.

We had to send for dozens of camp chairs from the
Grand Union Hotel to seat all the persons who came. The
whole downstairs of the house was filled. Those at the

greatest distance from the drawing room must have found it hard to hear the eulogy Father Whitehall delivered, but it was as well.

He had concocted it from newspaper clippings and a biographical article in the *Musical Courier*. I remember only a little of it—it went on very long—but I recall he reminded us of Rollo Walter Brown's phrase for Robert, "a listener to the winds." He said that Robert had composed the greatest piano sonatas since Beethoven, that others had called him the equal to Grieg, and that, like Grieg, he was a miniaturist of great scope. He quoted to us Robert's remark: "I never listen to other people's music for fear of being influenced by it." This the Reverend took to be a sign of Robert's great originality. He expanded upon it at some length.

Anna and I sat on chairs close to Robert's bier. We had been designated, together with Robert's brothers, Burns and Logan, the chief mourners. We both wore black dresses, and the brothers had wide black armbands sewn to their gray suits. What, who were they mourning? I wondered. They had not seen or communicated with Robert in years.

Everyone told me they admired the way I bore my grief. "My dear Mrs. Maclaren," said the Reverend, "you are holding up so well." I felt saddened, but it was buried. It was there, down beyond the display of tears. I mourned my wasted life in Robert's service, I grieved for his long absence from my conscious life, and mine, I think, from his. Only the curious unbidden thought of Miss Milly Martino at one point near the end of the service brought tears to my eyes. For what reason? I could not tell.

Perhaps thinking I was about to break down, Anna put her hand over mine. I grasped it tight and held it during the Reverend's long prayers, his last flights of fancy as he painted the dead composer in the image of a Parnassian god. I held her hand, thinking of the frightened, sick, troubled man in whose poisoned bloodstream spirochetes had raced like demented ants.

On foot we followed the casket, which was mounted, as Paderewski's had been, on the board of the farm wagon, to the spot Robert had designated. Anna had found his instructions for burial in his desk—have I written this already? Edward climbed down, stiff and sad-faced, self-important in his best clothes, and helped the three undertaker's men lower the casket into the grave. My mind was not in control that day. I was at the mercy of sudden irreverencies. At one moment, for no reason, I wondered if anyone had thought to line the grave with human hair in order to promote luxuriant immortality.

I took Anna's arm for protection against my fancies. We walked back down the road with Ida and Catherine Weeks, somewhat ahead of the others so we could see to the luncheon. It was all over: his short life, his long dying, the end of so much that began in promise, came to short fame, and ended in premature decay, long before death. As we entered the house, for the first time without Robert as its central inhabitant, I felt desolate, lost, in the way he must have meant when he said "Lost" to me, that time after Della Fox. Without him, the hub of my empty life, what would become of me? of the Farm?

First to leave were the relatives, and then Elizabeth, who had to return to her husband. As soon as the luncheon was over, the Maclaren brothers bowed stiffly, said a few polite words to me—after all, I could expect no more; we had not seen each other since my wedding—and took their leave. But the Weekses stayed on with us for a few days. Churchill was quite tired out by his long summer of teaching just concluded, by the trip to Saratoga Springs, and by his profound grief: he cried throughout the service, clinging to Catherine's arm. He touched Robert's hand just before the coffin was closed and murmured, "Good laddie." For two days afterward he stayed in bed, Anna and Ida preparing him special invalid foods. I took him his meals on a tray while Catherine visited the baths. We were all still in practice for invalidism. It seemed quite natural to be caring for someone.

"There are wonderful, healthful baths there," Catherine told us upon her return one late afternoon. "I think Churchill would benefit from them. The waters are warm and full of minerals—sulfur, I think, which the attendant at the Ladies' Bath says is beneficial for skin irritations."

"Does Mr. Weeks suffer from a dermatitis?" Anna asked politely in her professional voice.

"My, yes. Just recently he has recovered from a very

severe rash, everywhere, but mainly on his back. And the treatment was terrible, almost worse than the rash. But the doctor insisted on it."

"Treatment?" I asked, finding myself listening to Catherine for the first time. Often in the past I was able only to make an effort to appear to be listening to her cheerless, ill-tempered conversation. Now she seemed to be taking pleasure in the details of Churchill's affliction.

"Yes, he went daily for almost a month to the doctor's office. Often I came with him and waited while he had his treatment. Once I went in with him. I watched while he sat bare to the waist astride a special chair, his breast pressed against its back. An attendant squeezed a blue ointment from a large capsule onto his back and rubbed hard with his two hands, for almost half an hour. So hard that at times the pustules would break and spew out a yellow pus all over his hands. Church was not permitted to wash the terrible ointment off. He put over it a gauze shirt to wear under his clothes. Next morning he had to return to have a mercurial bath in a tin-lined tub, and then a hard alcohol rubbing, and then the treatment all over again.

"It was a terrible ordeal for him. It went on for weeks, every day, even Saturday and Sunday. Now of course he is somewhat better, so I am wondering if these baths might not benefit him. I should ask Dr. Keyes."

"They would not," said Anna curtly. "He should not go to the baths here. He may communicate his illness to others. I knew of a patient who abandoned such treatment because it was so unpleasant in order to travel to the Hot Springs in Arkansas, but it did him no good. It was very wrong of him to interrupt the treatment."

Catherine seemed impatient at Anna's interruption of her triumphant (or so it seemed to me) recital of Churchill's symptoms and treatment. She told us no more, and next day they departed. Church seemed very quiet and depressed, by Robert's death, I supposed. His two days in bed had left him weak and shaky on his feet. He said he dreaded the prospect of another difficult year of teaching.

The house was quiet, almost eerily calm that evening as Anna and I sat in the drawing room, once again restored to its old appearance. We played lotto for the first time in many weeks. My mind, however, was not on the game, being full of questions: "What do you think, Anna, about . . ."

"About Mr. Weeks's rash?"

"Yes."

"Only a doctor would know properly." She was short, not wanting to talk, I thought, perhaps because she liked to win at these games and was distracted by my interruptions. "I cannot really say."

"But, the mercury . . . I remember some years ago, a similar rash that Robert . . . Could it be?"

"It could be another thing. One can never tell from a story."

"But Dr. Keyes. You said he was a physician only for . . ."

"Well, yes. Dr. Keyes. That, of course, is something."

Alone in my room, on the following evening, I wrote a letter. I did not sit with Anna, as usual, because I was writing to her and because of the disturbing nature of what I had decided to ask her:

My dearest Anna:

When you took my hand during the service for Robert, I knew. I do not understand how I knew, or what it is I now want. I think it is this: to combine what remains of my life with yours, if you are willing, to spend our time together in the understanding, the peace, the easy conversation, the companionship we have already shared to some extent. My feelings for you are confusing to me. I do not understand what it is I am feeling, or even what it is precisely that I desire. I had thought my life would be almost over when Robert died. Now I see it was over long before, in one sense. For suddenly I have had a vision of an afterlife for me, for us, where we will nourish and sustain and, yes, love each other, in a new way. We are bound together now in sympathy for each other. Will you stay with me?

Thine,
Carrie

I never gave her this letter. I kept it among my papers, and I put it here, in this record, to allow it to speak for itself. Immediately afterward I wrote a second one:

Dear Anna:

This is a large house, and there is much to do in it. You

have made such a fine garden, you have been so good to Robert and me, that I have thought to ask you now: would you be willing to stay on, not as nurse or housekeeper, but as companion and friend to me?

Caroline Maclaren

Anna stayed. She didn't respond to me in words but simply went on with her constant helping, her activity in the house and in the garden, her gentle listening, and her comfortable talk. Her lissome, fine-boned, full-fleshed body hidden under the heavy dress and apron, she spent much time in the kitchen preserving the excess from the abundant garden harvest.

The time came to clear away the dead garden matter and to cover the area with leaves and bracken. In October Anna prepared the bushes for the onslaught of winter ice by wrapping them in coverlets of hemp cordage. Early each evening she would leave the house carrying two heavy watering pots: "It is necessary to spray cold water on the perennials and the bushes when there is a chance of frost. So that heat will be created by evaporation. This prevents frost-freezing."

My days and evenings were spent responding to the hundreds of letters of sympathy sent to me. Among the first letters to arrive was one from Henry Huddleston Rogers on stationery that informed me he was vice-president of the Standard Oil Company. He had been in touch with Robert ever since the accident with Paderewski. He wrote now that he wished to do something in Robert's memory: "What would you suggest?" Many other letters came that posed the same question.

I began to give serious thought to some kind of memorial for Robert. There was very little I could do alone, the taxes and the mortgage remaining on the Farm being almost more than I could pay at the moment out of my meager widow's money in the bank. Late that fall, I asked my faithful friend Lester Lenox of the bank in Saratoga who had helped us when we wished to buy the Farm to come for afternoon tea. I also invited a lawyer I knew in the village, Alfred de Wolfe, my longtime acquaintance Anne Rhinelander (who was good enough to come up from New York for the occasion) and Emily Chisolm, who traveled with her from New York, and of course my old friend Sarah Watkins.

I had written to Churchill, thinking that he, too, would wish to be part of the decision about a memorial. In return I had a short note from Catherine: "Churchill is ailing again. He is confined to his bed, has a high fever, and is at times incoherent. Tomorrow there is to be a consultation among our doctors to determine the treatment." She could not tell me the exact nature of his illness, as yet, but she had been informed by one physician that it was a variety of blood disorder, severe but curable.

We six, and Anna, met in the drawing room. I showed them the letters I had just finished responding to, pointing out how many had expressed a desire to do something. "What do you think should be done?" I asked.

Many possibilities were suggested: the award of a

medal in Robert's name each year to a composer of great promise, a national competition for a scholarship to a European conservatory, the endowment of a chair of music at a university. It was Lester, as I recall, who first offered the idea of a foundation to establish a summer community for musicians and composers.

"I have given this idea much thought," he said. "It would be fitting, very fitting indeed, to honor his memory in this way. Also, while we are raising the funds to prepare accommodations for the young composers who would come to the Farm, it may be possible, at the same time, to find funds to pay off the remaining mortgage on the Farm. So Mrs. Maclaren's security, too, would be assured. And the memorial will be established for the young and promising. Of course, the village of Saratoga Springs will benefit from it as well."

Mr. de Wolfe was enthusiastic: "By all means. I am so tired of our town being spoken of always as a gambling place or a racing center—or worse. A community for musicians on the outskirts would be a great improvement."

There was general agreement about the advisability of the plan. So it came to be. Those present became officers and members of the Maclaren Foundation, to be so listed in the charter. All but Anna, who said she would help in any ways she could, but she did not wish to be "listed." Entirely fearless in the presence of slugs, snails, spiders, earwigs, and aphids, and in her encounters with snows and rough winds, she had no self-assurance or courage in a gathering such as this. I think Mr. de Wolfe and some of the others may have been relieved at her retiring nature, not knowing quite what to make of her presence, of my insistence that she be part of the plan. To them she was a nurse, a companion, now inexplicably raised to equality with her mistress and employer. But not to me.

This is the time to place in this account an explanation of what Anna Baehr was to me. If it is distasteful to the Foundation officers who will read this, it can always be deleted. Nowadays a relationship such as Anna and I had may be openly declared. Women who love as we loved are called freely by the name of the isle inhabited by the Greek poetess. They walk hand in hand, I am told, in daylight through the streets of the city and proclaim their sexual preferences in public.

In my time—that is to say, in my middle years, in the afterlife I was fortunate enough to be granted by a compassionate and broad-minded Deity—such choices were hidden under the discretion of conventional appearances. We made no public announcement of what was, after all, a private intention. Nor was there any need for ostentation. The world would not have sanctioned it nor, or that matter, believed it of me.

Nor would an open admission have made one whit of difference to what *was*. We were two women of disparate class, living together in a farmhouse on the outskirts of a small village. We were disguised by my condition: marriage and widowhood, and by what came to be regarded as my mission, my work, assisted by Anna, on behalf of the memory of my husband and her patient, Robert Glencoe Maclaren.

If there was irony in this it was not seen by anyone but me. It must never have occurred to anyone that my intense determination to establish a memorial to him was in inverse proportion to the love that had been lost between us. Often I puzzled over this. Then I came to see that I had devoted myself to his public image, his music, not to his person as I knew it. I came to understand my activity.

But this strays from what I wanted to say about my profound love for Anna Baehr. During that first winter we were alone together in the house. Ida had to be let go because I could not afford to keep her, and Edward came only irregularly to do the outside chores. Anna and I did everything together. I wooed her quietly (yes, *wooed* is the word, there is no other accurate one), hoping to find in her something of the passion I felt, not knowing if I might frighten her, as indeed I myself was frightened, by my advances.

Our compatibility was very great; we talked often and of everything, together. But I soon knew that was not enough for me. I must be frank in this, and it is difficult. My fantasy, my vision of Anna and me together ended in the great bed. I wanted to sleep with Anna in my arms, to be held in her arms in Virginia Maclaren's bed, the bed in which Virginia Maclaren had slept with her son, the bed of her son's long death, the one I now so insufficiently occupied alone. I wanted to renew those old, soft linen sheets—with what? I was not sure what I would do, what we could do. I wished only for Anna's closeness, her warmth, her womanly presence and fullness, the touch of her soft skin against my small, thin, cold bones, in the center of my enormous bed.

My suit went no further than the tenderness of my first tentative steps: my fingers on the nape of her neck when she came in from her tiring physical labor in the garden and complained of a little stiffness. The gratifying feeling of her muscles relaxing, her shy smile of gratitude when I had finished. My kiss on her cheek as we said good night and went to our rooms. And after a while, her return of my kiss, her warm lips on mine.

Then all at once, I needed to go no further, there were to be no other trials. One night as we kissed good night she moved close to me, reached to my bony shoulders with her strong hands, and pressed me to her. I felt no surprise, no awkwardness. There was no spoken prelude to that night, and no verbal aftermath. It was understood: we no longer went to our separate beds.

To tell you what we had together that night, and during all the nights and the days that filled the next twelve years: how difficult it is to find words to hold it all, to capture the quality of close, understanding comradeship, to place inexpressible love into public phrases. I find I think most readily in images. But then I realize how one-sided are these images of mine. I could not tell at the time, do not still know, if Anna would have used the same ones, or any at all. She was not given to figurative language.

I think of the first, soft spring rain: she was moisture to my dried roots. I think of the way a certain configuration of notes played on the flute, alone, above the muted sounds of a symphony orchestra, can bring tears to one's eyes. Anna was those things for me. I had known "life" before that night, known what it was to be alive and to be aware of the horrors, too often, happening around me. I knew that life had substance without possessing any of it myself. I realized my own body not as a subject but as an object. Because of Anna I began to know it intimately, because she had touched me, given me knowledge of myself, with her loving hands.

Anna was a quiet woman. Words, especially abstract words like *love* and *happiness,* came hard to her. She never explained her feelings, rarely even mentioned them. Only her hands betrayed the humanity that burned in her. I knew what she felt when she touched me in places of my body to which I had always been indifferent, had known about only theoretically.

I remember one very cold night when we sat as close as possible to the fireplace. The fire burned high and hard, but it still did not seem to warm the rest of the sitting room. Anna said it might be better on the floor. So we gathered our skirts about our legs and lowered ourselves to the hearth, making cushions under us of our petticoats and skirts.

Suddenly I was very warm. I felt the heat invading my neck, my ears and armpits, almost piercing my skin. Anna must have felt as warm as I. She reached behind her neck and opened the little buttons that formed a long line down her back. I watched, marveling at her dexterity: usually we did each other's buttons. I wondered how she would manage those at the broad place of her back. She did. Then she reached to her shoulders and pulled her dress and the chemise beneath it to her waist, baring her full breasts, pale as snow. I wanted to touch them, to feel their extraordinary softness and warmth, but I waited. Her hands lifted her breasts toward me, I bent toward her and put my face down into their center. She took my head and held it there. I breathed the sweet warm odor of her skin, her glowing smoky flesh heated by the proximity of the fire.

It was enough, it was more than enough to compel us to our room upstairs, to the bed to which we climbed each night. Dousing the fire, we went upstairs. It was odd: for one of us to remove her dress, as Anna had done, was enough for us both. A single act represented two. The sensual pleasure we shared resulted, I have often thought, from the guesses we had made about ourselves and the answers we found in each other. Now I knew another like myself. My suppositions were confirmed.

I had discovered a strange thing about our love: when I held my breasts, thin and unsubstantial as they were, I was reminded of Anna's. I was touching her, re-creating the pleasures of contact with her on myself. To my inadequate self I assumed her lovely flesh. It was the very opposite of narcissism—it was metamorphosis.

I remember another time: in the early spring we were planting together, at the sunny side of the house, a place Anna had decided would be right for a wisteria vine. "It

[169]

will grow over the edge of the porch in time and make a cool place to sit." The roots of the little plant were tangled. On our knees we both reached into the shallow hole to disengage them. Our fingers came together around the stem. We looked up and smiled at each other, holding hands in the fragrant soil surrounding the young roots of the wisteria vine. In such silent but telling ways Anna spoke to me. She used gestures, sudden affectionate motions that were both symbolic and at the same time concretely warm: these came easily to her.

To me, the world we had discovered together at first seemed strangely unreal. My long education in connubial behavior before Anna had been so different. Between us there was no flirtatiousness, as there is so often in the world of men and women. We had no struggle for dominance, we experienced no submissiveness. We were each dominant and each submissive when we needed to be. Sometimes I took her in my arms, sensing her need for comfort. At other times I wished to be held, helped, comforted.

One wet fall day, I remember, I was taken by a very bad attack of lumbago, as it was then called, while kneeling on the damp ground to plant bulbs. The pain struck so quickly that I could not stand erect. Anna helped me into the house. I hurt so badly, I was a child again. How long it had been since anyone handled my body so carefully, so tenderly. She rubbed ointment into my spine, her gentle, capable hands full of remedy and assurance. I lay in bed, still sore and very tired. She sat beside me on the bed. "You are a born nurse," I said.

"Oh no," she said. "I was not born a nurse. It happened, my decision to be a nurse, after my sister got ill, a long time ago. My mother was gone then, and we were living with Frau Mundlein. She was very kind, kinder to us than I can remember my mother to have been. Sometimes I think she might have been . . . somewhat closer to us, but she was afraid, she once told me. Our mother might return and take us away and then she would feel a deprivation. She never kissed me or took me into her arms, and she kissed Rosa only once that I remember.

"Every day Rosa and I watched the post for word from our mother in Germany. One person on our street had a telephone, but Frau Mundlein did not. So we were able to tell ourselves that our mother called us often from across the waters but without an instrument there was no way for receiving her calls. We did not understand she was too far away to use such an instrument. Letters came frequently to Frau Mundlein containing money for our support. Frau Mundlein always read to us the sentence: 'Tell the girls I shall see them soon.'

"Rosa was very small for her age, very thin and pale. She was often sick and she recovered very slowly. I was in perfect health and never missed a day of school. Poor Rosa went to school very seldom. Frau Mundlein worked six days every week sewing shirtwaists in a factory near the East River. Often Rosa was alone in the house during the day, nursing her sore throat and the aches in her legs.

"Because of that I did not realize how sick she was when the diphtheria was in the city. Rosa was feverish and said her throat hurt her. She stayed in bed. When Frau Mundlein came home she made soup and milk toast for Rosa. That was all Rosa was able to swallow. I would get up in the night when she stirred in the bed beside me to get her water. She was always thirsty.

"But when she got very sick Frau Mundlein sent me to ask the doctor to come. We waited for him. It was two days before he climbed the stairs to our flat. He told Frau Mundlein angrily, 'There are sick people all over Yorkville.' He could not see them all when they wanted him.

"The doctor examined Rosa for a short time (I thought) and then came out of our room and told Frau Mundlein that Rosa had diphtheria. He gave her some white papers of medicine and said, 'Give her orange juice and weak tea.' He waited. Frau Mundlein said she would pay him next time. 'I'll come again tomorrow,' he said, but he didn't come, not until it was too late and Rosa was dead.

"People were dying of the disease, I knew, and from the time I heard that was what poor Rosa had, I was frightened. It was shameful, I still feel a hot shame, for I was frightened, not for her, but for me. I was afraid to go into our room. I did not want to catch the sickness. So I slept on the sofa in the parlor. I put my head under the blanket when I heard her call in the night. Frau Mundlein got up to get Rosa water.

"Even when she called, 'Anna,' that last morning, my heart beat so fast from fear that I could not answer or go in to see her. I was afraid to look on suffering. I was afraid I would see death as it came, I was afraid of being sick and dying myself, I was afraid of everything. I could not bring myself to be near her.

"Frau Mundlein stayed home from work the day Rosa's fever went very high. She told me not to go to school and instead to fetch the doctor. I went gladly. He said, 'I will come when I can. New York is full of sick people.' I remember still, to my shame, that I walked very slowly away from his office. I looked in store windows. I sat on a bench in front of a cigar store and studied a painted wooden Indian with his raised arm, his fingers holding a tomahawk. I spent long minutes at the glass counter of the newspaper store on the corner deciding to buy a rope of licorice with the penny I had. I thought of visiting a friend who lived around the corner and then remembered she would be in school.

"All this time my heart was pounding, my lips were dry, my tight fists were wet. I was mortally afraid. I did not want to go back home to see the dying and to be there when it came.

"And so I wasn't. When I got home Frau Mundlein was sitting in the parlor, holding a handkerchief. Her face was red and wet. 'She is dead,' she said and cried. And I? I am ashamed to say, I was flooded with relief that I had not seen it. Afterward, yes, I felt sorrow for my sister, my companion and friend. And pity for her, and terrible guilt at my cowardice.

"The doctor came and wrote out a paper and gave it to Frau Mundlein. Again he waited. Frau Mundlein gave him two dollars. Two men came for Rosa with a stretcher.

I stood in the doorway, watching them lift her from our bed. Before they covered her with a sheet, Frau Mundlein leaned over and kissed her on the lips.

"It is the way I remember Rosa most clearly now: lying on the stretcher, her eyes closed, her small nose pinched in and blue, great black patches on her cheeks and her chin. And Frau Mundlein bending over to kiss her. I have never put the sight of it away, nor the guilty ache I was left with. The memory of me, huddled against the frame of the door, afraid, lingering at the store, always afraid.

"In high school I took science subjects so I could go on to a nursing school. I would not be afraid again, I thought. I would learn what to do for the sick and acquire courage so that in all my life I would not run away at the prospect of suffering and pain. Even if I could not stop it, I would learn to stay with it, to help, to be with the sufferer, as I had not been able to be with my sister."

The work of the Foundation went along very well in the ten years that followed, as the press and the public who have been informed of these matters know. Mrs. Rhinelander conceived of the idea of the Maclaren Clubs, somewhat like the Mendelssohn Clubs, all over the country. I, and others in the Foundation, traveled to all parts of the nation helping to establish these clubs. The plan was this: once a month members of the club would come together for the performance of American music by American musicians, and the proceeds, after expenses and fees, would come to the Community's scholarship and building funds.

I traveled much in those years, accompanied always by Anna. On occasion I played some of Robert's piano music, but more often I spoke to groups of interested men and women about his compositions and his life as a student, a conductor and composer. I became proficient in my omissions, after a while not even considering that I was promulgating an authorized version of his life in which only the surface detail bore any resemblance to reality. I was, however, entirely successful in my apostolate: articles and books, encyclopedia entries, and histories of music and musicians have accepted and made permanent, and still retain, my descriptions. Only here, now, when Robert's name and music have fallen out of the public memory and are known only to a few dusty scholars, do I fill in the blanks I left in those speeches to raise money in his memory.

The sums donated to our enterprise astounded me: one and one-half million dollars in the first three years, beginning with a most generous sum from Mr. Rogers, another from Dr. Butler and the members of the Columbia University department of music. All of Robert's acquaintances, the doctors who treated him, musicians in the orchestras he had conducted, the publishers of his music, even dear Reverend Whitehall, who had become my good friend, all sent postal orders or checks. Young men and women who had studied his piano pieces when they were learning to play, as well as eminent persons all over the musical world: it was most gratifying. With those first years' contributions we were able to secure the future of the Farm by paying the bank what was owed on the mortgage and to begin to build the six studios in the woods we had planned to house our young resident musicians.

By the spring of 1911, I think it was, they were ready for occupancy. I wrote to persons I knew in the universities who taught music (not so frequent a thing as it is now) asking for the names of promising young persons who might want to work at the Maclaren Community, as it was formally titled in our chartered papers. One of these letters went to Churchill at Columbia. It was some time before I had an answer, and then it was not from Church but from the chairman of his department. I include the letter in this account for purposes of completeness:

Dear Mrs. Maclaren:

I took the perhaps unwarranted liberty of opening your letter to Professor Weeks because his widow, to whom it should rightfully have been forwarded, has returned to her home in Milwaukee, where she has again taken up abode. We are not in possession of her address there.

The sad facts are these: Professor Weeks died last summer after a long illness. He had left the faculty during the spring semester before, suffering from a long series of afflictions, to the liver, to the skin, and finally, I must tell you, to his mental faculties. Regrettably, we were forced to ask for his resignation. Mrs. Weeks much resented our decision. She appeared before the department committee in June to protest, claiming with some heat that her husband was only

temporarily ill and would be well in time for the opening
of the fall semester. The doctors, she insisted, had assured
them of this.

It was our feeling, after observing Professor Weeks's
rapidly deteriorating condition during his last term of teach-
ing, that this would be impossible. Indeed, this judgment
was, sadly, borne out: he died during the summer that fol-
lowed from a heart attack, Mrs. Weeks reported to us.

I hope you will permit me and my colleagues to send
our regrets to you, knowing of your late, esteemed husband's
long friendship with Professor Weeks. Finally, I wish to say
I am sorry to have been the one to convey this news to you.
Apparently, Mrs. Weeks, in her grief, must have neglected
to do so, and you must not have seen the short but respectful
obituary printed in The New York Times.

> *I am yr. most obedient servant*
> *Lawrence Vandersee*
> *Chairman, Department of Music*
> *Columbia University*

I tried to find Catherine's address in Milwaukee, without
success. I wanted to send her condolences. Not finding her,
I had no place to mail my note. I have never heard from her
and do not know if she is still alive.

Anna and I devised a routine for our six summer visitors to
follow. They arrived in late May and remained, if they

found the Community congenial, until early October. At first only male composers came to us. A few of them, oddly, found the life at the Community very hard. They were the gregarious fellows who could not withstand the long hours of enforced solitude. Our rules required that the days from early morning until evening must be reserved for creative work in the studios, alone. Some disliked the communal outhouse, which was cold at night and often inhabited by annoyances like spiders and mosquitoes. A few resented our communal approach to meals and other household chores. One man felt the lack of electric light in the studios was old-fashioned. We had hired a very good cook who came in midafternoon and stayed until dinner was prepared. So the clearing and washing after dinner was done by all of us together, to the dismay of a few of the young men whose talents had protected them thus far from close contact with domestic chores.

Professor Vandersee had enclosed with his letter a list of three names, graduates in composition now living precariously in New York, whom he recommended highly to me. One of them, a former student of Churchill's named Eric Anderson, was accepted for the first year.

Anderson was to prove our most faithful applicant and returnee. He was older than the others, in his late twenties when he started his attendance at the Farm, and had studied abroad as well as at Columbia University. He proved pleasant, willing, and surprisingly without the usual difficult temperament. His quietness was always welcome in the evenings, a little landing of silence in the midst of the general turbulence, the vocal excesses of the other, sometimes very arrogant, young men at our supper table. Anna and I were always glad when he applied to return for a summer and when the admissions committee, made up of established critics and composers, accepted him. Sometimes he played for us all in the evenings. The influence upon him of Robert Maclaren's music was evident: it was as though he had taken in from the air around him Robert's love of incorporating natural sounds in his melodies, his fondness for program pieces, his modest tunes and thin, delicate orchestrations. By the time the Great War began in Europe, Eric had become an expected part of our summer household as no other Community member ever was.

I can see him now, his six-foot-six frame bent over the piano keys, the lamp making his long blond hair, parted neatly in the center and reaching to his shoulders, even lighter, his huge hands wholly occupying the keyboard. He played Liszt with a kind of massive authority. He had his native country's light blue eyes. There was only one blemish to his blond handsomeness: a red mark, thin and salamander-shaped, which lay over his light skin from his eye to the corner of his mouth. Often he would sit with his hand over the mark, leaning on his elbow as he ate or listened to music. When he played, however, the scar darkened, although he seemed at those times to have forgotten it. The younger men called him the Quiet Swede. They appeared to resent his unusual reticence in the midst of all their racket and boisterous talk.

At the end of the summer of '15 we knew the war was

close to us. That fall we had fewer applications for the next year. Many of the possible candidates, I suppose, were expecting to be called away to the army. But in May '16 Eric came with three others and we settled into a quiet summer before the inevitable turmoil of war.

I never knew quite why—it may have been the remnants of Europe that still lingered in Anna's speech and manners —but Eric found it possible to talk to Anna and to no one else. One night as she and I were in bed she told me he had said two periods of his life had been spent in sanatoria for the insane: once in Sweden when he was in *gymnasium* and again in New Haven, Connecticut, while he was studying music in New York. His illness was depression. When it came upon him he could not play or write or eat or move from his bed or his chair. The first time he had to be carried to the hospital and kept there for a year until gradually it wore away. "I am well now. It is six years since . . . I have been working very well since . . . that last time."

Only in Anna did he confide, as I have said. But even to her he would not say anything about his parents. "He is a solitary man," Anna told me, "who can not bring himself to talk about himself. He lives alone because he has lost his confidence that anyone else would accept his history or trust his present and future." But at the Farm his way of listening intently to the others made him accepted, especially, I had noticed, by Anna, who favored him when she served portions in the kitchen at supper. She always provided his lunch basket with extra fruit and the sweets he loved.

During the first week of October we held our customary party to bid the young men good-bye. The visitors brought the wine and we provided sandwiches and cakes. We always preceded the feast with some hours of performance. Eric was more silent than usual, preferring, when his turn came, not to play. He sat beside Anna on the love seat and twice I saw him bend over to whisper something to her. He ate a great deal—our small sandwiches always seemed to disappear into his outsized hands—and he smiled steadily, receptively, but made no contributions to the general hilarity.

The other young men were like children about to be given their vacation from school. They drank much wine, joked loudly with each other, and talked about how good it would be to return to New York for the beginning of the opera and concert season. They seemed glad to be finished with the long summer's work and solitude: but not Eric. As always, he was regretful and sad.

The party lasted until midnight. At half past ten I said my farewells. They were all to make their way to the village railway depot early the next morning before I expected to arise. Anna remained to close up behind the young men after they returned to their studios.

I must have fallen asleep quickly and slept for some time. The sound of a door woke me. I looked at the clock that stands in the corner of our room. It was two o'clock. Anna was not there.

I went to the landing, feeling panicked. She was coming up the stairs in the dark and seemed startled to see me awake. We went back to the bedroom together.

"Where have you been?" I whispered, although why I do not know. There was no one any longer I might disturb.

"Talking. Talking to Eric. He said he wanted—very much—to talk." She undressed quickly, came into the bed and stretched out as though she were very tired. I sat up, now wide awake, waiting for her to speak. Suddenly there was missing the accustomed, loving easiness between us, the way we moved together at the start of sleep to lie close, often in each other's arms, the sense of creature warmth and security we kindled between our two bodies as we touched, the wonderful way we were always able to converse about anything, everything. The room, the bed, my heart felt cold, a new twist of jealousy, the rattle of fear knocking on the panes of the heart.

"Anna. Do you, do you—care for Eric? You must tell me at once if you do." There was a silence. Anna pulled the quilt over her shoulders to her chin. I lay down a short space from her, barely able to see the dark outline of her head on the pillow. Only thin moonlight entered the room.

"No, Carrie. I don't care for him—that way. Not in the way I care for you. But he is a troubled, lonely man. He has no friends, he tells me. He needs someone to talk with, to hear about his fears and worries."

Immensely relieved, I reached across what had seemed a chasm in the bed between us and touched her hair. It curled tightly about her head. "Does he care for you, Anna?" She turned to me, and I realized the chasm had been of my imaginary making. Once more warmth returned to the bed.

"I'm afraid, yes. He does, Carrie. He wanted to tell me

that before he left tomorrow. He says he has no hope, but he wants me to know, to think about him."

"Will you?"

"What?"

"Think about him?"

"Not in that way. I told him I would never leave you. But as a friend must think about another, of course I will. I said I would write to him in the winter. He is terribly afraid of the war, of America entering it, of being hurt or killed. . . ."

Her voice drifted off. Almost at once I could hear her steady, deep breathing in sleep. But I remained awake, staring into the darkness, somehow afraid of what could possibly happen. I slept very little that night.

That fall and winter, letters came regularly to Anna from Eric in New York. She read them all to me. They were frightened, depressed letters from a man alone in a studio on the Bowery in the bowels of New York (he called it that), trying to compose an opera on the theme of Oedipus, with no contacts with friends or fellow musicians. He had convinced himself, he wrote, that he must always stay indoors when it was light outside: "I must not be seen on the streets because my height, my strength, will call attention to me. I know the army has once said no to me because of my mental history, but I believe if they see me now on the street they will enlist me." He wrote that he went out only at four in the morning, when the wholesale markets in his section of the city were opening. He bought food and then raced back to his hole: "Literally, it is a hole," he wrote, "a basement from which I can see only the feet and lower legs of passersby."

Anna replied to him, composing her letters on the table in the evenings after we had finished our games, our reading aloud, our conversation. She showed me what she had written: "Do not stay indoors so much. It is bad for your spirits." She said she shared Eric's horror of the war, being rendered somewhat ambivalent by the call on her sympathies of her German and German-American friends and relatives. "Do not worry. The war in Europe cannot go on too much longer, perhaps we will not have to enter it, and then you will be safe. Are you planning a return to the Community in May? There will be a place for you. I will speak of it to Mrs. Maclaren."

Her letters were full of motherly negative commands: "Try not to stay so much within yourself. . . . Never eat unwashed salad greens or fruit." Reading her letters, I thought, Now that Robert is gone, Anna is nursing Eric. But I said nothing of this to her. Our relationship was so good, so open, that it admitted only of truth-telling between us. I was not tempted to disturb the tenor of our days. Our love sustained me and, I hoped, her. It was a source of psychic reassurance and, yes, physical pleasure as well. So that the presence of Eric among her letters did not disturb me. She was so loving a woman that there was, within her nutritive spirit, room for more refugees than me alone. Together with Anna, I, too, worried about Eric.

That year, in April, the United States entered the war. Foundation members met to decide what to do about the

Community and decided to open as usual in May despite the grave events. Anna and I volunteered to do our war work in addition to housekeeping for the Community. Evenings we worked in the public library. Miss Milly Martino was no longer there: by then she was retired because of the trouble in her hands and neck. The new librarian, a lady with the strange name of Mrs. Osnas Fitz, opened the reading room for war work in the evenings. Anna and I, with the other ladies from the village, rolled bandages for the Red Cross and knitted, and "finished off" for other knitters, scarves and caps and socks for our troops overseas. It was in this way that it came about that we were away, in the reading room of the library rolling bandages, when the fire started which destroyed the Farm.

But to go back a little. The last summer of the war, we had four musicians in residence, not our customary six. For the first time one of them was a woman, a most competent young flutist and composer named Dorothy Griffith who had come to the Farm to work on a sonata for her instrument. We assigned her the studio (Weeks, it had recently been named) nearest the house so that she would not have the long, dark walks home in the evening that some of the other studios required of their occupants.

Eric had returned, and two other young men were with us. One, from Massachusetts, Gerald Foster, had lost a leg in childhood, and the other, St. John Sterne (we called him

Jody), was weak in one eye and so was not called to the army. All four, for a wonder—usually we lost at least one the first week from restlessness or loneliness—found the Farm congenial to their work. They all got on well with each other, I thought, and with us when we saw them at dinner and during the evening musicales and gatherings.

The musicales were occasions of great pleasure to me. Sometimes, after the students had finished, I would play. Since the afternoon I went back to it, a year after Robert's death, I had regained my delight with the piano. The thick and oppressive quiet that filled our house during Robert's illness and, before that, my careful quiet so that he could compose undisturbed were ended, after what I had considered a decent interval of mourning.

Anna smiled at my "decent interval." I began to play *Lieder*, some pieces I had not looked at since my time with Mrs. Seton. To my great joy I discovered that Anna could follow the music and sing in a low, fine contralto. We began to study a song from Schubert's *Winterreise*.

There grows between accompanist and singer an unspoken bond. They signal to each other their readiness, and the accompanist plays the first note at the same moment as the singer begins. Between us there developed such a bond. I would hold my hands just above the keys. Anna, standing behind me, would place her hands lightly on my shoulders. At the moment I felt her touch I began, and so did she. Our understanding at these moments was complete.

Some notes were too high for her voice. But she managed the long ascent from "Manche Trän' aus meinen Augen" to the "Durstig ein das heisse Weh" with ease, only the final note giving her a little trouble. She would press my shoulder as she abandoned the attempt, and I would shrug and laugh. Then she would go on, to the long, slow, melodic descent to the end of that lovely song. I would applaud and she would blush. We were together in our amusement at our successes and our failures.

Always before, music had created a distance between Robert and me, a separation I served by my silence in deference to his greater accomplishments. With Anna it became collaboration, albeit an amateur one, and "in that union," as the Chinese sage who wrote the *Li Chi* said, "we loved one another."

That summer Eric found it hard, it seemed to me, to stay away from our house during the day. He would come to the kitchen at noon when Anna was preparing our luncheon and linger on one pretext or other. While I practiced in the afternoon I would see him from my window walking the road from his studio, cutting across the meadow to where Anna worked in the garden.

She always told me about his visits. Her openness to me about every thought she had was consoling at moments when I had twinges of the old fear. A day in July came when she told me Eric had asked her if she would consider him as a suitor. He said to her: "I want very much to marry. I think I might conquer my sickness, my fears, if I were not so alone all the time. If I marry it can be no one but you, Anna. My thoughts are full of you, winter and summer. Can it be that you feel nothing for me?"

Anna said she told him she could not leave the Farm.

" 'Why not? You are merely a companion, a paid person. She could find another.'

"He took my hand—it was very dirty, covered with soil, and held it very tight. 'Let me go,' I said. 'It is more than that.'

" 'What do you mean, more than that? Security? I can make a home for you. I am publishing and being paid for my work now. True, not much right away, but once the war is over, orchestras will begin to play American compositions as never before, I am told. I love you, Anna. I have never loved a woman before, except my mother, who died when I was ten, in a fire. Her room, only *her* room, in our summer house on Long Island was struck by lightning. No one in the house but my mother died in that storm. She burned up alone, in her bed, while my brothers and I slept, and my father was in the city working. . . . And since then, no one. I've felt nothing for anyone, until now, for you.'

" 'I am sorry.'

" 'You feel nothing for me?'

" 'I feel affection and friendship. But love, no. I don't love you, Eric.'

" 'How can you be sure? Perhaps you haven't felt what love is yet.'

" 'Oh, yes, I know what it is. I have felt love.'

" 'For someone else? Another man?' "

[188]

She did not know what to say then, she told me. She hesitated, and then said, " 'No.' "

She turned back to her weeding. When she looked up again, Eric was standing a little way off, staring at her: "His face was red, Carrie. He looked—he looked unbelieving, as though he were suddenly remembering a dream— I don't know. He ran his hand through his hair and shook his head, again and again. Then he turned away and left."

"Do you think he understood?"

"I'm sure."

But Eric did not give up trying to be close to where Anna was. He held her chair, he always took the seat beside her at dinner, he followed her onto the back porch in the evenings when we all left the dining room and went out to witness the sunset. He sat beside her on the stone benches where we waited for the moon to rise and the stars to appear. His pursuit was sad and mute. Anna told me he did not again speak to her of love or require anything of her except that she not reject his presence close to her. He always asked her permission: "May I sit beside you? Do you mind if I walk with you?" His great size hovering over her must have been noticed by everyone, in the evenings, in the dining room, when we were all together. I noticed, and watched, feeling within me a little rough place like a ragged fingernail that irritated and troubled my mind. But of course I said nothing of this to Anna.

Our union had always been without descriptive words. We accepted without comment what we had discovered with each other by chance, the miracle of love. It may have been the irregularity to the outside world of our life together that kept us from talking about it to each other, even in private—I don't know—or it may be that there was no need for talk. A fitting vocabulary for such discussion did not then exist, or at least, if it did, Anna and I did not know any of its words.

Anna's kindnesses to Eric intensified because, she told me, "I feel so sorry for him. The least I can do is see that he eats and that his shirts have their buttons returned, and that Edward brings enough kindling to his studio against the early-morning chill."

Late in August we had our traditional Sunday evening picnic. It had been a beautiful day, almost an early fall day, and promised to be a fine evening. Dorothy Griffith, Anna, and I prepared the food hampers, and the men carried them to the elevated grassy area near the graves. The four young musicians seemed in very good spirits, wine was consumed quickly, we ate sitting on shawls, and watched the sun set over the trees. So when it happened no one was prepared for the violence in Eric's voice. In the course of a small joke she was making, Dorothy had placed her hand over Eric's, apparently (I did not see it but Anna thought she had), and Eric was enraged by the comradely gesture.

"Don't touch me. I dislike being touched. Why are you always touching me?"

Dorothy blushed deeply, rose to her feet at once, and walked away from us, down the path to Weeks Studio. One of the men—I don't remember which—went after her.

The rest of us, surprised, gathered up the picnic plates and packed the two hampers.

Eric remained seated on the shawl, making no move to help us. He stared down, tracing the motifs in the shawl with a long finger.

"Anna, say something to him," I whispered to her as we packed. "Or shall I?"

"I think we should leave him be. He will be all right in a little while. It would embarrass him to be spoken to, I think."

Between us, Anna and I carried one hamper, leaving the other to be brought back later by the men. We said good night to Eric, who remained as he was, seated like a stone on the shawl, and did not answer. Once we had to put the heavy hamper down to rest our arms. I looked back. He was still there, but he was watching us, Anna and me, his light blue eyes looking almost red in the evening light. His hand was over the red blemish on his face, and he looked tragic, a giant child, seated on the ground in the dusk.

Edward drove us to the village for our two hours of war work in the library. He waited for us, and at eleven we started back.

We were near the Farm road when Anna noticed smoke on the horizon. I remember how I started at the sight, for the evening in town, all the women working together, had been so peaceful. Then we had been riding together on the seat of the farm wagon, feeling (or I know I felt, and I think she did too) the power of closeness, thinking our own thoughts. I will never know hers, but I was remembering

Eric on the ground, his hand to his face, a human island of desolation, looking despairingly after us. Knowing? Did he know? I will never have the answer to that.

"Look," she said.

The sky was gray with smoke behind the house. Close to the horizon we could see flames. Edward thrashed at the old horse. By the time we pulled up to the front of the house, the hill behind it and the woods to each side where the studios were, were covered with smoke. We could see Dorothy Griffith and Jody running about with buckets.

"Get ours!" I screamed to Anna and Edward. "We can fill them at the garden pump."

"No," Anna shouted back, as though I were deaf. "It would be better if I go for help. To the Wrights . . ."

There was no telephone at the Farm—we had never wished to have one installed even when our neighbors had done so. But the neighbors to the north, Charles and Ellen Wright, had an instrument. Anna ran toward their place, disappearing at once into the night.

Her hair singed and smelling of smoke, Dorothy came up to me. Her hands were black.

"Are you burned, Dorothy?"

"No, no, but we cannot get to the other studios through the smoke. We don't know where Gerald is—or Eric."

"They may be on the other side of the fire and cannot get through to us."

Even had we wished to find them at once, we could not have. The smoke grew thicker as we stood helpless, watching it mount higher and spread farther to the side. Then I saw a small snake of flames moving along the ground. "The house, the house," I remember screaming to no one in particular. The house was now in danger. Dorothy, Jody, and I began to splash water on the ground around it, on the walls and windows, everywhere. Our arms and legs grew weak from our repeated trips from the pump with heavy buckets.

The house was saved, not by our feeble efforts but because our neighbors, and then the fire wagons, arrived. The Wrights had telephoned at once: one engine and another equipped with a water pump came before the others could get to us on foot, while we were still wearily passing buckets to each other from the pump, now dousing the bushes and trees and grass near the house.

Anna returned with the Wrights, they took their places in the chain, and we were able to hold the little licks of flame away from the house until the firemen and their engines arrived. Their hoses were trained on the fire and the house itself. Little by little, the firemen moved forward into the woods, away from the house, their hoses creating massive yellow billows which rose above the charred trees.

Villagers, awakened by the smoke and by the fire bell calling for assistance, came to the farm and joined in the work. By the time the first light appeared in the sky I was too tired to do anything but watch—and pray.

Eric and one-legged Gerald Foster had not appeared. Anna was wild with apprehension. She ran from one fireman to another, pleading, "Find the others. For God's sake, there are two others back in there somewhere."

We were all so weary. We sat on the wet black grass—Dorothy, Jody, and I—too tired to raise our arms, to stand any longer, straining to see through the dense smoke, still searching for signs of the others. We told ourselves they must have escaped to the back road, they were now watching the fire from the east side of the property, across the road, worrying about *our* safety.

But when we found them, they were dead, suffocated as they tried to escape the encircling fire, we surmised. They died alone, a few hundred yards from each other. Gerald might have been trying to reach Eric; he was found stretched out across the footpath to Eric's studio, face down in blackened underbrush, his wooden leg entangled in vines. Eric had never left his studio. He had died stretched in the ashes around him, his face calm, his eyes closed. Only the red mark on his face still looked alive and resentful. His body was charred, yet his head had miraculously escaped the fire.

The firemen and villagers worked all night and much of the next morning to put out the last little pockets of fire that kept breaking out in the woods and fields. All six of the studios, which we had so lovingly labored over and constructed with such attention to detail, were destroyed. Around each one the faint, sour smell of burned pianos lingered for a long time. Twenty acres of our woodland were reduced to a naked forest of black stubs and sooty grass underbrush. Our fire pond, from which the firemen had pumped almost all its contents, was now a shallow dark cavity full of floating fallen branches and the black remnants of evergreen needles.

But we had saved the house. Like a magic island in an infernal conflagration, it remained untouched except by the pervasive smell and discoloration of smoke. By noon of the second day, Anna and I were able to enter it, to climb to our acrid-smelling bedroom and fall exhausted into sleep. Dorothy lay down on the couch in the drawing room, Jody on Robert's old horsehair sofa in the music room. The bodies of Gerald Foster and Eric Anderson were carried away to the funeral parlor in Saratoga Springs. We, the survivors, slept profoundly for almost fourteen hours.

Early the next morning—it was still dark—Anna and I, weary and very stiff, made our way downstairs to the kitchen to make some tea. The odor from the corner near the rear door reminded us that we had never unpacked the hamper. Before we boiled the water we thought it best to dispose of the decaying picnic remains. There, on top of moldering cheese and bread and decaying potato salad, was a folded piece of paper, addressed to Anna Baehr, from Eric Anderson. As she did with almost everything, she saved that letter. It was in her drawer among her handkerchiefs when she died. I put it here in this account:

Anna, my dearest:

I watched as you and Mrs. Maclaren walked away to the village. I understand, truly I do. I am writing this in my studio which I need now to clean, by burning my score of King Oedipus. *It is like my life: mediocre, and unlikely to amount to anything.*

Burning is cleansing. Perhaps the fire will spread to the

*studio and then to me. I was burned once before, by my
mother in an accident. She was very young, fifteen, and un-
married when I was born. One night she carried me to my
crib and dropped hot wax, by accident, from a candle she
was carrying in the other hand, onto my face. I was six
months old.*

*Perhaps this fire I am planning will cleanse all that
now seems vile to me: Dorothy's pursuit of me. The other
men's childish silliness. You and Mrs. Maclaren. The whole
idea of a memorial to her husband, the Community.*

*I don't wish you to burn, only be cleansed of—what?
Please forgive me.*

Eric

"He meant to burn us all—the whole Farm, the others,
us, everything?" I cried.

Anna, still staring at the letter in her hand, said, "No,
I don't think he meant that. He was discouraged about his
opera. I know that. The rest is just—wild declaration. It
doesn't mean he would do it. The fire spread out of his
control from the fireplace while he slept on his cot. . . ."

We never knew. I will never be sure. Sometimes I
wonder if the spectacle of our love and the burden of his
own goaded Eric to burn *my* Farm. Or was he gripped by
a religious fervor, a command to destroy Sodom, to repay
me for keeping Anna from him? Whatever, mad prophetic
gesture or miscalculated accident, the Farm lay outside our
blackened windows, a burned-out ruin.

Gerald Foster's body was returned to his family in Pittsfield, Massachusetts, I think it was. Eric was buried in our grave-yard. His mother was dead, and there was no one else we knew about for him. Edward put a field stone at the grave's head and sank it into the ground. There is no name on it, but he is there, and I could identify the stone, if it has not sunk down entirely from view by now.

Three months later the terrible war he so feared was over. Anna and I spent Christmas at the Farm, the first one in many years, for ordinarily we would be traveling in winter, raising money for the Foundation.

What was there now to travel for? The desolation from the fire, even the remains of the studios in the woods, square flattened foundations, were now all mercifully buried by the snow, the idea of the Community, the memorial, buried with them. That Christmas, we were alone. We exchanged little presents. Together we cooked a simple supper on Christmas Eve. Anna prepared to go in the sled with Edward to the village for midnight Mass. I asked if I might join her.

Her face lighted. "Of course. It would be wonderful if you came."

The altar of the church was vivid with red poinsettias (I thought at once of Dorothea Brooke's disease of the retina) and smelled of newly cut evergreens. The Mass was sung in Latin by young boys, their high, sweet un-tutored sopranos sounding like the Sunday-morning bells I had heard in Frankfurt. The church was dimly lit with candles and a little electricity, still a novelty and a pleasure, for we had not yet had the house wired for it.

I loved the Mass that Christmas Eve of 1918. I loved the bells, the organ, the sweetish smell of incense, the scrubbed little blond faces of white-robed choir and altar boys, the solemn elevated expressions of the two priests who, Anna whispered to me, were "the celebrants." The procession of "the faithful" (the priest who delivered the sermon referred this way to the people in the pews, who had come long distances through the cold night and the snow) to the altar "to receive": that was the way Anna described what she was doing up there. She would often say, "Today, I received."

My Unitarian sensibilities, restrained and intellectual, had not prepared me for what was going on among "the faithful" as they kneeled in their pews or at the altar rail. I understood not one word, except for the sermon and the reading from the Gospel. The heavily symbolic nature of the events escaped me entirely.

But Anna was there beside me, her lovely scrubbed countenance (a sister to the altar boys, I thought) never turning from the sedate pageant on the altar, her shining eyes fixed on something she must have been witnessing up there: I could not tell what. Outside, the wind rattled the stained-glass windows and rough snow puffs hurled themselves against the walls and the doors, but inside there were those serious, confident worshipers like Anna, glowing in the presence of their God, the extraordinary concentration, under the instruction of bells, of "the faithful."

Seated beside Anna while everyone else kneeled, I tried

to pray. I managed only to think, The destroyed Farm, what shall I do with it? Shall I start all over again? Will the Foundation want to help to restore it all? Is Robert's music still important enough to music lovers (who must have new favorites by now) to appeal to them again in his name? I floundered among questions vaguely directed to the Lord, but no supernatural answers presented themselves to me in that first hour of Christmas morning.

How do you pray? Do you command the Lord: "Grant me the time and the strength in which to rebuild, the Farm, my own life." Or question Him: "What do I do now?" Or petition: "Please, dear God, do not let me lose what little I have—the house, my friend, my love. . . ."

The Foundation members met in early April, as soon as it was possible for those scattered persons to negotiate the roads. Anna had been called away that day by old Dr. Holmes. An unusual number of persons in the village were ill with influenza, the result of the hard winter and the change of weather, he said. He needed Anna's help with a family in which four of the young children and their pregnant mother were very ill. So she was gone when the members arrived. They knew of the fire, the damage—the newspapers had carried accounts of it, reporting that nothing was known of the cause.

Mrs. Rhinelander was curious: "Have you ever found out what happened?"

"No," I lied, "we never have. We came home from the village to find the whole woods ablaze. The chief of firemen guessed it might have been sparks from an unbanked late-night fire in one of the studios. But we cannot know for sure because all the studios burned to the ground."

Lester Lenox gave us a dismal financial report: "There would have been enough to operate the Community for some time to come, under ordinary conditions. But not enough, by any means, to rebuild and refurnish. Prices are very high since the war. It could never be done on what is in the bank and what is invested."

We took everything into consideration on that long afternoon. There was no way. I heard in their voices a lack of enthusiasm for rebuilding, I sensed their feeling that Robert Maclaren's day had passed, and mine, and the best that could happen was that I might salvage enough to live on.

So it came to that. I did what they thought I should. I agreed to sell most of the property, all the burned acres, holding back only the land surrounding the house and corridor behind it which led to the hill and the knoll where the graves were. It was quickly sold: the township of Saratoga Springs was anxious to have land on the outskirts on which to build its storage sheds and to house its road-building equipment. Later, years later, the land was sold again, and subdivided. At present, I understand, although I have not been out to see it in some years, it has been much built upon. Roads have been cut through, there are power and telephone lines overhead going to the small houses which have, thrusting out from their roofs, television antennas as high as trees. There is no sign, I am told, of what once was there, the studios hidden away from each other in beautiful woods, "an idyll," the brochure used to say, "for the exclusive use of gifted persons." Now even the graves seem to have sunk, like the gardens of Persia, below the much trampled ground of the subdivision.

There was still enough money, I learned, for me (and so Anna) to live on in the house. We would need to be frugal, but hadn't we always been? With Anna's garden and our preserving, and doing so much of the necessary work about the house ourselves, we would make out well. I felt no longer young when that meeting was held. I knew the members were right. I needed to rest, not to travel so much. Yet the thought of discontinuing Robert's memorial, abandoning the summer Community of young musicians, was disturbing to me. So I persuaded the members of the Foundation to continue its existence and their membership on it for a while, to keep the idea alive until we saw what the future held: "It might be that the day will come when it will be possible to start again," I said to them.

They left the Farm, relieved, I thought, to be rid of the heavy burdens of administering the funds of the Community and glad of my willingness to let it all go for a while. Lenox, the Reverend Whitehall, and de Wolfe all urged me to come into the village more often: "Interesting things going on there now. Wednesday book club, church fairs and suppers. A ladies' garden society, that kind of thing," said de Wolfe, and I said I would try. I remember thinking, No more spectacle. Lillian Russell. The baths

closed down for repairs. Are the waters still drunk by colorful figures from New York, I wonder?

When Anna came back from her nursing stint the next
day, I told her what had transpired. All she said was, "It is
as well. Without Eric it would not be the same this year."
Her irises were almost white with fatigue. I remember she
went to bed at noon, having had no sleep during her long
night with the sick children. No more was said about it.

Losing the Community made a difference to my life, to
my pretense, you might wish to say, knowing now what
you do of me, to my pretense of devotion, to the apparent
duty of those years. True, to everyone I was Mrs. Robert
Maclaren, in the histories of music (if indeed I did appear
at all), in *Who's Who* under Robert's long listing. But
since his death I had begun to be Caroline Maclaren, the
woman who raised quite large funds for the Community by
playing Robert Maclaren's music and lecturing about him at
fund-raising gatherings all over the country, the adminis-
trator of the Community who headed the table in the dining
room during the summer sessions. In a small way, I had
become a person with a little authority.

With the Community gone, no, suspended, as I had
insisted, the township of Saratoga Springs removed what
it had called "the musicians' haven" from its travel brochure
in the summer of '19. The war over, the town had begun
to look for the return of the old flood of summer residents
and tourists. Reading that brochure, foolishly now it seems,
I was flooded with regret, almost, I must confess, so depressed by the loss, by the end of my life's work, no matter

how insignificant, that I hardly noticed Anna coming and going from the village at odd hours of the day and night, hardly heard her reports of the increasing number of persons stricken by the influenza. My depression closed my eyes to the signs, which must have been there, of her weariness.

The village had become an extended, crowded hospital. Never before in anyone's memory had an affliction spread so quickly and so lethally as the influenza of that year. It was no longer thought that the fierce winter was responsible, as Dr. Holmes had believed. Instead the theory now held was that the disease had been brought back from the front by young men who had survived the horrors of the trenches only to succumb in their beds, at home, having first communicated the germ, was it? spirochete? or what? to their families.

Anna insisted I stay away from the village. She carried whatever we needed to eat from the shops that lay along her path in her walk home up the hill. We ate hastily and at odd times. There were very few of our old long, comfortable, and companionable evenings together. For the sick in town needed her. And she did so well: she seemed to thrive under the hard new discipline—she had been away from it for a long time. The sense of service brought the shine back to her cheeks and the glow to her eyes.

There are persons whose vitality lies in the performance of their duty, in their service to others, which, I take it, is what duty really means. There are many more such persons than traditional history takes note of. We have been well educated, we have read chronicles and biographies, plays and novels, about rebels and revolutionaries, leaders of nations and battalions, kings and great criminals, theatrical stars and escape artists. But what do we know of those whose pleasure in life is service? The waiting classes, the pram pushers, the burden bearers up the sides of great mountains, the launderers of the sheets of others, the seamstresses of our cloaks?

More than all those, there are the ones whose hands distract the sick from their distress, who hold the frightened child they are paid to care for against their breasts, who comfort the dying while often the family waits safely outside the sickroom, who cool the distress of last moments. Anna was such a person. She made Robert's last days bearable to him, and to me. In the village she nursed the family of six, single-handed, until the mother and two of the children succumbed and until the two other children and their father recovered slowly and could leave their beds, and until —it was almost inevitable—she contracted the terrible illness, struggled weakly in her weariness against it, crying out and rambling incoherently, blind and deaf to me and to everything but the ancient, mad, frightened world she rehearsed in her head, and then died.

She was my friend, my companion, my beloved, she listened to me as no one, not my mother or my teachers or friends and surely never my husband, ever listened. She talked to me, not often about herself but about me, about us, and about others she loved. She filled the silences of a lifetime for me. Even at the end, as she lay in the middle of the great bed, bathed in the rank sweat of mortal sickness, red-eyed with fever, she talked to me, even when Dr. Holmes was there and she of course could not know that, was not aware that we were not alone: "Travel together. Should go to Germany. My mother. Alive still? Don't know. Afraid, always afraid. Must introduce you. So she knows about us, about me. Sees there is nothing to be afraid of in love. That I am her daughter. Even to her new husband. As I am your daughter. Your mother. Your husband. Your love."

I said in a low voice, "Shhh, Anna. Rest now, dear. Sleep for a while."

"Give her this powder when she is able to drink a little, Mrs. Maclaren." He put his silver tools away in his black bag and snapped the ends together. His face was very white. His reddened eyes looked strained and alarmed. He seemed eager to be gone. I wondered if he too was overtired, on the brink of the sickness himself.

"The Community dinners. When he talked and looked so long at me. To help him. To hold him close. Like a child. A son, a lover he wanted to be. Like Carrie. But hard to reach and frightened. Afraid like my mother. Wounded in the face. In the heart. Left alone. To the fire. We helped him not at all. How, Carrie? How could we help? I a nurse and not nursing. Died and was buried without the priest, without unction, without comfort. Burned again. Lying near the dog. Near the great man. He a boy and a man, without friends. I did nothing. Unspeakable crime."

She screamed. I held her, wiping the wet from her red,

shiny face, kissing her damp forehead, paying no heed to
Dr. Holmes. Was he still there?—I do not know—when
Anna talked, raved, when I pleaded with her to stay with
me, not to leave me in the dark, the loneliness from which
she had rescued me.

I whispered to her, "I'm not afraid, Anna. Not of being
alone. But of being without you. Stay with me."

But she didn't hear. She was out of her head, incoherent,
almost out of time, on the point of leaving the bursting
healthy life I had so loved in her. She had forgotten what
she knew for certain, and in her delirium remembered only
her doubts, her fears: "Know so much. The Foundation people. And Carrie. The great ones. The great man. How can
I be with them?"

I said into her ear, holding her beloved head, smoothing
her wet hair, "Love, you were with them all. Above them
all. Out of all the world, my choice. I wanted you, I want
you. Stay with me, love. There is no one else. Terrible loneliness without you, no one else. Not for me."

She could not hear me: "The long horsehairs. Long as
you can find. They spawn eels. Good for the soil. Needed.
In the garden. Long, long horsehairs."

But you know the truth already. At three in the morning
—I remember that a full moon had just disappeared over
the bend of the hill and the light in our bedroom disappeared—she woke and called, "Carrie?"

I moved from my chair, where I had dozed, to the bed.
"I'm cold."

"Anna, I'm here. I'll warm you." I went to the cupboard

for another blanket, a quilt, anything I could pull out quickly.

When I came back to the bed she said, "Carrie. Where is God?"

"God? What do you mean? The priest, do you mean the priest? Do you want me to call the priest?"

"Cold," she said. "God. Carrie."

And she died.

That was almost fifty years ago. (Can it be? Sometimes I lose count.) That early morning, in the darkened bedroom, Anna died. I have never found a comforting euphemism for it. She did not pass away, or leave this life, or go to her maker. I cannot accept "She is with God," which is what the priest who came the next morning said. None of those things. She died. She lay there, forever still. She turned cold and began to stiffen. There in the great Maclaren bed at three o'clock in the morning. My love became a thing, a motionless person-less strip of lifeless white matter.

I remember: I got into bed with her, lay beside her, touched every part of her body, as a student of sculpture would touch a classical statue to memorize its lines, to remember its curves and suggested softness. As long as I am able to remember (forever for me), her body will be alive in my mind, my eyes, under my finger tips.

The light was up when I climbed out of the bed, dressed, and walked to the village to tell Dr. Holmes ("It must be certified," she had told me when Robert died) about Anna.

I felt nothing at first but the cold of desertion. There would be no second resurrection for me, no third chance at life. I knew that. One is granted one great love if one is fortunate—and after that? Death while one is still in life. Endurance, waiting, survival, the slow, inexorable growth of a sense of loss and cruel grief until it floods the mind and drowns what is left of the self.

So it ended. It is an irony of my life that I have lived on for more than forty-five years, as the world would measure it. But to me the living time of my life came to an end long ago. Until Anna came, I had waited, prepared to be born. Life came, with her: the feeling that reached in to the bone and warmed it, the hours that were filled instead of passed through, the days I remember still, that swim in my memory, glow in my mind like phosphorescent fish. With her death, life for me was ended, but I lived on, a dead-live, half-woman, once again resembling the one who had lived so long with Robert, restored to the lonely solitary I had been during all the years of my marriage.

So. I have put it all down. I look back at the years since Anna's death and find it hard to remember what has filled the void. What have I done? I've waited—a long, still, terrible wait—to die. I've gone on living at the Farm because there was no other place I wanted to be or had to go.

Now and then I used to walk to the village—now a city, I must remember to say—to the library. I've read books, played music, listened to recordings, cleaned this house and then cleaned it again before it had a chance to grow dirty, sewn and repaired and darned, tended my garden—Anna's garden, at first—which now my visiting nurse tells me is weeds and dandelions. I've written a thousand letters, I would guess. Each day even now, I answer letters that come to me from musicologists, biographers, and historians questioning me about my husband, and about his friends in Europe, some of whom became very well known. Most of them are now dead.

Every day, summer and winter, I used to climb the narrow corridor between the house and the high knoll, to the graves, Anna's grave where she is buried to the side and below the great headstone that will be mine soon. I put a small stone at her head, with a cross and DUTY AND LOVE on it, and her beloved name and her dates. I used to take two bunches of flowers each week, one for display to place on Robert's grave, so that it would be seen by visitors, creating the illusion of a loving wife who faithfully remembered her husband all these years.

The other was a smaller bunch, a few wild flowers I would find as I walked to the knoll: meadowsweet and black-eyed Susans, violets and Indian paint-brush. Unshowy flowers for a discreet love, for my unremarked love who lies cold and silent, waiting, I believe, for me.

A new group, inheritors of the original Foundation, has

written to me. It seems that the government of the United States has a plan to endow the arts. One of the places they are looking at is our old Foundation, the long-since abandoned Maclaren Community. Of course, all the land is long gone. We could not rebuild here on the original site without dislocating thirty homeowners and the outbuildings of the City of Saratoga street-repairing department.

But Lester Lenox's grandson, Alexander, writes to me, from the Saratoga bank. I put his whole letter into this account:

We are asked to present the National Endowment for the Arts with a complete proposal. Part of that proposal— the bank's part—will consist of a statement of the present condition of the Robert Glencoe Maclaren trust, as administered by this bank in conjunction with you. Our assumption is that, if the proposal for the revival of the Community should be accepted, upon your death you would assign to the Foundation your rights to the estate.

A second part of the proposal will consist of a history of the Community. Of course, no one is better able to tell that story than you, Mrs. Maclaren. Are you willing? The committee from Saratoga working on the proposal (for of course we feel it would much benefit the city if we could re establish it here) can provide you with a secretary who would come to the Farm if you would like to dictate the history, as you remember it. Here at the bank we have all the books and financial records. Should your memory of the facts fail at any point; we can check such matters as names, dates, and financial details for you.

But I have already told this: I rejected the offer to dictate to a secretary, deciding I would celebrate my ninetieth year with a final effort to donate to paper my inner life together with the externals already known. I would put it down in my own hand as a way, I think, of signifying, attesting to the truth by the witness of my handwriting as well as the force of my own words.

And the facts? I read back over this lengthy statement and I find I have included too few facts. But then, what are facts but the catafalque upon which one hangs all the memories of an emotional life, the sticking points of one's memories out of which events have long since fallen, leaving only what seems real: disappointments, despairs, rare intense joys, and even rarer loves. And finally, for us all, the omnipresent aloneness of our lives.

We are all alone and lonely, wrote that novelist Virginia Woolf, who drowned herself. And so it was for me, Caroline Newby, raised by a lonely, heartbroken mother, taught to play the piano by the wordless Mrs. Seton, affianced to a prodigy who first loved his mother and then a man, once and fatally (I have now come to believe) before his marriage to me, a wife caught in a joyless, dutiful marriage, and freed from it at last by the deadly journey of infection through the rivers of her husband's blood. And then, after discovering love, unlikely and unsuspected, in a woman who dispelled her loneliness, left behind by her death, more alone than ever before, deserted by the single point of light, the one glowing coal, in a long, cold, dark life.

The Foundation will say: What you have managed to remember is perhaps only partial and personal, biased truth. You have not given us Robert's truth. Surely it would have differed from yours. I would reply: True. He never wrote about his life. Or Eric's truth, Churchill's. Even Della Fox's and Virginia Maclaren's and my mother's. The others. Anna's.

But, at the last, I think, the historian's view always superimposes itself upon history. Out of a vast amount of available facts from an infinite acreage he chooses what fits his limited and single vision and writes one story. In this case, the story is mine alone. It is all I am able to know.

At the last (I say this often, I notice, because at my age everything points to the end) I know this has been useful, not to the Foundation or to Washington, but to me. Writing it, I have freed myself. I have gathered in what I value and what I have hated. What is here, after all, but a few persons indistinguishable from their inevitable tragedies, a few hopes and visions, many fears, a long waiting, and a profound, extraordinary love that has lasted in memory far longer than most living passions.

Asked to write the history of a man and an institution, I have managed to produce merely a sketch of the chamber of one heart. Like Robert, I see, I am a miniaturist.

In ninety years I have made no significant journeys, traveled nowhere except into the interior of a single spirit, my own. Conceived in the age of the Centennial's bentwood sofa, I lived an almost empty life into an overcrowded and hectic century. Like Professor Watkins' migratory birds, I was the one who flew not a thousand miles but a few feet.

The wisteria Anna planted now blooms outside my bedroom window. Her memory for me has grown, reached up, covered, and supported the rest of my life. During the cold winter Saratoga nights when I lie alone and afraid in the great bed, I remember her way of protecting our trees from insects, her assurance that their brittle little skewered carcasses would enrich the roots. I still cannot believe in a higher purpose or a kindly Providence that will unite us. So I wait for the time when my remains will join hers to serve the useful soil.